A CATALOGUE
OF
THE INDIAN COINS
IN
THE BRITISH MUSEUM

First published 1936
Photolithographic reprint 1967

Printed in Great Britain in the City of Oxford
at the Alden Press and bound by the Kemp Hall Bindery

PREFACE TO REPRINT

THIS volume is a reprint, without alterations or additions, of the work by the late John Allan, Keeper of the Department of Coins and Medals, and originally published by the Trustees in 1936. The importance of the Museum's collection of the material covered by this catalogue and the authoritative nature of Dr Allan's work will hardly need to be pointed out to those engaged in Indological study, for whom such a catalogue will long remain an indispensable source of information. Moreover there have been very few significant additions to the Museum's collection of this material; we may mention only that some twenty punchmarked and tribal coins were included in the collection of Sir Richard Burn, acquired by the Museum in 1949.

G. K. JENKINS
Keeper

PREFACE

THIS volume of the Catalogue of Indian Coins in the British Museum, the seventh of the series, deals with the coins issued by native rulers from the earliest times to about A.D. 300. The coins of the foreign invaders of this period were described in the *Catalogue of Coins of the Greek and Scythic Kings*.

The size of the coins is given in inches and tenths, and the weight in grains. Comparative tables with other systems of measurement are given at the end of the volume.

The proofs of the text have been read by Dr. L. D. Barnett, Keeper of Oriental Printed Books and Manuscripts, and of the Introduction by Sir Richard Burn, C.S.I., to both of whom I am indebted for many suggestions. I have also to express my gratitude to Sir George Hill, K.C.B., for his stimulating interest in the work while Keeper of Coins and Director and Principal Librarian.

Considerable pains have been devoted to the many special types used in the volume, and their success is due to the draughtsmanship of Mr. C. O. Waterhouse of the Department of Greek and Roman Antiquities, and to the staff of the University Press, Oxford.

The text of the Catalogue was in print five years ago and a number of rectifications and additions appear in the Introduction.

J. ALLAN.

June 30, 1936.

CONTENTS

LIST OF PLATES

INTRODUCTION

§ 1. THE present volume of the Catalogue of Indian Coins deals with the 'Coins of Ancient India'. It covers the coins from the earliest period to about A.D. 300; its scope is that of Sir Alexander Cunningham's *Coins of Ancient India* and the coins described in it are largely from his collection.

§ 2. The coins fall into two main classes, uninscribed and unattributed, and inscribed or otherwise capable of attribution, with some degree of accuracy, to some particular period or area. The former may be divided into four classes, and the latter form one Part. The Catalogue may therefore be arranged under five heads:—

§ 3. Part I contains several classes of early silver coins distinguished from the well-known punch-marked coins by the fact that they have only a single type.

Part II contains the very large series of 'punch-marked' silver coins, the most characteristic of the early coins of India, which have regularly on one side a group of five punches found in a great variety of combinations, and on the reverse have one or more punches, usually different from those found on the obverse.

Part III consists of the equally numerous, though not so varied, early cast copper coins, which cannot be attributed to a definite area or period.

Part IV contains certain unattributed early punch-marked copper coins found in Northern India which, like the cast coins, cannot be definitely attributed.

Part V contains, alphabetically arranged, the coins which have been attributed to particular dynasties or districts on the authority of their inscriptions, types, or provenance; in the latter case the attribution is usually based on the authority of Cunningham, whose unequalled experience of such matters gives unusual weight to any pronouncements of his, even when detailed evidence of his reasons is not available. They may be conveniently referred to as 'Tribal Coins'.

§ 4. In dealing with the coins of ancient India we are at once faced with the difficulty that there is an unparalleled lack of historical, geographical, and chronological data which might enable us to arrange the coins of a dynasty in order, or in any way to check suggested attributions. Literary and epigraphic sources alike can do little to help us. The evidence of provenance which would often be of value has unfortunately not been recorded in such detail as to be useful for chronological purposes, although it yields a certain amount of vague geographical information. Cunningham's attributions in his *Coins of Ancient India* are valuable in this connexion as being based on his long experience, even when not fully documented. There are, however, certain known facts which enable us to do something for the chronological arrangement of the earliest Indian coins.

§ 5. The earliest literary reference to Indian coinage is the statement of Quintus Curtius, *Vit. Alex.* viii. 12, 42, that Omphis, king of Taxila, presented eighty talents of coined silver (*argenti signati lxxx talenta*) to Alexander the Great, which has generally been taken as evidence of the existence of coinage in India about 325 B.C.[1]

The inscriptions of Aśoka, which can be dated closely, yield a mass of epigraphical material with which the rare legends on early Indian coins can be compared from the point of view of chronology. Later definitely datable inscriptions are also of value in this connexion, especially such as contain names that can be identified with the issuers of coins.

§ 6. One chronological fact of the highest value is that Pantaleon and Agathocles copy copper coins of native Indian fabric of a type associated with Taxila, so that one type at least of the extensive

[1] We cannot follow Thomas (*P.E.*, i. 223) and Cunningham (*Num. Chron.*, 1873, p. 211) in finding a similar allusion in χρήματα ἀπηρίθμησαν of Arrian, *Alex. Anab.* 6. 16.

coinage attributed to this city was in existence *c.* 200–180 B.C. It is equally certain that the silver coins of the Audumbaras Mahādeva and Rudravarman are copied from hemidrachms of Apollodotos I Soter, and occur in finds with them, while on the silver coinage of Dharaghoṣa, the type of Viśvamitra is certainly copied from the Heracles on coins of Lysias and Zoilus. The silver coins of the Kuṇinda Amoghabhūti are also found with Indo-Greek hemidrachms of the second half of the second century B.C., and although their types are Indian, it is impossible to deny that they are influenced by the Indo-Greek hemidrachms. These few round silver coins are in striking contrast alike to the mass of copper coins among which they were issued, and in style and types to the silver punch-marked coins of ancient India.

§ 7. Another interesting point is the illustration of coinage on the Bharhut Stupa of about the middle of the second century B.C. and on the Mahābodhi Stupa at Bodh Gayā of about 100 B.C. The sculptures in each case illustrate the Buddhist legend of the purchase of the Jetavana garden at Śrāvastī, the owner of which fixed the price at the amount of money that would cover the garden. In the sculpture we see the garden being paved with coins, which it is interesting to note are mainly square. Whether the artist knew of square coins in his own time or thought that square coins were in use in Buddha's time is a question which is not important, as square and round punch-marked coins seem at all times to have been issued together, although some mints tend to prefer one shape and some another.

PART I.

VARIOUS EARLY SINGLE TYPE SILVER COINS.

§ 8. Class I. The first place in the Catalogue is given to a series of silver coins which can be shown to belong to an early period in the history of North-Western India. These are thick, slightly bent bars of silver stamped with wheel or sun-like designs, double on the larger denominations and single on the others. The general type is the same on all, but they vary in the insertion of an extra bar or pellet. It is probably to be connected with the six-armed symbol (§ 19) usually found on the punch-marked silver. The following variants of the type are found:

The interesting feature about these pieces is that they are struck on a Persian standard and represent double sigloi or staters, half- and quarter-sigloi. The siglos does not seem to be known.

§ 9. We know a little more about the provenance of these coins than is usual with early Indian coins. Setting aside Cunningham's specimens, which may have come from anywhere in North India, the Museum specimens from the Stubbs, Grant, and Whitehead collections point to the North-West, and Mr. Whitehead's specimens were purchased in Rāwal Pindī. Specimens were found in an early stratum of Taxila with punch-marked coins, and the same site yielded punch-marked coins with a gold coin of Diodotos.[1] Others were found in the Bhir mound at Taxila in a pot with punch-marked silver coins, a worn siglos, and coins of Alexander the Great and Philip Aridaeus.[2] Like the siglos, they were in a worn condition compared with the rest of the find. There are three specimens in the Indian Museum, *Cat.*, p. 136, nos. 4–6, weighing 169, 165·8, 174·1 grains, and six in the *Supplementary Cat.* (1923), p. 8, nos. 127–32, of similar weights. The coins of which the provenance is definitely known all came from that part of India which lay within the bounds of the Persian empire, from the end of the sixth to the middle of the fourth century B.C. As to the date of these pieces they are undoubtedly early, as the above-mentioned Taxila finds suggest, and the date of their issue may very well fall within the period of Persian influence in India or Afghanistan. We would suggest that they belong to the fourth,

[1] *Archaeological Survey Reports*, 1912–13, p. 42; 1919–20, p. 23; 1920–1, pp. 21–22.

[2] *Ibid.*, 1924–5, pp. 47–48.

or even fifth, century B.C., and that it may have been pieces such as these rather than the usual punch-marked coins that Omphis presented to Alexander the Great.

§ 10. Class 2 consists of a series of small oblong pieces with plain reverse and a single type on the obverse of which two varieties are known,  and . There is no definite record of the provenance of any specimens, but the Cunningham, Thomas, and Grant collections point to North India in the wide sense as distinct from South India, while the absence of specimens in the Whitehead Collection suggest they are not from the Panjab. The region of the United Provinces is therefore suggested. These pieces are all half-karṣapaṇas and no corresponding wholes appear to be known.

§ 11. Class 3 consists of a series of rude pieces with plain reverses represented in the Museum only from the Cunningham and Whitehead collections, which suggests Northern or rather N.W. India as their place of origin. One of Cunningham's specimens came from Mathurā. The central feature of the obverse type is a cat-like animal on a hill,  which suggests the , so common on certain types of punch-marked coins, but the animals clearly belong to different species. Various symbols are found in the field on the right, such as     . Two varieties are distinguished; the commonest has an uncertain object above which looks like a fish, but may be a rising sun. The second variety has a well-defined sun-like whorl in the same place. In this class also only half-karṣapaṇas are found.

§ 12. Class 4 is known only from one find, to which all the British Museum specimens can be traced, through the Elliot or Codrington collections. These are thick, slightly scyphate silver pieces with plain reverse and obverse type . Their fabric suggests an early date as it recalls that of the early copper coins of India, whose seal-like appearance suggests that they were made by impressing a die on a half-molten piece of metal. The known specimens all come from a find made in a field near Sultanpur, two miles north of Wai, in Satāra district. The find was published by Codrington in *J.B.B.R.A.S.*, 1876, pp. 400–403. Three denominations were found, double and single and half-karṣapaṇas or whole, half-, and quarter-kalinjas, of which the smallest is unrepresented in the British Museum.

The find consisted of fifty coins of this type and two others of similar fabric, neither of which is represented here. These are illustrated by Elliot, *C.S.I.*, Pl. II. 64 (wrongly described on the plate as gold, and one number is given to both as if they were obverse and reverse of one coin), and described on p. 55. One has a kind of quatrefoil design and the other a scorpion-like figure, which is probably the original of the cruder .

§ 13. Class 5 is also South Indian; besides being only known from the Elliot and Codrington collections, all specimens seem to be traceable to one find in the Konkan (Elliot, *C.S.I.*, pp. 50, 66, and 152 c, Pl. II. 61). The small size of these coins makes the types difficult to distinguish. The main type is certainly a bull  surrounded by a border of symbols or ornaments . Elliott, relying on specimens like Pl. I. 23, at first identified the animal as a lion, but later corrected this on seeing better specimens. The reverse seems to vary, but is as a rule  surrounded by a border of  &c.; on some it seems to be similar to the obverse. The weights of these small pieces are very uniform.

Classes 6 and 7, which seem to be connected in weight, are represented by three and one specimen respectively here. The fact that they are all from the Cunningham collection suggests a northern provenance. The design in Class 6 is an arrangement of small symbols to form  : the reverse is plain, as is that of Class 7. The obverse design of the latter approaches the regular punch-marked type, and it is probable that like these it had five punches on it.

Part II.

SILVER PUNCH-MARKED COINS.

§ 14. The problem of the coins to which the name punch-marked[1] is given is one of the most difficult in the Indian series. The belief that the various stamps or punches upon them were struck at different times by different hands through which they passed has hitherto prevented their real nature from being recognized. It is true that the punches on them were put on separately and not by a single die, but they were stamped at the same time by the authority issuing them and not from time to time by private individuals. A close examination shows that the types are really as distinct as those on any well-known series. They are far from being a primitive type of coin. Unfortunately we are not able to go much further at present, owing to the absence of information from literary sources and the lack of detailed information about finds from which alone we can hope for a precise chronological and geographical classification. It is to be hoped that the detailed examination of future finds on the lines laid down in this Catalogue will enable progress to be made in this field, and in time enable us to give a classification with a historical significance. One remarkable feature about them is that they show no signs of evolution.

§ 15. The collection of punch-marked coins in the British Museum represents the accumulation of a century and a half. The coins have been gathered in quite haphazard fashion, and the significance of the types was not realized. The result is that

[1] The term seems to have been first used by Prinsep, *J.A.S.B.* (1835), iv. 627.

the collection is probably not so complete as it might have been; some types are very strongly represented because the original owner happened to choose a large number from a find which came his way; other types are poorly represented because the original collector was content with a few pieces which he believed to be representative, and did not make the most of his opportunities. The collection seems on the whole to be a not unrepresentative one, to judge from the fact that specimens brought casually to the Museum are usually already represented here. The few finds also that have been published in detail and well illustrated seem to contain nothing new to the Museum collection, with the exception of the Patna find published by Mr. E. H. C. Walsh in the *Journal of the Bihar and Orissa Research Society*, 1919, pp. 16–72, the types of which are unrepresented in the Museum.

§ 16. On coming to catalogue a miscellaneous accumulation like the Museum collection of these pieces, one had to examine them minutely again and again in search of any distinguishing features. We may here mention that shape is of no significance. There are almost as many round as square, the latter term being a convenient one to use to mean 'not round', and not meaning that the pieces are in any way rectangular—round and angular would describe them better. The flans were either cut out of a sheet of metal or cast in globules. The former gave square, the latter round coins. The first thing one noticed was that a few were struck on only one side, which we may call the obverse; a large number have only one, or at most two stamps, on the reverses; others again had many small stamps on the reverse, which really suggest the 'shroff' marks, which it had been suggested all the punches were, no one of which seemed more significant than another.

On examining the obverses of the first and second of these classes which seemed more promising at first than the third, one could not help noticing that the same punches occurred over and over again, notably the sun, a circle round a pellet with three 'taurine' symbols and three arrow-heads alternately around, a mountain, an elephant, a tree in railing, &c. In time it was possible to make out all the figures used to make up the types, and to try to arrange them in some sort of order. It was soon found, for example, that all coins with the same reverse type did not have identical obverse types, so that a minute classification had to be based on the latter; there is, however, an association between groups of obverse symbols and certain reverse symbols. Having made out every symbol on the coins in the collection, many of which had to be reconstructed from several coins, it was found that every obverse bore five distinct punches. The task of getting the large number of combinations into some sort of probable order has been a long one, and one cannot claim that the arrangement finally adopted is absolutely satisfactory and final, but it is hoped that it will facilitate publication of future finds, and that the realization of the fact that these coins have types as distinct as those of Roman coins will in time enable them to be classified as easily as if they bore rulers' names. One is still disturbed by the occasional wide separation of identical reverse types and by the intervals which occasionally separate some of the rarer obverse symbols.

Of the five punches, two are almost always the sun [see § 18], and a variety of the circle with pellet in centre surrounded by two sets of three arrow-heads, taurine symbols, &c., of which there is a number of varieties [see § 19]. It is interesting to note that on the very few types on which these two symbols do not occur and are replaced by others, the remaining three symbols show them to be closely connected with other pieces of the usual type (cf. e. g. var. *f* and *g* of Class 2, Group I, with vars. *a–e*, pp. 17–24, vars. *c–h*, with *a–b* of Class 2, Group II, pp. 25–27, var. *f* of Group VII, which should perhaps go with var. *g* of Group II, with *e* and *g*).

§ 17. The five symbols which make up the type are always beautifully executed and neat pieces of minute engraving. Many of them are readily recognizable, and it is only lack of material for comparison that prevents us identifying many of the others. One thing that can be definitely said about them is that, generally speaking, they seem to have no religious significance, neither Buddhist nor Hindu. They are drawn mainly from the animal and plant world, or are combinations of symbols the meaning of which we do not know. Human figures are very rare, and only one of these is probably a deity. The number of reverse symbols is much smaller than those found on the obverse, and with very few exceptions the symbols found on the obverse do not occur on the reverse, and vice versa. A striking feature about the symbols on the silver punch-marked coins is the complete absence of some well-known Indian symbols very common on other series of coins, such as the svastika and simple triskeles, the so-called Ujjain symbol in its various forms, and the Nandipada so common in more or less elaborate forms elsewhere, the hollow cross common at Taxila. On the other hand, the symbols provide a few links with other series, especially in the reverse symbols. It is also worth noting that some of the commoner obverse symbols, such as  and , are not found on other series.

§ 18. Before proceeding to discuss the classification of these coins, we give a list of the symbols found on them.

The commonest of the symbols is the sun, which occurs on the obverse of every coin except the few small series already mentioned at the end of § 16. Four methods of representing it are distinguished in this Catalogue.[1]

1.  (Pl. X. 17)

2.  (Pl. X. 8)

3.  (Pl. VIII. 1)

4.  (Pl. VI. 25)

Nos. 1 and 2 are both very common; the difference is that in no. 2 the rays are thinner and longer than in 1. No. 3, which is a whorl, is rarer, and no. 4 is very rare. Nos. 1–3 occur on the obverse only, and no. 4 occurs on both obverse and reverse of the only coin on which it occurs, which is very unusual; on the

[1] The plate references are to coins showing the symbol very clearly.

obverse, however, it is a second symbol, the sun being represented in the commoner form 1; it may therefore be a star rather than the sun.

§ 19. We may next take the symbol, one variety of which always accompanies the preceding, and which is absent on the few varieties which do not bear the sun. Its general structure is a circle with a pellet in the centre; around the circle are six arms, three (more rarely two) of which are arrow-heads[1] and the other three are taurine symbols, fishes, triskeles in an oval, taurine in an oval, &c., and 'dumb-bell' symbols, which we meet elsewhere. It is simpler to give the forms that occur than to describe them in words. None of these symbols occurs on the reverse. Similar symbols occur, but very rarely, on other series. The following are the variants that occur on the silver coins:

1.  (Pl. III. 14)   2.  or  [2]   3.  (Pl. XLI. 23)

4.  (Pl. IV. 20)   5.  (Pl. VI. 21)   6.  (Pl. VI. 26)

7.  (Pl. IV. 9)   8.  (Pl. VIII. 11)   9.  (Pl. VIII. 14)

10.  (Pl. VIII. 21)   11.  (Pl. II. 13)   12.  (Pl. IX. 6)

13.  (Pl. VIII. 1)   14.  (Pl. IX. 11) or  [3] (Pl. X. 3)

The six-armed symbol [§ 8] which occurs on the silver bars described on pp. 1–2 belongs to this class of symbol.

[1] We use the term to indicate shape only. Theobald, *J.A.S.B.*, 1890, p. 215, calls them *chhatras* or umbrellas, in which he is followed by Mr. Walsh in his accounts of the Patna and Gorho Ghat find, *J.B. & O.R.S.*, 1919, pp. 16 f. and 443 f.

[2] The latter is no doubt the correct form (Pl. VII. 19), of which the other is only a cruder representation (Pl. VIII. 2).

[3] It is probable that the former of these forms is much the commoner and should more frequently replace the latter in the text.

§ 20. One of the commoner symbols on the punch-marked coins, and the one which can really be said to be common on other series also, is that which represents a mountain.[1] This is one of the symbols which is also found on the reverse, but a careful examination shows that the form used for the obverse is never exactly identical with one used on the reverse; it has not been always possible to cut special forms to indicate this in the text. This conscious differentiation is notable in Group I, where the reverse  is made slightly taller and thinner than the obverse . This suggests that it is important to be able to distinguish the various punches. The following representations of a mountain occur on the obverse:

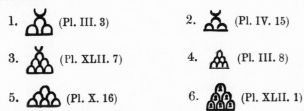

1.  (Pl. III. 3)
2.  (Pl. IV. 15)
3.  (Pl. XLII. 7)
4.  (Pl. III. 8)
5.  (Pl. X. 16)
6.  (Pl. XLII. 1)

It is difficult to separate no. 6 from the others in spite of the dumb-bell-shaped objects in the arches. Theobald suggested that they are reliquaries, one in each chamber of a stupa. As the same object is found in many other combinations, usually with the 'taurine' symbol, where it can hardly be a reliquary, we need not be prevented from identifying this type as a mountain also. In some forms this symbol has an inverted crescent on top; the fact that the two forms seem to be used indiscriminately on the coins of the Andhras and the Western Satraps, suggests there is no special significance in the crescent, especially when we remember that on the latter coins the sun and moon are already represented beside the 'mountain'. This symbol in one form or other is found on a number of other series of coins of ancient India, notably on copper coins attributed to Taxila, and in the two series above

[1] The evidence for this identification, i. e. that it is not a stupa or 'caitya', is summed up by Ananda Coomaraswamy in the *Ostas. Zeitschr.*, N.F., iv, pp. 175–9.

mentioned. It does not seem, in spite of its wide distribution, to occur on the numerous series of punch-marked copper coins here attributed to Eran and Ujjayinī. It is not found on the coins in this Catalogue associated with the 'Ujjain symbol', so that the close associations of these two symbols on the coins of Śātavāhana family is of interest (Rapson, *Cat. of Coins of A. & W. K.*, Pls. VI and IX). We may note its occurrence on a seal from Pāṭaliputra, *A.S.R.*, 1912–13, Pl. XLIX. 10, and also on Pl. XLIX. 6. We may now take the forms of this symbol found on the reverse only (see also § 39):

7.  (Pl. II. 5) 8.  (Pl. XLII. 2)

9. 

No. 7 is distinguished from 1 by being thinner; and 8 is a small copy of no. 1. In the text (e.g. p. 50, no. 48) no. 9 has been occasionally used on the reverse. It is really different from no. 2, however, being somewhat smaller. It is of course not possible to cut type for every variety. We may here note that the 'river' symbol, which is not uncommon on other series and associated with the mountain, is not found on the punch-marked coins.

§ 21. We may next take a small group of symbols of which the basis is the 'mountain' type. These are:

10.  (Pl. IV. 10) 11.  (Pl .VII. 13)

12.  (Pl. VII. 18)

and may for convenience be described as a peacock or dog (it may well be a jackal) and a tree on a hill. No. 9 is an important reverse type, and is one of the very few symbols which are used on the reverse in a form absolutely identical with the reverse type. Nos. 10 and 11 are found on the obverse only. Each belongs to a different group of coins. They are, so far as we know, not found on any other series with the exception of no. 10 on the unique and uncertain coin described on p. 279, no. 1. With no. 10 we may perhaps compare the type of Class 3 (pp. 6–7, § 11), but the animal is different. No. 12 is found on some rare early Andhra coins (Rapson, *C.A.W.K.*, Pl. II. 17–18).

§ 22. We now come to the animals used in the types. The first of these is the elephant, which is found on the obverse in two well-marked and distinct groups of coins in forms which we have distinguished as 1 and 2:

1.  (Pl. II. 6) 2.  (Pl. VIII. 8) 3.  (Pl. IV. 24)

Nos. 1 and 2 are only found on the obverse; no. 3, an elephant surrounded by small 'taurine' symbols, is very rare, and only occurs as a countermark on the reverse of a well-known type. In other series the elephant is especially found on the cast copper coins and on the coins here attributed to Eran and Taxila. Although a common type it seems therefore to have a local significance.

4.  (Pl. III. 16)

It is difficult to know how to describe no. 4, which is very distinct on Pl. III. 16 (on its side) and 17. It is characteristic of a little group of coins, most of which (var. *e–g*) of Class 2, Group I, do not bear the sun and six-rayed symbol. It occurs nowhere else.

§ 23. The bull is a very common type on the punch-marked as on the coins of ancient India generally. On many series it is undoubtedly the bull Nandi of Śiva, but that one ought to attribute so definite a religious significance to it on the punch-marked coins is unlikely. The following forms occur:

1.  (Pl. II. 10) 2.  (Pl. III. 3)

3.  (Pl. XLII. 6) 4.  (Pl. VI. 4)

5.  (Pl. VIII. 16)

No. 2 is only found with the 'taurine' symbol in front of it, and no. 4 only with the two fish-like symbols which, like the taurine, frequently occur in combinations. While the bull is a common type, there are large and well-marked groups on which it does not occur. It is a common type on many of the tribal series, very frequently accompanied by a tree in railing, but its absence from Taxila and rarity on the varied types of Eran and Ujjain may be noted. The bull does not occur as a major reverse type, nor is it found on any reverse in the British Museum collection. It occurs, however, on one of a number of punches on the coin on Pl. II. 43, in Mr. Walsh's Gorho Ghat find.

§ 24. The next common animal type is one which might conveniently be described as a dog seizing a young hare or rabbit; in its clearest form it is certainly an animal of the dog type seizing a young animal, but it is perhaps too much to identify them (nos. 1 and 2) definitely. It is Theobald's no. 44, fig. 27 (*J.A.S.B.*,

1.  (Pl. XLII. 17)

2.  (Pl. X. 13)

3.  (Pl. V. 14, 16)

4.  (Pl. II. 6)

5.  (Pl. II. 5)

6.  (Pl. IV. 5)

7.  (Pl. V. 8, 18)

1894, p. 221), and Mr. Walsh's no. 45 on Pl. IV of the Gorho Ghat find. We group here with it a number of other symbols, some of a similar animal alone (no. 6) and others which seem to be crude copies of this type (nos. 3, 4, 5). No. 41, incomplete in British Museum specimens, is shown in full in Mr. Walsh's Pl. IV, nos. 16, 17, and 19. This symbol characterizes several well-marked groups of coins, and is absent from certain classes. It never occurs on the reverse, nor is anything like it found on any other series of coins. A parallel type is that of a large fish seizing a small one, which is not on any coin in the Museum, but is shown by Thomas[1] and by Theobald, *loc. cit.*, no. 46 (Pl. I. 30). We may include in this paragraph the curious animal (no. 7) with a taurine symbol for a head or in its mouth.

[1] *Ancient Indian Weights*, Pl. I, l. 7, nos. 1 and 2.

§ 25. We may class together two symbols in which an animal is associated with a tree, although this is really the only feature they have in common:

1.  (Pl. XLI. 12, 16) 2.  (Pl. VI. 11)

No. 1 always has a vase on its side above it. Theobald (no. 224) describes no. 1 as a goat browsing on a vine. The animal certainly seems to be horned, but that it is a goat is more doubtful. It is more probably of the deer family, an animal such as is found on the coins of the Kuṇindas. Theobald calls no. 2 a jackal looking up at a tree in a railing, and adds that it looks as if designed to perpetuate the fable of the 'fox and grapes', which certainly sums up the type admirably. Neither type occurs on any other series where the association of a bull and occasionally of a deer with a tree in a railing is common. Neither symbol is found on the reverse, and the series of coins on which they are found are closely connected. Both are absent from large classes of punch-marked coins.

§ 26. An animal which forms a characteristic symbol on one group of coins is the rhinoceros, which survived in the Panjab

1.  (Pl. VIII. 8) 2. 

down to the sixteenth century. The horn is always represented as curved forwards as on the 'unicorn' of the Mohenjo-daro seals. This type is not found on the reverse nor on any other series. The wolf (no. 2) is of rare occurrence, but may be identified as the animal no. 15, on p. 44.

§ 27. The rabbit occurs on several varieties of coins either alone or in combination with symbols. No. 3 is the most interesting,

1.  (Pl. VII. 5, 7) 2.  3.  (Pl. III. 17)

4.  (Pl. VII. 8) 5.  (Pl. VI, 26)

a rabbit in a crescent, which presumably represents the crescent moon and may be compared with the type on the coin of Viṣnudeva, p. 147, no. 3 (**Pl. XIX. 13**). No. 2 may also represent the moon. Nos. 1–3 are found only on the obverse, and no. 4 on the reverse, possibly on one obverse also. It is probably the same animal that is represented on the rare symbol . No. 5, the little animal that occurs on a well-marked class of coin, is probably of a different family like the weasel. Theobald thinks it might be a jackal or fox.

§ 28. The scorpion (no. 1) is a rare type, as is the snake of which

1.  (Pl. VIII. 17) 2.  (Pl. X. 5)

3.  (Pl. VII. 13) 4.  (Pl. VI. 17)

two forms (2 and 3) are found, evidently representing different species. No. 4 seems to be a double snake, but it is not clear on the only specimen on which it is found.

These conclude the animals found on the punch-marked coins in the Museum. Two animals which are found on other series of Indian coins, the lion and the horse, are not found here; the tiger is another notable omission. Birds are not found alone at all, and the only birds are the peacock on a hill and a bird on a tree in a rare type. A bird of the bustard type is found on a reverse (cf. § 39, no. 26).

§ 29. Fish and other denizens of water are well represented, and are characteristic of a number of varieties. The commonest type

1.  or 2.  (Pl. X. 20) 3.  (Pl. VI. 21)

4. 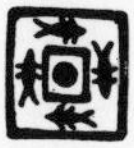 (Pl. VIII. 10, 11)

is that representing two or four fishes in a tank. No. 3, four fishes in a square tank with probably a lingam on a square pedestal in the centre, is a characteristic mark of a large class of coins, and occurs nowhere else. Nos. 1 or 2 (the fish may be represented either to right or to left) is found on several varieties of different classes. It is also found on the rare Uddehikā coins and at Ujjayinī, where we also have no. 3. These types are only found on the obverse.

5.  (Pl. IX. 22),  (Pl. II. 15)

6.  (Pl. X. 20) 7.  (Pl. IV. 9)

8.  (Pl. X. 4)

No. 5, two fishes with a spear-head between them (with it we put another symbol occurring incompletely on one coin only; it may be the same type); no. 6, a fish in a crescent; and no. 7, a little fish in a rectangle, are all rare, and each occurs on the obverse of one variety only. No. 8 only occurs on the reverse. These, which we might call conventional fishes to distinguish them from the more realistic representations of actual species, are also found, like the taurine symbol, as constituent elements of a number of symbols.

9.  (Pl. V. 17) 10.  (Pl. VIII. 24) 11. 

12.  13.  14.  15. 

Nos. 9–13 are the varieties of fishes found on the obverses; no. 11 is occasionally found on the reverse, and nos. 13 and 15 only on the reverse; no. 14 is not found alone but only in combination on one variety with .

15.  16.  17.  (Pl. VI. 15)

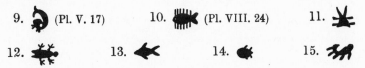

The frog, either alone (no. 15) or between two taurine symbols no. 16), occurs on varieties only as does the tortoise with a taurine symbol. The frog is also found on a few rare coins from Ujjayinī, but the tortoise (no. 17) seems to be unknown elsewhere. Both animals are found on the obverse only.

§ 30. Trees and branches play a prominent part among the types of punch-marked coins. The commonest are conventional representations of a sacred tree in a railing, which is one of the commonest of Indian symbols. Representation of particular species of trees and branches from them are also found. Nos. 1 to 5 are

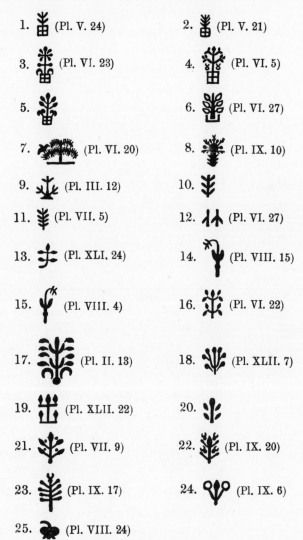

1.  (Pl. V. 24)

2.  (Pl. V. 21)

3.  (Pl. VI. 23)

4.  (Pl. VI. 5)

5. 

6.  (Pl. VI. 27)

7.  (Pl. VI. 20)

8.  (Pl. IX. 10)

9.  (Pl. III. 12)

10. 

11.  (Pl. VII. 5)

12.  (Pl. VI. 27)

13.  (Pl. XLI. 24)

14.  (Pl. VIII. 15)

15.  (Pl. VIII. 4)

16.  (Pl. VI. 22)

17.  (Pl. II. 13)

18.  (Pl. XLII. 7)

19.  (Pl. XLII. 22)

20. 

21.  (Pl. VII. 9)

22.  (Pl. IX. 20)

23.  (Pl. IX. 17)

24.  (Pl. IX. 6)

25.  (Pl. VIII. 24)

forms of the tree in railing found on varieties of the obverse type; nos. 1 and 2 are also found on the reverse. No. 3 occurs once on the reverse as a countermark on an otherwise well-known variety. The tree in railing is one of the commonest types on the early cast copper coins and on the tribal coins. It is perhaps a little rarer at Taxila. No. 6 is found on a rare type so distinct as to form a class by itself. It is evidently a representation of a particular tree, as is no. 7, a tree with a bird settling on it, which is characteristic of one variety, and recalls the type of a series of cast coins. No. 8, which is characteristic of a group of coins, is clearly also a particular species of tree. No. 9 is classed here as it is probably a conventional representation of a tree and branches. It is characteristic of a well-marked series of coins. Nos. 10 and 11 are branches and are found only on the reverses. No. 12, which is only found on the reverse of a rare variety, may represent two branches. Nos. 13–20 and probably 24 are all more (notably 14–15) or less accurate representations of branches or sprays, and are characteristic of varieties of obverse type. Nos. 21–23 are conventional branch-like figures formed of or combined with taurine symbols. They also are only found on obverses. No. 25, which we may include here, is the only flower found on these coins, and is found on the obverse of one variety only.

§ 31. Weapons and tools are exceedingly rare. No. 1 is a bolt-like object which occurs on a rare variety. The bow and arrow

1.  (Pl. XLI. 1) 2.  (Pl. IX. 5) 3.  (Pl. IX. 15)

with (no. 2), and without (no. 3) a taurine symbol are found on the obverse of two groups. It is a common type on early Andhra

4.  (Pl. IV. 12) 5.  (Pl. IX. 4) 6.  (Pl. IX. 18)

coins from Kolhapur (Rapson, *C.A.W.K.*, pp. 5–9, Pls. I–IV). The steelyard (no. 4) is the essential element in a type found on the obverse of a number of varieties of a group of coins. It is also the type of some coins attributed to Ayodhyā. Nos. 5 and 6 are two varieties of wheels found in obverse types; we include them here as their rarity suggests that they are simply wheels, and not of any religious significance. No. 6 may be a water-wheel.

§ 32. A large group of symbols is formed by combinations of taurine symbols. None of them is common, and most of them are characteristic of varieties only.

1.  (Pl. IV. 17)
2.  (Pl. VI. 14)
3.  (Pl. IV. 15)
4.  (Pl. II. 13)
5.  (Pl. VI. 20)
6.  (Pl. II. 12)
7.  (Pl. IV. 22)
8.  (Pl. IX. 5)
9.  (Pl. IX. 4)
10.  (Pl. X. 17)
11.  (Pl. X. 17)
12.  (Pl. IX. 24)
13. 
14.  (Pl. IX. 17)
15.  (Pl. XLI. 4)
16.  (Pl. XLI. 6)
17.  (Pl. IX. 19)
18.  (Pl. VI. 26)

With the exception of no. 18 in a smaller form these are all confined to obverses; a small form of no. 1, , is however a common reverse symbol. They are found throughout the series, and there is scarcely a group without one of them, so that their distribution is very general. They are peculiar to the punch-marked series, and have no parallels on the other series of coins of ancient India.

§ 33. Along with these we may group a number of symbols in

1.  (Pl. VIII. 4)
2.  (Pl. X. 17)
3. 
4.  (Pl. XLII. 23–24)

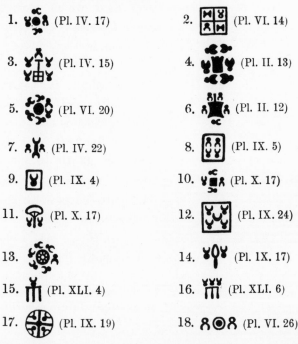

the formation of which the 'taurine', fish, and other symbols only play a secondary part.

No. 1 is found on the obverse of several groups of a large class of coins. The object without the taurine symbols is a common one on several other series of coins.  and  are found on various cast coins, and  on coins of Kauśambī, Taxila, and Ujjain; in a railing it is found on coins of Eran. A similar object occurs on Andhra coins and on the disc from Pataliputra, *A.S.R.*, 1912–13, Pl. XLIX. 6. Prinsep calls it a *jayadhvaja* (*J.A.S.B.*, iv, p. 628). It evidently represents some familiar object. Nos. 2, 3, and 4 are all rare, and found on the obverses of varieties. A form of no. 1 is found on reverses.

§ 34. One very common symbol has not yet been mentioned. It occurs (no. 1) on many varieties of coins in Class II, and in a slightly different form in a group of Class 6. It consists of three circles lying on a straight line, in the one form touching each

1.  (Pl. V. 1) 2.  (Pl. X. 7)

other, and in the other at a little distance from each other. It has been called a caduceus, with which it really has no relationship. A somewhat similar object is found on the coin of Viṣṇudeva, p. 147, **Pl. XIX. 13.** No. 1 is also a very common reverse symbol, and is among the few that are found on both obverse and reverse of the same coin; the reverse form is perhaps slightly smaller than that of the obverse, but otherwise it is indistinguishable. Common as it is on the punch-marked series, the type does not seem to be found on other series. It seems to have an ancestor on the seal from Mohenjo-daro, *A.S.R.*, 1925–6, Pl. XLV. 20.

Arrangements of squares and triangles are not common. No. 3

3.  (Pl. IX. 11) 4.  (Pl. IX. 9)

5.  6. 

is only found on the obverses of a very distinctive little group of coins. No. 4, the pentagram, occurs on the obverse of one variety only. The hexagram is found on coins from the Golakhpur find. Nos. 5 and 6 are rare, and are also found on the reverse.

§ 35. There is a little group of symbols which may represent edifices of some kind.

1.  (Pl. II. 15) 2.  (Pl. XLII. 25)

3.  (Pl. XLII. 17) 4.  (Pl. X. 1)

5.  (Pl. III. 5) 6.  (Pl. X. 21)

Nos. 1 and 2 are called by Theobald a raised grain-store with a pole in front, which certainly describes it. It is probable that there is only one form, and that the pole in var. *a*, Group X, should have a spear-head as in var. *b*. This symbol occurs on the obverse of this group only. Nos. 3 and 4 are fairly common on the obverse of a number of varieties of Class 2. No. 5 is found on the obverse of one variety and the reverse of another variety of Group I of Class 5. No. 6 occurs once only on an obverse of one variety of Group VII of Class 6. None of these is found on any other series of coins.

§ 36. The remaining obverse symbols, with the exception of those representing human figures, are the following:

1.  (Pl. V. 12) 2.  (Pl. V. 7)

3.  (Pl. IV. 7) 4.  (Pl. IV. 19)

5.  (Pl. VII. 10) 6.  7. 

No. 1 is a neat little symbol occurring on several varieties; it looks like three spear-heads on an oval which stands on two legs. No. 2 is a triskeles combined with the curious symbol already mentioned above, § 33, no. 1. The triskeles is a common reverse type, but is only found in this combination in the obverse. Similarly, the common reverse type  (no. 3) is only found in combination on the obverse. No. 4 is a rare symbol. It is possibly a hand. No. 5, four adjacent circles with pellets in the centre occurs on obverses only, usually as a countermark. No. 6 is of rare occurrence. No. 7, of rare occurrence, is probably only a part of § 33, no. 4.

§ 37. Representations of the human figure or of deities are rare, but are occasionally found. The most striking is the group of three struck from one punch (no. 1), which occurs on certain varieties of Group II of Class 2, and seem also to occur on a rare coin of Ujjayinī (**Pl. XLIV. 22**). The three figures struck from separate punches on var. *g* of Group I, Class 2, are presumably

1.  (Pl. V. 13) 2.  (Pl. III. 17)

identical with this group. They occur on the obverse only, except in one case (**Pl. XLII. 23**) as a countermark, and not as a regular reverse type. The interesting point about these three figures is that they occur only on the rare groups of coins which do not have the sun or a figure of the form . In the case of the second group a number of variants have been distinguished in the text (pp. 21–23), but they are presumably only due to the die-cutter.

3.  (Pl. XLI. 10) 4.  (Pl. V. 9)

5.  (Pl. V. 19)

No. 3 is one of the most interesting of the punch-marked coins, as it is one which is found identically on another series—the copper coins attributed to Ujjayinī (see p. 248, **Pl. XXXVIII. 11** and **14**). This enables us to identify the figure as Kārttikeya, who appears six-headed on some coins of Ujjayinī, and may therefore be recognized in the other forms in which he appears there. This type is also represented facing at Ujjayinī (cf. p. 245). No. 4, which looks like a rudely made human figure with the 'dumb-bell' symbols at either side, is found on coins closely related to those which contain nos. 3 and 5, and is probably the same deity (cf. Ujjayinī, p. 263, **Pl. XXXVII. 7**). These two figures are found on the obverse only of two clearly related varieties. No. 5 is a vigorously represented little figure. The only other representation of the human figure on punch-marked coins is confined to the reverse (cf. below, § 39, 29). Hanumān, the monkey god, is found on one coin (**Pl. XLVI. 17**).

§ 38. The reverses of the punch-marked coins may be divided into two classes: those which have a definite type; in this class we would include the large number which have two or even three punches, because on examination it is usually found that the second and third are later countermarks. In most cases the earliest punch is more worn than the later one, and even in cases where it is not obvious to the eye, it is probable that the punches were put on at intervals. The second class consists of coins which have a large number of small punches on them, none of which has the prominence nor probably the significance of the reverse type of the first class. In most cases it is quite impossible to identify the individual punches in the confusion in which they are struck; still less has it been possible to cut special type to illustrate them in this Catalogue.

Classes 1–5 of this Catalogue belong to the first class and 6–7 to the second. The two classes show a marked difference in fabric, the second being larger and thinner than the first. The coins with plain reverses do not form a distinct class. Their obverses always bring them into one of these two classes.

§ 39. With one or two exceptions the types of the first class of reverses are not found on the obverses. The symbols found on the reverses are much fewer in number than those found on the obverse. The significant reverse types are the following:

1.  (Pl. XLII. 7) 2.  (Pl. VI. 25)

No. 1 is probably a representation of the sun, but it is not exactly like the common form on the obverse. It is very rare. No. 2 may also be the sun or, as already suggested (§ 18), perhaps a star. It is very rare. Next we may distinguish three well-

3.  (Pl. II. 5) 4.  5.  (Pl. II. 15)

marked types of the mountain symbol, all of which are common. This, as already remarked, is a prominent type on other series, notably on the copper coins of Taxila. Nos. 6–12 are all also found on the obverse, and have been already mentioned above.

6.  (Pl. IV. 10) 7.  (Pl. V. 1)

8.  (Pl. V. 24) 9.  (Pl. VII. 6)

10.  (Pl. XLI. 5, 24) 11.  (Pl. VI. 5)

12.  (Pl. IV. 5)

Three very common reverse symbols (nos. 13–15) are not found on the obverse. No. 13 is a pellet surrounded by four semicircles,

13.  (Pl. IV. 21) 14.  (Pl. IV. 1)

15.  (Pl. VI. 1)

a type which has been associated with Taxila from its frequent occurrence on coins found there, e.g. **Pl. XXXV. 12.** In no. 14, of which 15 is a smaller form, two of the semicircles are replaced by the conventional fish so common in the formation of symbols. This type is also found at Taxila, e.g. on the unique gold coin, **Pl. XXXV. 11.** No. 16 is a small form of a not uncommon

16.  (Pl. IV. 19) 17.  (Pl. V. 12)

obverse symbol. No. 17 is found on the obverse, but there it is always combined with another symbol (see § 36, no. 2). No. 18 is another form of the triskeles. No. 19, the taurine symbol, and

18.  (Pl. VI. 4) 19.  (Pl. V. 8)

20.  (Pl. V. 13)

20, the 'dumb-bell' symbol, are both very familiar constituents of obverse symbols, but the latter is not found alone on the obverse and the former very rarely. Nos. 21–24, none of which are common,

21.  (Pl. IX. 8) 22. 

23.  (Pl. XLII. 17) 24. 

25.  (Pl. VI. 27) 26.  (Pl. IV. 24)

are not found on the obverse. Representations of animals are rare; we have, however, an elephant surrounded by taurine symbols (no. 26) which occurs several times, in each case as a countermark; it is not found on the obverse; a curious bird is also found once (no. 27). Two forms of fish are found, one (no. 28) a particular

27.  (Pl. IX. 8) 28.  (Pl. VI. 15)

29.  (Pl. X. 4)

species, and the other (no. 29) a conventional fish in a circle. The only representation of the human figure found is a little figure of a deity holding a staff and bag (no. 30), who is perhaps the same

30.  (Pl. V. 19) 31.  (Pl. XLII. 23)

as § 37, no. 3, who is probably Kārttikeya, but the two figures are not quite identical; on one coin a group of three figures occurs on the reverse, but the coin is not in sufficiently good preservation to identify them with certainty. They are probably (no. 31) the same as the obverse group, § 37, no. 1.

§ 40. These reverse types belong to Classes 1 and 2 of this Catalogue, the coins in which are linked together by their obverse types, and we find some reverse types recurring through these series, although in a general way an agreement between obverse and reverse type can be noted in the groups or in several varieties together. The following notes on reverse types will be useful in the ultimate classification of the punch-marked series. The following groups of symbols are found with identical obverses:

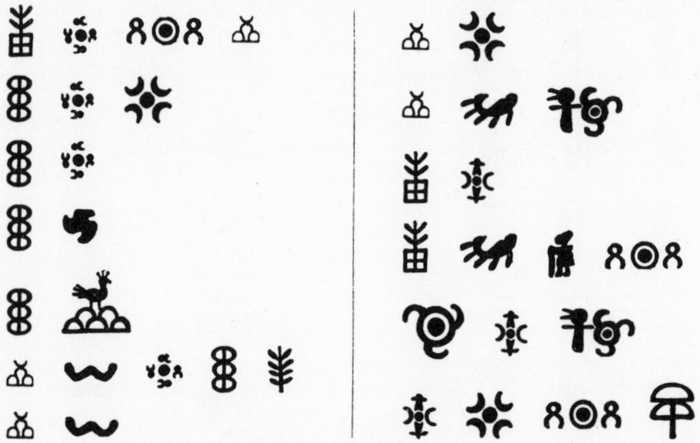

§ 41. It is very unusual to find countermarks as evidence of re-striking on the obverse; only one countermark is found, but it occurs several times, namely, . With the reverse it is different, and we find two or even three symbols stamped on coins, which in many cases can be seen to have been done at intervals. We have noted the following associations of reverse types on punch-marked coins:

 is countermarked on 

 is countermarked on 

 is countermarked on 

 is countermarked over 

 is countermarked over  and vice versa.

  and  are found together, probably having been countermarked in this order.

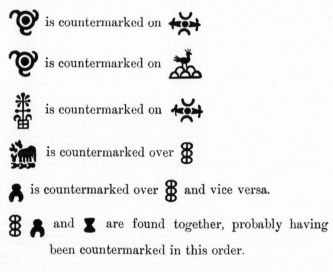

The following groups are found together on one coin, but it is impossible to say whether they were struck at the same time or not.

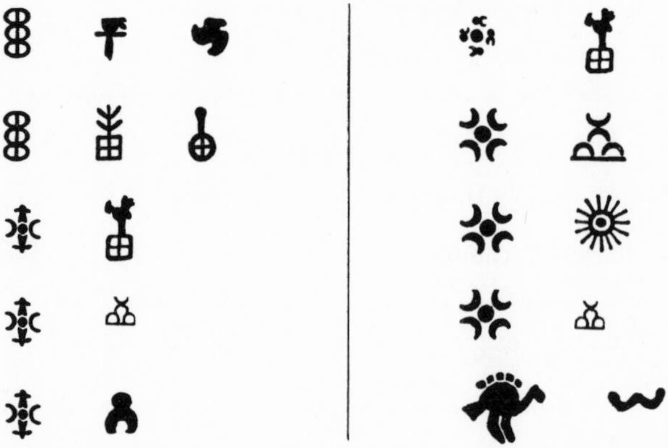

§ 42. It is impossible to treat the second class of reverses in the same detail. The reader may be referred to the coins illustrated on Plates VII to X. The symbols on these are smaller, and it is impossible to pick out one as more significant than the others. It is probably right to say that none of the reverse symbols of the first class occur among them. One of course finds some similar, such as a small mountain, fish, branches, &c., but they are not really connected with those of the first class. Geometrical patterns and arrangements of pellets are common. Among these reverse symbols we may note the following:

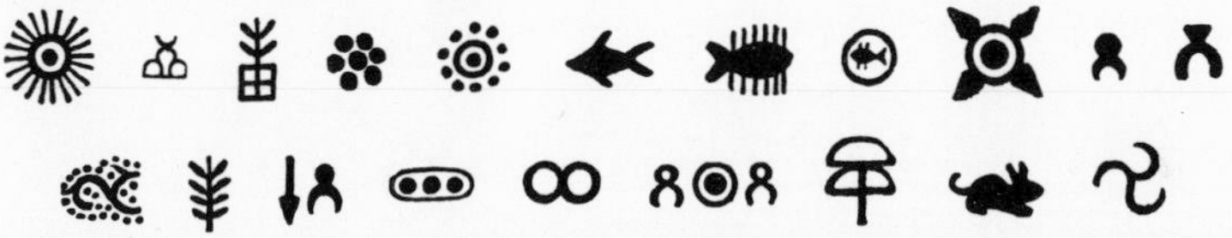

For convenience the same type has been used for some of these symbols as in other series, e.g. the sun, tree in railing, but they are not to be taken as identical.

§ 43. We have here collected the information available about finds of punch-marked coins. Very few hoards have been fully published, and little is recorded of the constitution of most of them. The evidence of provenance is of some interest, and there is some valuable evidence for chronology.

We may first record what is evidently an unpublished find in the British Museum. This consists of the coins from the Swiney[1] collection here catalogued as varieties *a–c* of Class 1. These coins, in addition to similarity of type, have a similarity of fabric, and are characterized by a reddish tinge acquired during their period of deposit in the earth. All the coins have the same reverse punch  not found exactly in any other class. The find contained three types of obverse of the form *a b c d e*, *a b c d f*, *a b c d g*, i.e. four fixed and one variable. Nothing is known of the provenance of the hoard, but the other coins acquired at the same time point

[1] Captain G. C. Swiney, nephew of General Swiney, not the celebrated collector Dr. Swiney.

to the Panjab: and similar coins have been brought to the Museum with Afghan and Panjab coins.

§ 44. A very important find not yet published in full is that recorded by Sir John Marshall[1] from the Bhir mound at Taxila. It consisted of 1,167 silver coins and some jewellery in an earthenware pot six feet below the present surface in association with the second stratum, which had already been judged to belong to the third or fourth century B. C. Some of the coins were the oblong bars described in this Catalogue on pp. 1–2, **Pl. I. 1–3**; others were the minute pieces punched on one side only, described on pp. 286–7, **Pl. XLVI. 18–19.** Most important are two coins of Alexander the Great and one of Philip Aridaeus, 'fresh from the mint', and an Achaemenid siglos of the type of Hill, *B.M.C. Persia*, &c., Pl. XXVII. 19–20, i. e. of the fourth century B. C. The remainder are punch-marked coins. Of the specimens illustrated in the Plate nearly all belong to Class 6 of this Catalogue, and a few seem to belong to Class 2. It is not always possible to identify the coins accurately from the Plate, but the following are represented:

Class 2, Group VII, var. *i*.
„ „ VIII, var. *d*.

Class 6, Group I, var. *a*, *e*.
„ „ II, var. *e*.
„ „ III, var. *b–f*.
„ „ IV, var. *a–f*.
„ „ V, var. *a*.
„ „ VI, var. *d*.
„ „ VII, var. *e*.

A number of other coins can be attributed to these groups, without its being possible to identify the exact variety. This find affords important support for the classification here proposed. The date of burial of the hoard cannot be much later than the early third century or even the close of the fourth century B. C.

[1] *Archaeological Survey of India, Annual Report*, 1924–5, pp. 47–8, Pl. IX.

§ 45. Another important find from North-West India was published by Dr. D. B. Spooner in the *Arch. Survey Rep.*, 1905–6, pp. 150–5, Pl. LIV. It was found in an earthenware vessel nine or ten feet below the surface at the southern end of the grounds of Government House, Peshawar. Dr. Spooner's article is the first serious attempt to classify punch-marked coins, to call attention to constant groups of symbols on the coins, and to insist that they are not haphazard. His insistence on the Buddhist character of the symbols seems hardly justified.

Sixty-one coins from the find were recovered and examined, but it is not known how many were originally in the hoard. If the coins recovered were typical of the whole, then the bulk of the deposit consisted of coins of our Class 2, Group I, var. *a*, with the 'Taxila' symbol on the reverse. The remainder were of the following varieties:

Class 2, Group II, var. *c*.
„ „ IV, var. *e*.
„ „ V, var. *c*.
„ „ VII, var. *i*.
„ „ VIII, var. *e* and a new var.
„ „ X, var. *b*.

In addition a number of coins were clearly of these groups, although it is impossible to identify the exact variety from the photographs. Group III is probably present in one of the coins on which the symbol  is legible. In any case it is clearly so closely connected with Group IV that its absence is not serious. The absence of Group IX is interesting as it is really a very distinct group, although connected with Class 2 by the symbol  on the obverse. Some of the coins in this find, e.g. Pl. A. 26 and B. 13, seem to be new varieties. There is no clue to the date of the hoard; the large number of one variety (I, *a*) present probably means that these are the local issues rather than the latest in date. Cunningham (*A.S.R.* xiv, pp. 19–20, Pl. X. 1) has noted that three-quarters of the coins from Shāh Dheri, i. e. Taxila, were of this type (Class 2, Group I, var. *a*).

175 punch-marked coins were found with a gold coin of Diodotos in a single deposit in the Bhir mound[1] at Taxila. These were of 'copper with a slight admixture of silver, and most of them had on the reverse the so-called Taxila symbol', i. e. they were of Class 2, Group I. The only specimen illustrated (Pl. XL. 1) is of Class 2, Group I, var. *a*. This find is further evidence of the association of this type with the Taxila region. The date of this hoard is indicated by the coin of Diodotos as the latter half of the third century B. C. The coins in this find were probably originally plated. The British Museum has very few of these plated coins, but they are quite common. They are of the same type as the silver, and traces of the plating occasionally survive, but the majority at first sight seem to be copper.

The miscellaneous coins found at Sirkap (Taxila)[2] included punch-marked pieces and silver bars of the type described in § 8 with the corresponding small round pieces. With them were well-known copper coins of Taxila, and some clue to the date is given by the fact that a coin of Demetrius was found in a slightly later stratum.

In a monastery at Taxila[3] punch-marked coins were found with coins of Kadphises I and II, Kanishka, Vasudeva, and Sassanian coins of the third to fourth centuries A. D.

In the Lower City of Taxila many punch-marked coins were found as well as coins of Apollodotos, Philoxenos, Maues, Azes I and II, Gondophares, Soter Megas, Kadphises I and II. These two records show that punch-marked coins were still in use in the first centuries B. C. and A. D.

§ 46. A little find of ten coins was made in a hillock north-west of Thatta[4] in the Pindigheb tahsil of the Attock district. Nine of these were punch-marked pieces 'of the local Taxilan' type, i. e. Class 2, Group I. From the symbols mentioned—bull, taurine,

[1] Marshall, *A.S.R.*, 1912-13, p. 42.
[2] *A.S.R.*, 1919-20, pp. 21-2.
[3] *A.S.R.*, 1923-4, p. 26.
[4] *A.S.R.*, 1926-7, p. 229.

and tree—they were evidently again of var. *a* of this group. With them was a hemidrachm of the horseman type of Philoxenos, which puts the date of burial of the hoard in the latter part of the second century B. C.

§ 47. A small collection of punch-marked coins was published by Mr. R. D. Banerji in the *Num. Suppl.* to the *J.A.S.B.*, 1910, § 76, as a find from Afghanistan. They were given to the Asiatic Society of Bengal by the Amir of Afghanistan when in Calcutta. This seems the only reason for describing them as having been found in Afghanistan. That they were found together is probable, as there seems to be little variety in the types. The coins, forty-four in number, were in very poor condition, and it is impossible to identify many of them accurately. It is clear, however, from the occurrence of symbols , , and  upon them that they belong mainly to Group VII of Class 2, and one (no. 27) on which  is clear, may be of Group XI. From a comparison with the finds already described above, a north-western provenance seems indicated, and the coins may well have been found within the boundaries of modern Afghanistan. One coin (no. 38) bears a 'Taxila' symbol. We are unable to follow Mr. Banerji in finding Brāhmī letters on these coins. What he took for letters were no doubt incomplete portions of well-known symbols.

§ 48. A find of punch-marked coins was made in the Shahpur district of the Rawalpindi division in 1895, and is briefly recorded in the *Proc. B.B.R.A.S.*, 1896, p. xli. The British Museum received four coins from this find; these were of Class 2, Group I, var. *a* (no. 17), var. *d* (no. 38), Group VII, var. *a* (no. 10), and Class 6, Group III, var. *e* (no. 36), so that it seems to have had the same constitution as the finds already mentioned from Taxila.

Unfortunately we have no details of the few punch-marked coins found in the Kangra district about 1853[1] with silver coins of Antiochus II, Philoxenos, Lysios, Antialkidas, and Menander,

[1] Cunningham, *Num. Chron.*, 1873, p. 209.

but their much-worn state is contrasted with the freshness of the Greek pieces.

§ 49. It is unfortunate that few finds from parts of India other than the north-west have been published in any detail. There are, however, two notable exceptions in the two finds from Bengal so carefully published and discussed by Mr. E. H. C. Walsh. They are from Gorho Ghat [1] in the Bangaon thana of the Bhagalpur district and from Golakhpur in Patna city.[2] The Gorho Ghat find which, with the pot containing it, was recovered intact, contained fifty-eight silver punch-marked coins of types represented in this Catalogue. So far as they can be identified from the plates and descriptions with coins in the British Museum, the hoard included the following types—one cannot always be sure of the exact variety with certainty:

Class 2.	Group I,	var.	*a* (nos. 1, 3)
,,	,,	,,	*b* (2, 4, 6)
,,	,,	,,	*e* (7, 8, 9)
,,	,,	,,	*h* ? (19)
,,	,, II,	,,	*a* (20, 21, 43)
,,	,,	,,	*e* (53, 56)
,,	,, III,	,,	*c* (44)
,,	,,	,,	*g* (45)
,,	,,	,,	*i* (13)
,,	,, IV,	,,	? (49)
,,	,,	,,	*u* or *v* (22, 23)
,,	,, V,	,,	*a* or *b* (37)
,,	,, VII,	,,	*a* (14-18)
,,	,,	,,	*h* (47)
,,	,, X,	,,	*k*
Class 6.	,, I,	,,	*a* (46)
,,	,, II,	,,	*d* (43)
,,	,,	,,	*e* (41–42)

[1] *Journal of the Bihar and Orissa Research Society*, 1919, pp. 463–94, Plates I–III.

[2] *Ibid.*, 1919, pp. 16–72, Plates I–IV.

Class 6, Group III, var. *c* (44)
" " " *g* (45)
" " IV, " *a* (48)
" " " *e* (50)

When thus tabulated this find resembles that of the Bhir mound find (§ 44), but it is to be remembered that the proportions are very different. This find consists almost entirely of coins of Class 2 with a small proportion of Class 6, while in the Bhir mound find the vast majority of the coins belong to Class 6.

§ 50. Another find from the Bhagalpur district is mentioned by Cunningham.[1] He says he had seen in the Indian Museum in London seven punch-marked coins found by Grant in a subterranean passage in Bhagalpur. They bear the 'usual figures of the sun, bull, chaitya, tree, soldier with shield and dog'. These coins are probably now in the British Museum, but no record of provenance came with them from the India Office. They may have been of Groups III, VI, and VII of Class 2.

§ 51. The other find published by Mr. Walsh consists of coins of a type hitherto unknown. It was found at Golakhpur in Patna city in a jar in the river bank, and contained 108 coins. It was a very homogeneous find. The coins are remarkable for their large fabric which enables the punches to be distinctly and separately impressed without merging into one another as is so common on smaller coins. Like the coins with which we are familiar, they always have five punches on the obverse, of which two are the sun and a form of the six-armed symbol .

The other three symbols vary and are mainly new to the series of symbols. They are usually geometrical patterns, notably a hexagram and arrangements of dots. Animals are rare, but the bull and elephant are found. A remarkable type is one which Mr. Walsh describes as a bull's head with a wreath round it. It is very clear on Pl. II. 83, and we would rather suggest that it is

[1] *A S.R.*, xv, pp. 31–2.

a beetle of some kind. The bow and arrow is a symbol occasionally found on coins with which we are more familiar. Another feature of these coins is the complete absence of the taurine symbol or the conventional fish or any of the numerous combinations in which these occur. It seems natural to suppose that these coins are typical of a local issue, and it is a little remarkable to find again at Bhagalpur, at so considerable a distance farther east, coins of a type with which we are very familiar on the north-western frontier.

The remainder of the information available about the provenance of punch-marked coins is very slight, and does not enable us to identify the coins in question.

§ 52. In excavating at Belwa [1] in the Saran district of Tirhut, Mr. H. Panday found 'seven punch-marked coins and three of copper coated with silver, three copper coins of the Kushan dynasty including one of Kanishka'. The earliest buildings were of the second and first centuries B.C., and the date of burial of the coins may have been as late as the first or second century A.D.

Mr. Ratan Tata's excavations at Pāṭaliputra [2] yielded numerous copper and a few silver and silver-plated punch-marked coins along with coins of the Kushan and Mitra dynasties.

In 1925, 254 silver punch-marked coins were found near the village of Trogna [3] in Masaurhi, in the Patna district.

In 1913, 2,873 silver punch-marked coins were found at Patraha [4] in the Purnea district of the province of Bihar and Orissa, but no details are available.

At Bodh Gayā Cunningham found five silver punch-marked coins and 'a curious medal of the Indo-Scythian king Huvishka'; [5] one of them was of the type of **Pl. V. 16**, Class 2, Group II, var. *e* (cf. Cunningham, *Mahabodhi*, Pl. XXII. 15, p. 20 (probably no. 44)).

In the *Proc. A.S.B.*, 1882, p. 112, there is a reference to some coins from Toomluk sent up by the collector of Midnapur, which

[1] *A.S.R.*, 1918–19, p. 16. [2] *Ibid.*, 1912–13, pp. 84 f.

[3] *Ibid.*, 1925–6, p. 168.

[4] *Ibid*, 1916–17, p. 17; *J.B. & O.R.S*, 1919, p. 20.

[5] *A.S.R.*, xvi, p. iv.

these included early cast copper, silver punch-marked, and a copper coin of Kanishka.

The neat-little coin, Class 3, var. *a*, no. 1 (**Pl. VI. 26**), was found by Cunningham at Dharāwat[1] in Bihar. 1191 silver punch-marked coins of all shapes were found at Chaibasa in Singbhum in the Bengal Presidency, mostly of silver, but a large proportion of a very base metal.[2]

§ 53. Of finds made in the United Provinces, the following may be noted here:—

A find made at Mirzapur in 1895, from which a selection reached the British Museum as Treasure Trove from the Asiatic Society of Bengal included

Class 2.	Group I	var. *d*.
„ 2.	„ VII	var. *a*.
„ 6.	„ III	var. *e*.

From Indor Khera,[3] eight miles SSW. of Anupshahar in the United Provinces, Carlleyle got punch-marked coins and Indo-Scythian and early cast copper pieces. The only punch-marked coin described in detail was of Class 2, group II or III.

At Bhuila,[4] Carlleyle found punch-marked coins with coins of Wima Kadphises and a coin of Purushadatta.

At Bua-dih (Kurda),[5] Carlleyle found a square punch-marked coin with coins of Wima Kadphises and Kanishka.

In 1886, 141 much worn punch-marked silver coins were found in the Etawa[6] district of the United Provinces.

In 1886, 164 extremely worn silver punch-marked coins were found at Ballia[7] in the United Provinces.

In the *A.S.R.*, xxii, p. 106, Cunningham records that many ancient punch-marked coins have been found at Chiriyakot (Chiraiya-kot), twenty-five miles NW. of Ghazipur in the Benares district of the United Provinces. Some of these are now in the British Museum:—

[1] *A.S.R.*, xvi, Pl. XIII, p. 46.
[2] *Proc. A.S.B.*, 1885, p. 126.
[3] *A.S.R.*, xii, p. 40.
[4] *Ibid.*, pp. 145 and 164.
[5] *Ibid.*, p. 206.
[6] *Proc. A.S.B.*, 1886, p. 67.
[7] *Ibid.*, 1886, p. 68.

Class 4, var. *a* (no. 1) and var. *d* (no. 6). Class 6, Group I, var. *a* (nos. 2 and 5). Class 4, which is of a very distinct fabric, recalling that of the Golakhpur (Patna) find, has symbols not found elsewhere and may therefore belong to this district. Of Bairaṅt in the same region, Cunningham records that punch-marked coins are found there with early copper cast and struck coins (*ibid.*, p. 114).

In 1875–6 Cunningham procured 45 punch-marked and cast coins with 2 coins of Huvishka at Sanchankot.[1]

In 1881–2 he found at the Fort of Kaṛṛa,[2] thirty-seven miles NW. of Allahabad, a punch-marked silver coin, two cast copper coins, and a large Kosambi coin, which suggested to him a site of the second century B.C.

At Pāḍham[3] in the Gangetic Doab, in the Mainpuri district of the United Provinces, half-way between Elah and Shekohabad, Cunningham found some punch-marked coins with single specimens of coins of the satrap Ranjubula and his son Śoḍāsa, and 20 coins of Kanishka and Huvishka.

At Sankisa[4] in the Farrukhabad district of the United Provinces, in 1876, Cunningham made a large collection of coins, including 3 silver punch-marked coins and several cast copper coins. On the same site were coins of Ranjubula and his son Śoḍāsa; then came coins of Wima Kadphises, Huvishka, and Vasudeva. At Sankisa[5] Cunningham at an earlier date found square silver punch-marked and early cast square copper coins.

About twenty years ago a find of 1,245 silver punch-marked coins was made at Paila in the Kheri district of the United Provinces. I had an opportunity of seeing specimens from this find which came home with the late Mr. W. E. M. Campbell's collection. It consisted of a very distinct class of coins represented in the Museum by the two coins forming Class 7 (see p. 84). The important thing to note about the find is that it contained a distinct type of coin, and had, we believe, none of the common classes 2 and 6 in it.

[1] *A.S.R.*, xi, p. 54.
[2] *Ibid.*, xvii, p. 89.
[3] *Ibid.*, xi, p. 38.
[4] *Ibid.*, xi, p. 25.
[5] *Ibid.*, i, p. 276.

§ 54. From Rajputana and Central India the following information is available on the provenance of punch-marked coins:—

At Tambavati Nāgari,[1] twenty miles north of Chitor, in Udaipur State, Rajputana, Carlleyle in 1871–2 found numerous punch-marked coins. The earliest inscribed coins from this site seem to be of the second-first century B.C. Of the coins he describes (p. 216), one can be identified as of Class 2, Group III, var. *f*.

At Chandravati or Jhalra Patan,[2] in Jhalawar, Carlleyle found square punch-marked coins and uninscribed early copper coins.

At Sarangpur,[3] eighty miles NW. of Bhilsa, in Central India, Cunningham found numerous punch-marked and early uninscribed cast coins.

In his excavations at Besnagar, two miles NW. of Bhilsa, Mr. D. R. Bhandarkar found numerous punch-marked copper coins of the Eran and Ujjayinī types and a few plated silver punch-marked coins[4] of Group III or IV of Class 2. The date of burial might be as early as the second century, but may be as late as the second or third century A.D.

In 1875–7 Cunningham[5] had discovered similar coins on this site:—6 punch-marked, 50 of the Eran and Ujjayinī copper types: other coins were found of the Satraps, Nāgas, and Chandragupta II.

At Eran,[6] fifty miles NE. of Bhilsa, in 1874–5 and 1876–7 Cunningham found numerous early struck copper coins of the Eran and Ujjayinī type. The punch-marked coins obtained here included one which he illustrates on Pl. XXIV. 3; it is of Class 6, Group III, var. *f* (**Pl. VII. 13**). Here, as at Besnagar, the silver punch-marked coins formed a very small proportion compared with the copper. The 'broken die' illustrated by Cunningham on Pl. XXIV. 1, is probably a mould for forging or casting coins in copper of some variety of Class 6, Groups III or IV, which would be afterwards plated with silver. It was made from an impression of a genuine coin as the position of the dog to left instead of right

[1] *Ibid.*, vi, p. 197, 200–1.
[2] *Ibid.*, ii, p. 264.
[3] *Ibid.*, p. 288.
[4] *Ibid.*, 1913–14, p. 210 (Pl. LXIV. 16–17).
[5] *Ibid.*, x, p. 37.
[6] *Ibid.*, pp. 77–9.

shows. There is no case of a silver punch-marked coin being struck from a single die. All the evidence shows that the punches were put on separately.

We may also record here a find made in Palanpur state in 1918, a selection from which was presented to the British Museum by the Bombay Government; it included:—

Class 2. Group VII, var. *g*.
„ 6. „ III, var. *a*.
„ „ „ „ var. *c*.
„ „ „ V, var. *a*.
„ „ „ „ var. *c*.
„ „ „ VI, var. *d*.

Two finds have in recent years been made in the Central Provinces:—

One, discovered at Hinganghat in the Wardha district of the Central Provinces in 1924, from which two coins were presented to the British Museum by the Director of Industries, contained coins of

Class 2. Group XI, var. *c*.

The other from Thathari, in the Central Provinces, discovered in 1925, from which a selection was presented to the British Museum through the Director of Industries, included:—

Class 2. Group V, var. *e*.
„ „ „ VII, var. *j*.
„ 6. „ „ var. *h*,

and the very small pieces called Class 9 (pp. 286–7).

§ 55. Several finds are recorded from Bombay and Madras Presidencies and South India:—

192 silver punch-marked coins were found in the village of Shinhi near Kolhapur, in the Kurveer Petta, along with a gold ring. Dr. Bhau Daji reported on them to the Bombay Branch of the Royal Asiatic Society at their meeting of 11th April 1872 (*Proceedings*, pp. xxi–xxii). 'They have a few punch-marks or symbols on one side and frequently one punch-mark on the opposite side. Generally a corner is cut off. The 30 coins recovered varied in weight from 45 to 53 grains. The gold ring had the name of the

owner engraved upon it in characters 2,100 years old, i.e. nearly the age of Aśoka, in Devanāgarī characters, *Nadibhagasa* = (ring) of Nandibhaga.' It was octagonal on the outer surface with a symbol on each facet. These were a lion or tiger, two standing figures, elephant, tree and railing, horse and fishes, deer, some of which types are common on punch-marked coins.

§ 56. An important find of punch-marked silver coins was made several years ago in the Karimnagar district of Warangal in Hyderabad, and acquired as treasure trove for the Hyderabad Museum. Mr. T. Streenivas has described the coins, some 420 in number, very fully in the *Annual Report of the Archaeological Department of H.E.H. the Nizam's Dominions*, 1931, pp. 39–44, and Pl. XVI: 39 coins are illustrated on the plate, and they belong to the following varieties of this Catalogue:—

Class 2.	Group I.	var. *a*.
,, ,,	,, ,,	var. *g*.
,, ,,	,, IV.	var. *d* to *h*.
,, ,,	,, ,,	var. *i* or *j*.
,, ,,	,, ,,	var. *m*.
,, ,,	,, ,,	var. *n*.
,, ,,	,, V.	var. *b*.
,, ,,	,, ,,	var *c*.
,, ,,	,, VII.	var. *a*.
,, ,,	,, ,,	var. *h*.
,, ,,	,, ,,	var. *j*.
,, ,,	,, ,,	var. *l*.
,, ,,	,, IX.	var. ?
Class 6.	Group I.	var. *a*.
,, ,,	,, II.	var. *l*.
,, ,,	,, III.	var. ?
,, ,,	,, ,,	var. ?
,, ,,	,, V.	var. *c*.

On account of the condition of the coins, Mr. Streenivas was not able to make out all the symbols on all the coins, but it is quite evident from his descriptions that the coins on the plate are quite representative of the find; one or two varieties might be added, e.g. no. 60 is Class 2, Group IV, var. *a*, but all the groups seem to be represented on the plate. Class 2 seem to preponderate, so that the find resembles that from Gorho Ghat (§ 49). A number of coins of Class 2, Group IX, were present, e.g. p. 52, no. 51 (not illustrated, No. 52, is the coin on Pl. XVI. 22). This group is absent from the similarly constituted Gorho Ghat and Bhir mound finds. We have, therefore, evidence of the association of Classes 2 and 6—to which the majority of punch-marked coins belong—from Taxila in the north-west, Gorho Ghat in the east, and Karimnagar in the south.

§ 57. A find at Trichinopoli in 1910 consisted, so far as can be judged from some very worn specimens sent to the British Museum, of Classes 2 and 6; only one was worth cataloguing (p. 65, no. 7).

A find made in the Bimlipatan taluk of the Vizagapatan district of the Madras Presidency in 1896, from which a selection reached the British Museum as Treasure Trove from the Madras Government, included:—

Class 2.	Group IV.	var. *e*.	
,, ,,	,,	,,	var. *m*.
,, ,,	,,	VII.	var. *j*.
,, 6.	,,	XI.	var. *a*.
,, ,,	,,	V.	var. *b*.
,, ,,	,,	,,	var. *d*.

In 1808, Mr. William Garrow, collector, of Coimbatore, wrote to Col. Mackenzie to report that a number of ancient silver punch-marked coins had been found in a tumulus at Chavadepalyam in that district; these coins were, he said, identical with some others discovered four years previously in a field at Penar, also in Coimbatore district, among which was a denarius of Augustus.[1]

§ 58. The find-spots mentioned in the preceding paragraphs fall into well-marked groups. The first is in the extreme north-west:—

[1] Sir Walter Elliot quoting from the Mackenzie MSS. in *Transactions of the International Congress of Prehistoric Archaeology*, 1868, p. 255; cf. also Elliot in *Numismatic Gleanings*, p. 10 = *Madras Journal of Literature and Science*, N. S., III, p. 227-8 (1843-4), and James Bird, *J.B.B.R.A.S.*, Vol. I, p. 294.

Peshawar, Taxila, Thatta, Shahpur, and Kangra (§§ 43–8). The second belongs to the Ganges valley: Indor Khera, Pāḍham, Paila, Etawa, Sankisa, Chiriyakot, Mirzapur, Ballia, Patna, Trogna, Belwa, Bodh Gaya, and Bhagalpur (§ 48–53). The Chaibasa and Midnapur finds may be put in this group or classed together. In the west we have a third group:—Palanpur, Tambavati Nāgari, Jhalra Patan, Sarangpur, Besnagar, and Eran—in southern Rajputana and Malwa, the area between the Aravalli and Vindya mountains, drained by tributaries of the Jumna. The Hingaghat, Thaithari, Karimnagar, and Bimlipatan finds belong to the basin of the Godavari. The Kolhapur, Coimbatore, and Trichinopoli finds appear rather isolated in the south, although the two last are not so remote from each other. This tells us little more than that punch-marked coins are found in what were in ancient times also the most important and thickly populated parts of India. When, however, we come to examine, with the limited details available, the coins in the individual finds, we find that the composition of the finds is almost everywhere the same. They consist of our classes 2 and 6. The finds which contain coins of classes other than these contain coins of quite different classes only. These are the find which contained our Class 1 which belongs to somewhere in the north; the Paila find (Class 7, § 53) which was made somewhat north of the area delineated by the finds in the Ganges valley; and the Gorho Ghat (Patna) find which contains a class of coin unrepresented in the Museum. At first sight the constant association of Classes 2 and 6 is surprising. They are very different in style and fabric. Class 2 consists of small thick pieces and Class 6 of large thin pieces. Speaking generally, the coins of Class 2 have a definite reverse type, while those of 6 have a very large number of small punches on the reverse, none of which appears to be of special significance. The obverse symbols of the two classes cannot be linked together as they can within the classes. We were at first inclined to think on the evidence of the provenance of individual specimens that Class 2 belonged to Northern India and Class 6 to the Deccan (cf., for example, the frequency with which coins from Bombay and Madras appear in Class 6 in this Catalogue and the coins illustrated by Elliot (*Num. Glean.*, Pl. VII, VIII), all belong to Class 6). The evidence of the Bhir mound find (§ 44) with a large proportion of Class 6, and of the Karimnagar find (§ 56) with a large proportion of Class 2, forbids any such hypothesis. Classes 2 and 6, to which most of the known coins belong, therefore circulated together from Peshawar to the mouth of the Godavari, and from Palanpur in the west to Midnapur in the east. The distinction between Classes 2 and 6 is not one of place: they must have been issued by the same authority and have circulated together throughout the area where that authority prevailed. Below we show that the different groups and varieties of Classes 2 and 6 are linked together in a way which shows that the issues are closely connected. The similarity of constitution of the various hoards suggests they were buried about the same time, and had we an accurate analysis of all hoards it would be possible to confirm this and construct a chronological arrangement of the coins. In other countries, hoards are usually buried in troubled times—for example, the commonest period for finds of English coins is that of the Civil War. The authority that issued these coins must have ruled the Ganges valley, the upper Indus valley, thrust its way up the tributaries of Jumna to the west and come along the east coast through Orissa and penetrated far into the Deccan. This is what the find-spots suggest. If we assume that these hoards were buried in a time of war and insecurity, this power must have collapsed about the same time everywhere in its vast empire, for there is a great similarity in the hoards. All this suggests the period of the Maurya empire—which ruled all the regions mentioned and suddenly collapsed everywhere at the beginning of the second century B.C.—for the issue of these coins, and the above rough grouping of the find-spots corresponds quite well with the distribution of the Aśoka inscriptions.

§ 59. The chronological evidence available from hoards is slight, but, such as it is, it points in the same direction as the geographical evidence. The Bhir mound find at Taxila (§ 44) contained two coins of Alexander the Great, and one of Philip Aridaeus and an Achaemenid siglos. It must therefore have been buried after the time of

Philip (323–316 B.C.), probably about 300 B.C. The same site yielded a find deposited with a gold coin of Diodotus which must therefore have been buried about 250 B.C. To about this same date belong the coins from Sirkap, where a coin of Demetrius was found in a somewhat later stratum. Elsewhere at Taxila punch-marked coins were found associated with coins of the Greek kings of the first century B.C. and first and second centuries A.D., Maues, Azes, Gondophares, Kadphises, and Kanishka, that is to say they still circulated in the Scythian and Kushan periods.

The small find from Thatta contained a drachm of Philoxenos which puts the date of burial at about 100 B.C. The Kangra find also contained coins of Philoxenos, but other Greek kings like Antimachus, Menander, and Lysias are represented; the date of burial again is about 100 B.C. In the Ganges valley, the Belwa find was associated with Kushan coins and the Ratan Tata excavations at Pāṭaliputra showed that punch-marked coins circulated with Mitra and Kushan coins, i.e. of first and second centuries A.D. At Bodh Gaya and Midnapur (Toomluk) the same association is again found. At Indor Khera, Bhuila, Bua-dih, and Sanchankot, punch-marked coins came from sites which also yielded Kushan coins. At Pāḍham, punch-marked coins were found with coins from Ranjubula to Huvishka, that is to say of first and second centuries A.D. Conditions at Sankisa were similar. In these cases from the Ganges valley we are not dealing with hoards but with isolated coins from sites. The most reasonable thing to suppose is that the punch-marked coins immediately preceded the Scythian and Kushan series when these are all found on the same site; but it is possible that they continued in circulation down to the Kushan period, and the complete absence of silver coins of the later Śaka-Pahlava and Kushan rulers makes this very probable. These sites certainly show that punch-marked coins circulated in the second and first centuries B.C. It is only in Northern India that we can expect to find other coins with them which can give a clue to the date of punch-marked coins. We omit the frequent association of silver with early copper uninscribed coins, as the latter do not help us. In Central and Southern India we have a find near Kolhapur with a ring 'inscribed in Aśoka characters', probably of the second century B.C.; and the finds from the district of Coimbatore are interesting as one of them yielded a denarius of Augustus, so that the coins were probably buried in the first century A.D.

§ 60. The period of circulation of punch-marked coins may therefore be put at the third and second centuries B.C.; that they continued in circulation later is most probable, and that they may go back to the fourth century B.C. is possible. Their issue does not cover a great period in time, otherwise the hoards would differ considerably in composition. The great variety of combinations of symbols cannot mean that each obverse belongs to a different reign for example. And, as we shall show below, the obverse types are linked together in a way that shows they must fall into practically contemporary groups. The change of one minor symbol must have been made very frequently, and the relative permanence of two of the symbols also suggests a limited period of issue.

§ 61. The classification of the many combinations of obverse types is a somewhat difficult matter, and it is complicated by the fact that the reverse types do not always agree when an obverse arrangement has been settled. The reverse type is evidently of considerable significance on Classes 1 to 5, for it is on this side only that we find countermarks (e.g. p. 20, no. 36, p. 30, no. 24), and the countermark is usually another known reverse type, or at least a type not found on the obverse. In the second group, Classes 6 and 7, it is impossible to say that any of the numerous reverse punches has any special significance, and the only countermark found appears on obverses (e.g. p. 65, no. 12). While we have the same reverse with a closely linked series of regularly changing obverses, we also have the same obverse with a number of different reverses. The arrangement we here propose will no doubt be emended and simplified in time from an analysis of finds, but we may run through it here to show how the numerous issues are linked together, and to suggest that for this reason they do not cover a great period in time. We have divided the coins into seven classes: the great bulk of them belong to 1, 2, and 6; 3, 4, and 5 consist of a few coins each, which differ in fabric or have unusual symbols and seem to stand apart. Class 7 is certainly very distinct from the others, and it is unfortunate that it is so poorly represented in the Museum. The evidence of finds shows that 1, 2, and 6 are more closely connected than the differences of fabric suggest.

We have given the name Class to large series of coins of the same fabric and characterized by certain symbols. These we have divided into groups within which the same symbols recur; they usually have each a symbol or two peculiar to them. The varieties are the individual issues. It is unfortunate that we are unable to say whether these distinctions are chronological or geographical.

§ 62. Class 1 consists almost entirely of square coins of very regular size with the reverse symbol . Four varieties are distinguished, one symbol varying in each. These are:—

	Obverse.					*Reverse.*
Var. *a.*						
Var. *b.*	”	”	”	”		”
Var. *c.*	”	”	”	”		”
Var. *d.*	”	”	”	”		”

The evidence of this isolated group of coins from a single find suggests we ought to be able to arrange all the coins in groups with a single reverse and regularly changing obverse symbols. It is not certain that var. *d* is of this Class.

§ 63. Class 2 is divided into eleven groups, each characterized by certain symbols but linked together by others.

Group I consists of coins all of which have the so-called Taxila symbol, , on the reverse. Vars. *a*, *b*, *c* should perhaps not be distinguished, as *b* and *c* are countermarked specimens of *a*.

abc, *d*, and *e* differ in one symbol.

Obverse.
Reverse.
Vars. a, b, c.
Var. d.
Var. e.

f and *g* have two symbols in common with *e*, namely  and ; they are closely connected in not having the sun and six-armed symbols, but they differ in the symbols which take their place.

Var. *h* has a different and rare reverse symbol, , but is closely connected with *g* by the three little figures on the obverse. It is interesting to note then that var. *h* is quite closely linked with *a*, although the two varieties have not a single symbol in common.

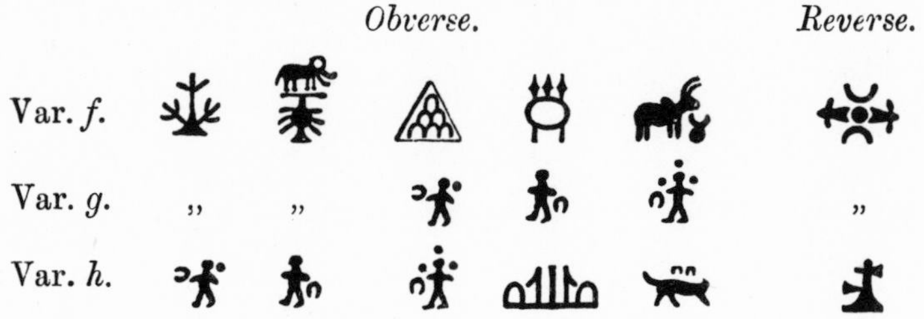
Obverse.
Reverse.
Var. f.
Var. g.
Var. h.

§ 64. The characteristic symbols of Group II are , , and : var. *b* is only a countermarked form of var. *a*, and the countermark, it may be noted, is also found in Group I, var. *b*. Vars. *a*, *b*, *c*, and *d* have the same reverse; var. *c* substitutes the three men  for the first three symbols of var. *a*, and *d* has only one symbol in common with it. It may be noted that two of the symbols on var. *d* also occur in Group I, var. *f*, another type which has neither the sun nor six-armed symbol. Var. *e* is connected with *c* by three of its obverse symbols as is *f*, which has the same reverse symbols as *e* and *g*; var. *g* is also connected by obverse with vars. *d*

and *e*. Var. *h* is connected by obverse symbols with *a*, *e*, and *g*. The possession of the reverse type  links *e*, *f*, *g*, and *h*.

§ 65. Group III is characterized by the symbol  which links it with Group II. It is also the characteristic reverse of this group. The countermark  is again found in this group on specimens of var. *a*, and on var. *b*, which is really a countermarked form of *c*. Var. *g* is var. *f* countermarked with a rare symbol  only found as a countermark. The symbol  on these is found on coins of Ujjayinī (p. 248).

The obverses of this group are as follows:

Var. *a*.	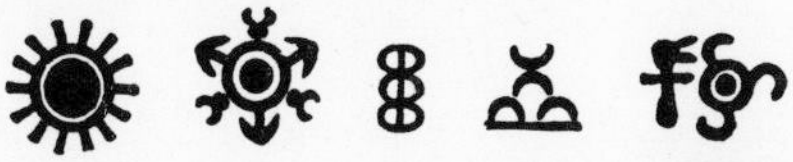				
Var. *b*, *c*.	”	”	”	”	
Var. *d*.	”	”	”	”	
Var. *f*, *g*.	”	”	”	”	
Var. *h*.	”	”	”	”	
Var. *i*.	”	”	”	”	
Var. *j*.	”	”	”		”

h, *i*, and *j* are connected by the same reverse symbols, a taurine countermark being added to the regular  of this group. We have put here a coin which is connected with Group II or IV.

Obverse. *Reverse.*

§ 66. Group IV is connected with III by the symbols  and . Its characteristic symbols are  and .

Obverse. *Reverse.*

Var. *a.* 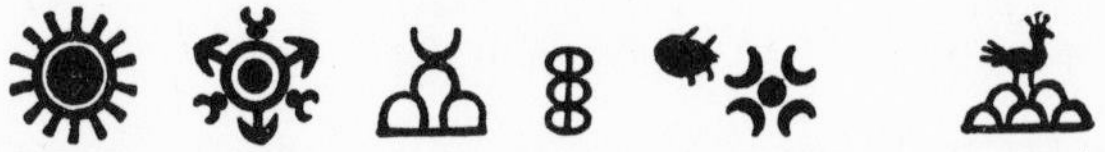

Var. *a* is connected by four of its obverse symbols with Group III and by reverse with Group II, but the fifth obverse symbol is one not found elsewhere. Var. *b* differs in only one symbol on the obverse , but has reverse  connecting it with Group III. Var. *c* substitutes  for  and has the same reverse as var. *a*. Var. *d* is the same but with reverse of *b*. Vars. *e* to *h* are similar but show different forms of the six-armed symbol, *e*, *f*, and *g* having  (not  as in the text), with 'dumb-bell' symbols in place of the fishes, while *h*, *k*, and *l* have a remarkable form, , not found elsewhere. *f* and *g* have new reverses,  and , to be found again later. *i* and *j* have the same obverse as *b*, but reverses  and  respectively; *k* to *o* are connected by the symbol ; *m* and *o* by ; *q* to *t* are connected by  and a new form of six-armed symbol , and with *d* and *e* by 'the tree in railing'. *u* and *v* are connected by two of their symbols, but it is their reverses that bring them into this group. A number of new reverses, , , , , , appear in this group.

§ 67. Group V is connected with IV by the use of most of the reverse symbols just mentioned. Its characteristic symbol is . Vars. *a* and *b* have four symbols in common and differ in their fifth; that of *b*, a hare[1] in a crescent, the symbol of the moon, is not found elsewhere on punch-marked coins but we have it on the coin of

[1] I take this opportunity of correcting 'rabbit' to 'hare' on p. xxviii, last line, as Sir Richard Burn has pointed out to me that the rabbit is not known in India.

Viṣṇudeva (p. 147). Var. *c* is connected with *a* by a special form of branch; it has a remarkable six-armed symbol, ; var. *d* is connected here by its reverse and two obverse symbols; the most notable obverse symbol is that of a bird alighting on a tree.

§ 68. Group VI shows the same variety of reverses as IV and V. The obverses of *a*, *b*, and *c* are connected by the symbol 'tree in railing'. *d* is connected with *b* by its reverse type, a little figure of a deity with a staff or spear. The gesticulating little man on the obverse of *b* is not found elsewhere. The obverses of *d* to *f* are connected by a bull, while *e* to *g* are connected with *c* by three of their symbols. Var. *h* is remarkable in having a star or lotus  on obverse and reverse.

§ 69. Group VII is a large one, the characteristic symbols of which are what we may call the 'dog and rabbit' , although the latter is not a rabbit, and the former may not be a dog, , and . Vars. *a* to *d* differ only in reverse types, with all of which we are already familiar. Var. *f* has not the sun and six-armed symbol, and like some other coins (Class 2, Group I, var. *f*, and Group II, vars. *d* and *g*) which omit them includes  and  in its symbols. Vars. *e* and *g* substitute  for , and var. *h*  for , for which var. *i* again has an elephant. *j*, *k*, and *l* each differ in one symbol from the variety which precedes it. The reverses of this group show an increasing number of punches, but it is still possible to pick out one as the most important. Vars. *i*, *k*, and *l* have , not  as in the text. The cobra on var. *l* may be noted.

Group VIII is linked with VII by the symbol 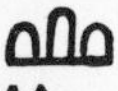 and 'dog and rabbit' on *a* and *b*; *c* is connected with *a* by , and *c*, *d*, *e* by the elaborate symbol  and the remarkable .

Group IX consists of a series of very neatly made coins, all with the same obverse, and showing five different reverses. It is connected with preceding groups by  on the obverse and by its reverses. Its characteristic symbols are  and . I again take the opportunity of correcting the  of the text to .

Group X, the characteristic symbol of which is , is connected with VII by ; the fifth symbols on each of the varieties do not occur elsewhere. The reverses are those of the preceding groups but show an increasing number of small stamps.

Group XI still shows the same reverses, but the characteristic obverse symbol  of *a* and *b* suggests a separate group; the place of var. *c* is uncertain.

§ 70. Class 3 consists at present of two very neat coins with the same obverse: one with a plain reverse and the other with reverse . The obverse symbols  and  connect it with Class 2, but the other three, , , and , put these coins in a class by themselves.

Class 4 contains a number of coins of large fabric, with normally plain reverses. The symbols on the reverse of one specimen of var. *b* (no. 4) are probably countermarks. It is characterized by a whorl form of the sun and unusual variants of the six-armed symbol,  and . *a* and *b* are connected by four of their symbols, and *c* is connected with them by the bow and arrow, and *d* with *c* by  and with *a* and *b* by the elephant. Var. *e* really has only four symbols on the obverse and should be transferred to Class 7. The first symbol is not a snake but .

Class 5, like Class 3, consists of two neatly struck coins, one with plain reverse and the other with a symbol on it. Its characteristic symbols are  and . Var. *k* of Group III, Class 6, should be transferred to this class as var. *c* of it.

§ 71. The coins of the very large Class 6 are linked together by their obverse symbols and by the fact that their reverses have numerous small punch-marks, no particular one of which seems to have the significance of the large and distinct reverse types of Classes 1 and 2.

The characteristic symbols of Group I are the rhinoceros or unicorn, , and a square tank with four fishes around a central pillar or lingam .

Vars. *a* to *d* have four symbols in common and differ in their fifth, , , , and . Var. *e* is connected with *c* by four symbols but substitutes a little animal  for the tank. Vars. *f* and *g* are connected with *c* and *e* by their fifth symbol, and *h* with them by . A number of variants of the six-armed symbol are found in this group.

§ 72. The characteristic symbol of Group II is  which serves to link it with I, with which and II, it shares the bull and elephant. Vars. *a*, *b*, and *c* have four symbols in common and differ only in their fifth, , , and . Var. *d* substitutes a bull for  of var. *b* and *e*, an elephant for another symbol of *d*.

§ 73. Group III, to which a large number of coins belong, is characterized by the symbol  and shares the bull with other groups of this Class. The connexions of the obverses of the variants may be conveniently exhibited as follows:

Var. *a*.     

Var. *b*. ,, ,, ,, ,, 

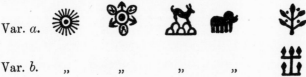

Var. *c*.					
Var. *d*.	,,	,,	,,		,,
Var. *e*.	,,	,,	,,		,,
Var. *f*.	,,	,,	,,		,,
Var. *g*.	,,	,,	,,		,,
Var. *h*.	,,	,,	,,		,,
Var. *i*.	,,	,,	,,	,,	[?]
Var. *j*.	,,	,,	,,		

Var. *k* ought to be transferred to Class 5, as var. *c* of it.

§ 74. Group IV is connected with the preceding by  and the bull; its characteristic symbol is . Symbols peculiar to it are the frog and little animal surrounded by a border of pellets and taurine symbols.

Its variants are connected as follows:

Var. *a*.					
Var. *b*.	,,	,,	,,	,,	
Var. *c*.	,,		,,	,,	,,
Var. *d*.	,,		,,		
Var. *e*.	,,		,,		
Var *f*.	,,	,,	,,		,,

Var. *d* does not contain the characteristic symbol of this group but is too closely connected with *c* to be separated from it. Similarly var. *f* can hardly be separated from *e*.

§ 75. Group V is connected with the preceding classes by the elephant, and its characteristic symbols are a palm-tree and a little animal surrounded by taurine symbols.

Var. *a* which is one of the commonest coins of Class 6 has obverse type 

Var. *b*. ,, ,,  ,, ,,

Var. *e*. ,, 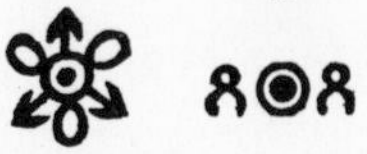 ,, ,,

Var. *f*. ,, ,, ,, ,, 

Var. *c* is the same as var. *a*, as probably is var. *d*. The symbol  on the latter is a countermark, and not the original type which was probably a palm-tree. It is very doubtful whether the next two varieties, *g* and *h*, are properly placed here. Var. *g* is much countermarked and it is difficult to say what the original type is; the elephant shows that it belongs to one group of Class 6. Var. *h* has an unusual form of the six-armed symbol found only on Class 4, and the frog connects it with Group IV of Class 6.

§ 76. Group VI is connected by the elephant and bull with other groups of this Class; its characteristic symbol is a tree growing out of a hill, .

Var. *a* links this group with other groups of Class 6 by the elephant and bull. Its obverse is:

Var. *b* substitutes  as its fifth symbol, and var. *c* .

Var. *d* cannot be separated from *c* although it has not the tree on a hill among its symbols, for which it substitutes a fruit ; otherwise it is as var. *c*.

Var. *e* resembles var. *a* but has a small wheel surrounded by taurine symbols in place of the bull. Var. *f* is probably similar, as I am now inclined to think that the symbol  only occurs as a countermark and is not part of the original type. Var. *g* has the three usual symbols of this group, but the fourth and fifth  and  are unusual on the obverse. Var. *h* has as fourth and fifth symbols four fishes in a tank, found in Class 2, Group V, and on varieties of Group I of Class 6, and a branch found in Group III, var. *a*; this branch is the link which puts var. *i* somewhat doubtfully in this group. Var. *j* may belong to the preceding Group.

§ 77. Group VII consists of a number of coins which are remarkable for their large, thin fabric. The elephant on var. *a* connects them with the other groups of this class, but many of the symbols are unusual and peculiar to the group.

Var. *a* has obverse

Var. *b* is connected with this by the unusual form of mountain, as is *c*, but the symbols  and  are new.

Var. *d* is not clear. The wheel is a very rare symbol and the fifth symbol is not quite clear; it seems to be two rows of pellets. The symbol  connects this variety with Class 6. Var. *e* is connected with *a–c* by the form of mountain symbol; the fish in a crescent is not found elsewhere. Var. *f*'s claim to be here is rather doubtful; it may belong to Group VI. The coin we have put here as Group VIII of Class 6 should more probably be connected with Class 2. The symbol  is also found in Group IX of that class. The *nāga* symbol is not found elsewhere on silver punch-marked coins. It is the numerous punches on the reverse that connect this coin with Class 6.

§ 78. Class 7, of which the Museum only has two specimens, differs entirely from all the preceding coins and belongs to a different territory or time. The feature of the coins in this class is that they have only four punches on the obverse. These are an elephant, the uncertain little animal seen on fig. 3, p. 84, the symbol , and . The reverses have a number of stamps, none of which is especially prominent;  is common among them. This is the type of the Paila find (§ 53). The coin here catalogued as var. *e* of Class 4 (p. 59, no. 7) should probably be now attributed to Class 7 as it differs from the usual type only in having  in place of the little animal. The first symbol is not, as given in the Catalogue, a snake  but .

We had made a Class 8 (p. 286) of one coin, a small, square, thick piece which appeared to have a figure of Hanuman on it; apart from the fact that this is in relief, and not a punch, the resemblance is purely fortuitous and caused by the punches leaving a raised area between them. The head of the little figure is really an arm of the symbol . The coin is only a poor and incomplete specimen of some variety of Class 2.

Class 9, which should now be Class 8 (p. 286), consists of very small coins with obverse type a form of ; these come from the United Provinces, the Thathari find in the Central Provinces, and were also in the Bhir mound find (§ 44).

§ 79. While these pages are going through the press, Mr. Ajit Ghose has presented to the Museum three specimens of a new class of punch-marked coin which we may call Class 9. These are from a find of some 500 pieces from Set Mahet in the Gondā district of the United Provinces, which consisted of this class only, and contained none of the other classes. The characteristic feature of this class is the reverse type, which is a ball surrounded by three S-shaped lines; this device is repeated twice or thrice to fill the whole area. The obverse symbols are also new, except a bull, which is, however, of a distinct type; on one specimen they are five in number, on the others there are numerous countermarks which obliterate the original type. As in the case of other outlying classes, the symbols do not include the sun and six-armed symbol. The five distinct symbols are a long thin bull, a circle with a pellet in the centre surrounded by ten pellets, struck twice, an object like a spear-head, which may, however, be a bud, and a symbol . Among the symbols on the other specimens are a lotus, a whorl, and a circle divided in three parts by three radii. Like the Paila (§ 53) and Golakhpur (Patna) (§ 51) finds, these coins represent a currency distinct from the great majority of punch-marked coins. They were found on a site of the ancient city of Śrāvasti, the old capital of Kosala, the date of whose incorporation in Magadha is unfortunately unknown.

§ 80. The known punch-marked silver coins, then, may be classed as follows:—Classes 2 and 6 are closely connected and are regularly associated in finds over a very wide area; Class 1 so closely resembles the first groups of Class 2 that it is not to be separated from them. Classes 2 and 6 are the issues of one kingdom, if not of one dynasty. The wide distribution of their find-spots, and the evidence that they were circulating in the second, third, and probably early fourth centuries B.C., suggests that these classes are the coins of the Maurya empire (§§ 58–60). The very small classes 3 and 5 may be separate issues of small states, but it is probable that they should be made groups of Class 2. Group IX of Class 2 is a similar issue of coins with distinct symbols, which we have not felt justified in separating from Class 2. Class 4, coins of unusual size with plain reverses and uncommon obverse symbols, is clearly a distinct class, but in the absence of sufficient evidence from finds we can say no more about them. Class 7 is also quite a distinct type, the large Paila (§ 53) find which consisted of this class came from a spot which lay outside the circle of find-spots of Classes 1–3, 5, 6. Similarly, the Golakhpur (Patna) find (§ 51) and the Set Mahet (§ 79) finds are the issues of quite distinct authorities, and the latter is also outside the area of the find-spots of the great majority of these coins. The Golakhpur find was made on the site of the ancient city of Pāṭaliputra, and contained none of the usual classes. The inference is that it was buried before Classes 2 and 6 were struck. While distinct in fabric and having secondary symbols peculiar to them, these coins resemble 2 and 6 in having a sun and a variety of the six-armed symbol —not, however, found elsewhere—on all of them. They are therefore struck on the same principle. Are we to see in them a coinage of the Nandas or of one of the other kingdoms which became incorporated in the Maurya empire? Does the Set Mahet find represent the coinage of Kosala and the Paila find that of Pañcāla?

The occurrence of three isolated finds of distinct types certainly suggests that they are issues of smaller kingdoms or republics, and are rlier than the great mass of widely distributed coins, for the latter were not found with them.

§ 81. While we have little doubt that most of our coins belong to the Maurya period, there is then evidence—apart from the possibly very early, even fourth-century, date of the Bhir mound find—that coins were known before the Maurya period. It is not impossible that the tradition of the great wealth of the Nandas owes its origin to their having been the first to issue coins on a large scale. In any case there is no evidence that coinage in India is older than the Nanda period, and the earliest finds, Paila, Set Mahet, and Golakhpur, may indicate the region in which punch-marked coins originate. The similarity in constitution of the usual finds indicates that punch-marked coinage did not exist over a very long period; the fact that it had not been long established is indicated by the rapidity with which the new coins with type and inscription struck from a single die ousted the punch-marked coins from the second century B.C. onwards. It is very possible that the idea of a coinage came to India in the late fifth or early fourth century B.C. from Achaemenid territory, being suggested by the sigloi, although its character is entirely Indian.

§ 82. That these coins were issued by a government authority and not by private individuals there is not the slightest doubt. Only a central authority could have carried out such an apparently complicated, but no doubt—if we had the clue—simple, system of stamping the coins in regular series. The regular occurrence of five symbols on the obverse naturally suggests a board of five, such as Megasthenes says was at the head of most departments of Mauryan administration. It can hardly be that the symbols are those of the five officials actually concerned in the issue of each piece, as some symbols like the sun and the six-armed symbol occur over a wide range of coins. The punches, though not struck with one die, were struck at one time. They may represent a series of officials of diminishing area of jurisdiction. The last and most frequently changing symbol would represent the actual issuer of the coin. The constant symbol, the sun, would represent the highest official, perhaps the king himself, and the next commonest, the various forms of six-armed symbol, the highest officials next under him. It is, however, difficult to reconcile the existence of coins with the same obverse symbols and different reverse symbols with this suggestion. The association in finds of Class 2 with significant reverse symbols with Class 6 with numerous small punches like shroff-marks and no definite symbol is another puzzle. The latter may be the earlier issues, struck before the adoption of a regular reverse mint-mark. The frequent occurrence of the so-called Taxila symbol in finds from the north-west suggests that the reverse symbol on these coins which have one indicates a mint. A similar deduction may be made from Class 1. Whether the reverse symbol is the badge of a district or of a ruler we cannot say. The countermarks on Class 2 also suggest that the reverse symbol is a very significant one. It is only reverse symbols that occur as countermarks in Class 2 (§ 41). In Class 6, where we have no significant reverse symbols, countermarks are placed on the obverse (§§ 41, 75–76). The case of Gautamīputra countermarking the coins of Nahapāna shows that each ruler or country had a characteristic symbol, which we might almost call a coat of arms. We can say little more, but only appeal once more for a careful examination of finds on the lines laid down here. This alone can give the answer to our problem.

§ 83. As to the meaning of the symbols we can only suggest that each is the mark or signet of an official. The coins have preserved a great deal of a very elaborate system of symbolism which disappears completely with the spread of the Kharoṣṭhī and Brāhmī alphabets in India from the third century B.C. onwards. Many of the symbols are simple and taken from the animal and plant world. Others are quite unintelligible at the present day, and some of them may be conventionalized forms of forgotten pictographic symbols. They are of course not inscriptions in any sense. Three thousand years is a long period to bridge and, while it is impossible to connect the majority of the symbols with anything on the Mohenjo-daro seals, we may point to the part played by fishes in both, to the survival of the rhinoceros—if it is not some extinct unicorned animal—and to the symbol . Writing, as we know it, seems to have been unknown in India before the fourth century B.C., and the root *lip* (*dip*) itself is of Persian origin.[1] It is not till the second century B.C. that we find inscriptions becoming regular on coins.

§ 84. We get no assistance from literature about the date of these coins. The frequent references in the *Sūtras* to *kārṣāpaṇas* and other coins do not take us beyond the third century B.C. Nārada's[2] statement that the *kārṣāpaṇa* is a silver coin in the southern country may indicate that the use of punch-marked coins survived longer in the Deccan than elsewhere, which is in any case very probable. The numerous references in the *Jātaka* and other Buddhist literature to monetary transactions reflect the conditions of the period in which they were written and not those of the sixth century B.C. The parable of the *Visuddhimagga*[3] telling how a lot of coins would strike different observers may be mentioned here. A money-changer, we are told, would know at once at what village, town, city, mountain, or river-bank and by what mint-master a coin was

[1] E. Hultzsch, *Inscriptions of Aśoka*, *C.I.I.*, vol. i, p. xliii.

[2] Nārada Smṛti, App. 57, *S.B.E.*, vol. xxxiii, p. 231.

[3] *A.S.R.*, 1913–14, p. 226; D. R. Bhandarkar, *Indian Numismatics*, p. 99 f. and p. 147 f.

struck; this only tells us that the symbols had very definite meaning to the expert, who knew at once exactly where the coins were issued. More interesting is the description of the shape of the coins—irregular, long, rectangular, and round—which shows that the author was quite familiar in his day with punch-marked coins, so that they may have survived long into the Christian era. The story in the *Mahāvagga*[1] of Upāli's parents choosing a career for him may also be quoted. His mother says, 'If Upāli studies coins (learns money-changing) his eyes will suffer'—a sentiment which appeals to any one who studies punch-marked coins, and shows that a knowledge of their types was a special subject even when they were current. The use of the word *rūpa* here to mean money is interesting, as it does not seem to be found later, although *rūpya* is common. It has been suggested that coins were known as *rūpa* because they had figures or symbols (*rūpa*) stamped upon them. It may, however, simply mean silver as the beautiful metal. Silver was rare in ancient India, and the metal for the coins was probably imported. Gold was of course well known. So rare was silver, however, that it is called white or bright gold (*rajatam hiraṇyam*) in the *Śatapatha-Brāhmaṇa* (xii. 4, 4, 7). It may have been then that silver was rarely seen except in the form of coins in the period with which we are dealing, and that money and silver were synonymous.

Part III.

UNINSCRIBED CAST COINS.

§ 85. Among the commonest coins of ancient India are the uninscribed cast copper pieces. They have a strong family resemblance but several groups can be distinguished. Certain symbols are very common, especially the elephant, tree in railing, and the 'mountain' symbol. Insufficient attention has been devoted to finds of these pieces in the past and there is little to assist in attribution. They are usually found on sites which yield punch-marked silver coins, and are probably of the same period. They have been grouped in the Catalogue as follows:

[1] *S.B.E.* xiii. 201 f.

Varieties *a* and *b* are known only from one coin each and they are not connected with the common types. The obverse of var. *a* seems to have three standing figures, the central one facing and the other two turned towards him (or her). The general attitude recalls the puzzling reverse of the Pratāpa type of Kumāragupta I (B.M. Cat. of *Gupta Coins*, p. 87). It is quite possible that the type of this coin, which is in poor condition, is really the *abhiṣeka* of Lakṣmī, which is a very probable type. The reverse has an elephant and a tree in railing with the ladder-like symbol often found below the elephant on copper coins. The types of var. *b* are quite unusual: *obv.* a female with her right hand grasping a tall tree and a building of some kind on the left. The *rev.* has a tree in railing of the type found in var. *n* and a lingam. Var. *c* has obverse type, lion, svastika, and the symbol , and *rev.* tree in railing, Ujjain symbol  and a hollow cross ; some of these symbols are found on other varieties. Var. *d* is connected with this but has an elephant instead of a lion on the obverse, and a wheel instead of the Ujjain symbol on the reverse. Var. *e* has the obverse of *d* and a reverse, tree in railing, wheel, and Ujjain symbol, which is related to both *c* and *d*. Var. *f* has the obverse of *d* and *e* but substitutes  for the tree in railing of the *rev.* of var. *d*. Vars. *g* and *h* differ only in the arrangement of the obverse symbols, elephant, , , and svastika. The *rev.* of both has a very elaborate tree in railing with a small hollow cross surmounted by a taurine symbol on one side and a small mountain symbol on the other. Vars. *i*, *j*, *k*, are closely connected. The reverse is the same in all, a tree in railing, taurine symbol, hollow cross, and mountain symbol. Var. *i* has *obv.* elephant, , and hollow cross. Var. *j* has *obv.* elephant, , svastika, taurine symbol, and the ladder-like symbol. If the omission of the last symbol in var. *k* is merely accidental, the two varieties should not be distinguished; but the large number of specimens suggests that it is a distinct variety. Var. *l* is a very distinct type of coin, *obv.* a well-executed elephant, and *rev.* a realistically executed tree in railing on the branches of which four birds are perched. Var. *m* is a unique piece of exceptional size for this class of coin, *obv.* hollow square (or quatrefoil) and *rev.* mountain symbol. It came from the Bhagvanlal Collection, which suggests a Western Indian provenance; var. *n* has a similar obverse and a tree, not conventional, in railing, on the reverse. Var. *o* consists of neatly made square coins, *obv.* mountain symbol with pellets in the field or in the compartments, and *rev.* a conventional tree in railing. Vars. *p* and *q* are closely connected. The obverse of *p* has an elephant and rider, and of *q* the same elephant without rider; both have  on reverse: specimens of this variety are occasionally found in pairs just as they were originally cast together. This shows how these coins were cast in batches. On most of these coins one can still see where the coin was broken from the mould and the adjoining piece. Var. *q* is one of the most extensive series of cast coins. Var. *r* and var. *s* are closely connected, the *rev.* is  with a taurine symbol on either side; the *obv.* of *r* is a bull to r. with a trisceles above and of *s* a lion to l. with  in front. These coins therefore fall into certain main groups. Vars. *c* to *k* are closely linked together; *l*, *m*, and *n* are probably all quite distinct; *o* also is a separate class; *p* and *q* are closely connected and so are *r* and *s*.

§ 86. We have very little to assist us in distinguishing these coins geographically. It will be noticed that neither Whitehead nor Elliot occur among the sources of the Museum specimens. This suggests that they do not come from the north-west or the south of India. The impression one gets from the frequent but not specific references to early cast coins in the *A.S.R.* is that they belong mainly to Central India and the United Provinces. Cunningham[1] sums up the distribution as follows: var. *q* is found all over North India;

[1] *C.A.I.*, p. 60.

var. *r* and var. *s* are rarely found in the Panjab. Var. *j* is found chiefly about Benares. Var. *o* he describes as rather rare.

The specimens of var. *q* illustrated by Prinsep[1] come from Kanauj and another specimen came from Central India. Cunningham obtained specimens of this variety at Masaon,[2] Bairaṅt,[3] and Bhitari.[4] They were also found in the excavations at Pātaliputra,[5] and Besnagar.[6] Prinsep illustrates a specimen of var. *f* from Jaunpur and a specimen of var. *s* from Central India. Specimens of *j* and *k* were found in the Besnagar excavations.[7] Most of the evidence of provenance is vague. Early cast coins usually described as 'Buddhist' have been found with silver punch-marked coins at Indor Khera,[8] Bairaṅt,[9] Sanchankot,[10] Masaon Dih,[11] Kaṛṛa,[12] and Sankisa,[13] all in the United Provinces. In the West a similar association was noticed at Jhalra Patan,[14] Sarangpur,[15] and Besnagar,[16] in Central India. So far as one can judge, the area covered by these coins is not by any means so great as that in which punch-marked coins are found. The United Provinces, Rajputana, and the Central Provinces seem to be the limits within which they are found. We have little clue to their date. Their frequent association with silver punch-marked coins on sites which yield only these classes of coins suggests that they are of about the same time; they are frequently found with Indo-Scythic copper which they must have preceded. They closely resemble in general style, and are probably the immediate predecessors of many classes of inscribed coins which cannot be earlier than the second–first century B.C. The evidence then suggests the third–second century B.C. as their date. More careful observation of provenance will have to be made before we can say much definitely about their classification.

[1] *P.E.*, I. p. 84, Pl. IV. 8.
[2] *A.S.R.*, XXII. 103.
[3] *Ibid.*, XXII. 114.
[4] *Ibid.*, I. 27.
[5] *Ibid.*, 1911–12.
[6] *Ibid.*, 1913–14.
[7] *Ibid.*, 1913–14.
[8] *Ibid.*, XII, p. 40.
[9] *Ibid.*, XXII. 114.
[10] *Ibid.*, XI. 54.
[11] *Ibid.*, XVII. 89.
[12] *Ibia.*, XXII. 103.
[13] *Ibid.*, XI, p. 25.
[14] *Ibid.*, II, p. 264.
[15] *Ibid.*, p. 288.
[16] *Ibid.*, 1913–14, p. 210, Pl. LXIV. 22 f.

Part IV.

PUNCH-MARKED COPPER COINS.

§ 87. Copper coins with punch-marks are, as Cunningham observed, much rarer than silver punch-marked coins. They seem to be of one class only. At one time the only specimens known were those in Cunningham's collection (*C.A.I.*, Pl. I, 20–2, p. 59), and now in the British Museum (nos. 58, 133, and 217). In 1911, however, the Museum acquired from Mr. W. H. Valentine what was evidently a find of these pieces which had been kept intact by a previous owner. No details of provenance were available, but the general character of the collection of which they formed part suggested the southern part of the United Provinces, coins of the sultans of Jaunpur forming a large proportion of the collection. These coins are all catalogued here; they offer no variety in type, but the great variation in weight is worth putting on record. The method of manufacture is apparent. The flans were chopped out of long bars of copper and then punched with symbols, five on one side and four on the other. These symbols are, on the obverse (as we may call the side with five symbols on the analogy of the punch-marked silver):

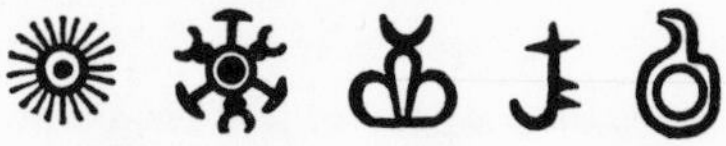

and on the reverse: 

The obverse resembles the punch-marked silver of Class I and many groups of Class II in that three of the symbols are sun, six-armed symbol, and mountain, although in no case are the symbols exactly the same. The fourth symbol resembles  which is only found on the reverse of the silver coins. The fifth symbol is not found elsewhere. The reverse differs from all other punch-marked coins in having four distinct symbols impressed upon it: one of these is a lotus, recalling a symbol found on coins of Eran, the second is a conch-shell, the third is the somewhat elaborate svastika. The fourth is probably a variant of the common 'mountain' symbol but is not found elsewhere in this form.

A find was made of similar coins a few years ago at Madhipur[1] in the Bhagalpur district of Bihar; 54 specimens were acquired by the Indian Museum, Calcutta. They weighed from 163·9 to 286·7 grains. Bhagalpur is the ancient Campā, the capital of Anga, which was incorporated in Magadha in the sixth century B.C. The find of coins previously mentioned (§ 49) probably came also from the ancient kingdom of Magadha. These coins are similar in their obverse type to the punch-marked silver coins, and the fact that the first three symbols are the sun, a six-armed symbol, and a 'mountain' connects them closely with Class 1 and Groups I–VII of Class 2. We have no evidence that they are as widely disseminated as the punch-marked coins, but one does not expect copper coins to travel far. They cannot be coins of Anga in view of its early loss of its independence; they must therefore be of Magadha of a date after the incorporation of Campā in Magadha. These pieces then are most probably the local coins of Magadha in the Maurya period.

PART V.

TRIBAL COINS.

§ 88. IN this section are included the coins which can be more or less definitely attributed from their legends or otherwise. They may be conveniently called tribal coins; indeed, on several, the word *gaṇa* (tribe) actually occurs in combination with the proper name: thus we have the *gaṇa* of the Yaudheyas and of the Ārjunāyanas. The attribution is in many cases still very problematical. Cunningham's attributions are almost everywhere followed even when his reasons for them are not on record. His long experience as a collector in India and his unrivalled knowledge of coins and their provenance make it very difficult to differ from him.

§ 89. ACYUTA (pp. 117–19). The small copper coins bearing the legend 𑀅𑀘𑁆𑀬𑀼 *acyu* in Brāhmī characters of the fourth century A.D. on the obverse, and a wheel on the reverse, have been attributed to the

[1] *A.S.R.*, 1925–6, p. 154, Pl. LX, fig. *f*.

Acyuta who is mentioned in the Allahabad inscription in the list of kings of Āryavarta conquered by Samudragupta. The epigraphy points to this period and the module of the coin and its reverse type, a wheel, suggest that it is not remote in time or place from the coins of the Nāga dynasty, one of whom, Gaṇapatināga, shared the fate of Acyuta. The coins appear to be of two denominations, one of which is half the other. The coin on Pl. XIV. 6 with the syllable *Pṛ* on the obverse and a somewhat similar wheel on the reverse may be connected with this series, and it is retained in this place in the Catalogue until a more certain attribution is found for it. It is later than the *acyu* coins and may quite well be Hūṇa. The rare coins with the obverse type, a bust to right and legend *A–cyu* on either side of it, and a similar wheel on the reverse, are not represented in the British Museum collection. Like the common type they come from Ahicchatra and must be of about the same time. There is no reason to doubt with M. Drouin (*Rev. Num.*, 1898, p. 141) Vincent Smith's reading of the inscription, nor need one suppose direct Roman influence. Although unusual on copper, busts had been for long a familiar feature on silver coins, e.g. of the Western Kṣatrapas, and in the fifth century a portrait is a very common obverse type on the extensive copper coinage of the Hūṇas. The coins should be attributed to a local dynasty of the fourth century A.D. at Ahicchatra in the Bareilly district of the United Provinces.

§ 90. Almorā (p. 120). We are fortunate in knowing the provenance of the three unique coins here catalogued under this head. They were found together 'in Almorah in the Himalaya mountains', and passed into the possession of Sir Henry M. Elliot and ultimately became the property of Sir H. Clive-Bayley, who sold them to the Museum (Prinsep, *Essays*, i, p. 224, figs. 1 and 2). They differ in style, fabric, and size, from all other coins of ancient India, nor are their types to be paralleled. Almorā is in the Kumaun division of the United Provinces and is almost all within the Himālayas. The inscriptions are in large Brāhmī characters of the latter half of the second or first half of the second century B.C. The names Śivadatta (𑀲𑀺 𑀯 𑀤 𑀢 𑀲 *Sivadatasa*), Sivapālita

([ ] [:] *Śivapāli*[*ta*][*sa*]), and Haridatta ([ ] *Hari*[*da*]*tasa*) are quite unknown to history. The pieces of Śivadatta and Haridatta are connected by obverse type and their legends are in Prākrit. In place of the which occupies the centre of these two coins, that of Śivapālita has a rude figure—human or divine—in the centre, with at his side. All three coins have the legends around the central type, with a bull before a tree in railing at the beginning of the legend. The use of the two different sibilants, dental and palatal, in the same word Śiva within so brief a period on these coins, is typical of the laxity in their use in early inscriptions, e.g. in Aśoka's edicts (cf. Bühler, *E.I.*, iii. pp. 136–137).

The elaborate reverse type  which is common to all three pieces is not found exactly elsewhere, although it is built of well-known symbols. It appears to be an altar surmounted by with an elaborate *nandipada* symbol on its face. A very similar reverse is found on the uncertain coin in Pl. XLV. 20, p. 282, 20–21, the obverse of which includes the bull and tree and the symbol characteristic of the coin. The coins, however, differ so much in style that a connexion is very doubtful. The only other coin known of this series is one in the possession of Captain R. F. C. Martin, R.E. The types are similar to those of Śivadatta. The name cannot be read with certainty but the consonants appear to be *M-g-bh-t-sa.*

§ 91. Aparānta. The coins attributed by Cunningham[1] to Aparānta are not represented in the Catalogue. The coins with incomplete legends (p. 182, nos. 80–84) here attributed to Mathurā, are probably of this class however. A specimen with full legend has recently been acquired.

Obv. Lakṣmī as on coins of Mathurā, standing facing with star on left.

[1] *A.S.R.*, xiv, pp. 136–137.

Rev. The Mathurā three elephants type.

On r. *Maharajasa.*

On l. *Apalatasa*, reading outwards.

Aparānta is the Northern Konkan and these coins come from the United Provinces and Rajputana. Their fabric and types make it impossible to remove them from the Mathurā series. The legend naturally means 'of King Apalata' and one does not expect Apalata to be a territorial designation. We need not doubt the equation Apalata = Aparānta, but the legend must mean 'of King Aparānta' and not 'of the king of Aparānta'. The coins should therefore be attributed to a ruler of the dynasty of Mathurā possessing the unusual name of Aparānta.

§ 92. Ārjunāyana. The coins bearing in Sanskrit the name of the Ārjunāyana tribe are very rare and are known in several varieties. The full legend is Ā(r)junāyanānāṁ jaya[-] 'Victory of the Ārjunāyanas'—a type of inscription also found on other tribal coins, e.g. those of the Yaudheyas. The types are var. *a*: obverse a bull to l. apparently standing on a hill, while the reverse has a standing female figure, who may be identified with the Lakṣmī, familiar from the coins of Mathurā, &c. She stands between  (a lingam ?) and a tree. Var. *b.* has an animal before a tree in railing, as above. It may be a bull, as one would expect, but in the Indian Museum specimen (Pl. XX. 10) it is, as Vincent Smith points out, more like an elephant with uplifted trunk, as on the coins of the Audumbaras. The reverse type is certainly a bull before a lingam, as in var. *a*, which makes the presence of a bull on the obverse more doubtful. The third variety has a bull on the obverse; on the reverse a svastika with taurine symbol at end of arms 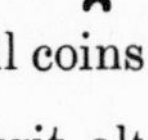, and a branch or palm leaf 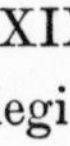. These coins recall certain small coins of the Yaudheyas (Pl. XXXIX. 16–20). The language is Sanskrit, although the *r* in *rj* is not legible on any of the Museum specimens. The earliest reference to the Ārjunāyanas is in a commentary on Pāṇini, while they appear with the Yaudheyas as a frontier people in the

Allahabad inscription of Samudragupta and later in the Bṛhat-saṁhitā, where Varāhamihira puts them in the northern division. Cunningham procured his specimens in Mathurā. The epigraphy of the coins suggests a date about 100 B.C. and the lands of the Ārjunāyanas probably lay within the triangle Delhi–Jaipur–Agra.

§ 93. AUDUMBARAS. The coins attributed to the Audumbaras fall into three classes: a series of square copper coins bearing the name of the tribe, a few rare silver pieces, and a group of round copper and billon pieces, the attribution of which is due to Cunningham and is supported by provenance, but has not yet been further confirmed or overthrown.

The coins which may be presumed to be the earliest, as distinctly Indian in type and showing no trace of foreign influence, are the square copper coins, once very rare but now well known from the large find made at Irippal in the Kangra district of the Panjab in 1913, and published by R. D. Banerji.[1] The type was already known from Cunningham's excavations at Pathankot.[2]

The obverse type is a tall tree in an enclosure; this type is so common on early Indian coins that it is doubtful if we need identify it, as Cunningham does, with the *udumbara* fig-tree: on the right is the forepart of an elephant to l. The reverse type is a two-storied domed and pillared stupa beside which stands a trident with an axe-head on the shaft; the latter bears no proportion to the stupa, nor is the elephant on the obverse in proportion to the tree, so that the four elements of the types are probably quite separate from each other. The obverse inscription is in Kharoṣṭhī characters, and the reverse in Brāhmī. The names of four kings have been found on these pieces:—Śivadāsa, Rudradāsa, Mahādeva, and Dharaghoṣa. As *Mahādeva* is also found as a regal title on these coins, it is possible that some of the specimens attributed to him in the Catalogue are really incomplete specimens of coins of other rulers. There is no reason, however, to doubt the existence of a ruler of this name, especially as we have also a silver coin bearing it.

1 *J.A.S.B. Num. Suppl.*, xxii. § 134, p. 247 ff.

2 *A.S.R.*, v, p. 154, and xiv, p. 116, Pl. XXXI. 1–2; *C.A.I.*, p. 67, Pl. IV. 2.

The full legends, which are in Prākrit, are:—

a. *Mahadevasa raña Sivadasasa O*[1]*du(ṁ)barisa.*
b. *Mahadevasa raña Rudradasasa* „
c. *Mahadevasa raña Dharaghoṣasa* „
d. *Mahadevasa raña Odu(ṁ)barisa.*

The epigraphy points to the first century B.C. The Pathankot coins were found with coins of Zoilus, Vonones, and Gondophares, as well as of Kanishka and Huvishka, so that the Audumbara coins probably preceded the coins of these invaders. The dialect on each side is possibly the same, but the fragmentary nature of the inscription does not permit us to decide. There appear to be slight differences of dialect on the silver coins. Both Brāhmī and Kharoṣṭhī show the genitive *Oduṁbarisa*, the use of the genitive suffix of the *a*-stem in stems in *i* and *u* being quite usual in the Prākrit of this period.[2]

§ 94. Of the rare silver coins attributed here to the Audumbaras, there is no doubt about one at least, that of Dharaghoṣa, for not only is there a Dharaghoṣa known from the copper coins, but this piece, like them, bears the tribal name Odu[ṁ]barisa and has the same legend as the copper pieces. Its connexion with the latter is further shown by the reverse type, which is the trident with axe on shaft beside the tree in enclosure, each familiar from obverse and reverse of the copper pieces. The obverse type is a bearded male figure with right hand raised, clearly copied from the type of Hercules crowning himself, such as we get on the hemidrachms of Lysias, for example. The club has disappeared from his left arm, but the lion's skin still hangs there. The figure, however, is labelled Viśpamitra, i.e. the sage Viśvāmitra. A parallel to *śpa* for *śva* is found in the name Aśpavarman.[3] Viśvāmitra's connexion with the Audumbaras is otherwise unknown. This coin, which, like the other silver pieces, is obviously modelled on the Graeco-Indian

[1] On the occurrence of *guṇa* for *vṛddhi* in the dialect of these and other ancient coins cf. Rapson, *J.R.A.S.*, 1900, p. 429.

[2] R. O. Franke, *Pāli und Sanskrit*, 1902, p. 65.

[3] Cf. Franke, *op. cit.*, p. 117.

hemidrachm, may be dated in the middle of the first century B.C. There is a similar coin in the Lahore Museum.[1]

Of Mahādeva, the British Museum has two round silver coins with types elephant and bull, recalling the very common hemidrachms of Apollodotos, although the great majority of the latter are square. The attribution of these pieces to the Audumbaras is based on the name Mahādeva, the type elephant with a trident in front, and general similarity to the coins of Dharaghoṣa. The frequent omission of long vowels on these coins makes the reading of the exact dialect difficult. The marginal legend *Bhagavatamahadevasa* in Prākrit is the same in the Kharoṣṭhī and Brāhmī forms. This is presumably for *Bhāgavata-Mahādevasya*, 'Mahādeva, the worshipper of Bhagavat'. The legend *rajaraña* in the exergue of the obverse, corresponding to the Sanskrit *rājarājnaḥ*, is represented by *rājarāja* on the reverse, which is a puzzling form; the second *j* is possibly an error for *jñ*:[2] this is a very early occurrence in a Hindu dynasty of the title 'king of kings'. The obverses of the two known specimens differ in the direction of the bull and in the form of the lotus.

§ 95. The third ruler of whom a silver coin[3] is known is Rudravarman. His types are those of Mahādeva, except that the elephant is to the right. The elephant and trident with axe on handle again suggest the attribution to the Audumbara dynasty. The marginal legend on both sides, in Kharoṣṭhī and Brāhmī, is in Prākrit,

Vijayaya-raña Vemakisa Rudravarmasa
and
Vijayaka-rajñ[o] Vemakisa Rudravarmasa.

In the text (p. 125) I had adopted the reading *vijayata* given by Cunningham, Rapson, and others for the word in the exergue in Kharoṣṭhī. There is no doubt, however, that the word is *vijayaya*, a Prākrit equivalent of *vijayaka*[4] which, and not *vijaya*, is the

[1] Whitehead, *Panjab Museum Catalogue*, i, p. 167, Pl. XVI, no. 136.

[2] Perhaps as Bergny suggested (*J.R.A.S.*, 1900, p. 412) it is *rājarājasa*, the two final *sa*'s running into one another.

[3] Whitehead, *Panjab Museum Catalogue*, i, p. 167, Pl. XVI, no. 137.

[4] On *ya* for *ka* cf. Pischel, *Grammatik der Prākrit-Sprachen*, 1900, § 598.

correct reading of the corresponding word in the Brāhmī inscription where it begins the legend. It is an adjective meaning 'victorious'. The Kharoṣṭhī legend also shows that the word before the king's name is *Vemaki* (for *Vaimaki*, like Odumbara for Audumbara). The legend means 'of the victorious king Rudravarman, the Vimaki', the latter being an otherwise unknown family of the Audumbaras.

The resemblance of the silver coins of the Audumbaras to those of the Kuninda Amoghabhūti is remarkable in many ways, and one of them was found with three of the latter and twenty-eight hemidrachms of Apollodotos at Jwālamukhi in the Panjab.[1]

§ 96. Following Cunningham, we have retained the attribution to the Audumbaras of a group of coins of kings whose names end in -mitra, which are not in type or style particularly closely connected with the coins bearing the name *Odumbari*. A link is perhaps found in the elephant, usually, however, with rider on the obverse, and, though rarely visible, the tree in front of it. The obverse type is the figure of a male deity, Kārttikeya, or perhaps simply a warrior holding a spear in his right hand; on some coins an axe-head seems visible on the shaft, which recalls the trident-axe of the preceding series; on the right is a perpendicular wavy line. The inscriptions are Prākrit in Brāhmī and Kharoṣṭhī: *Raña* (*Rajña*) *Ajamitasa* = *Rājna Āryamitrasya*. Three other kings' names are found:—Mahīmitra, Bhānumitra, and Mahābhūtimitra. The smaller coins of Bhānumitra have, in place of the male figure, three well-known symbols 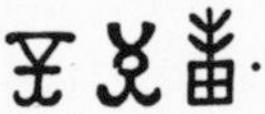. The obverse type, however, makes the attribution certain. These coins come from the Panjab, notably from the Hoshiarpur district, and are to be dated in the first century B.C. or A.D. A unique bronze coin of *Bhāgavata Mahādeva*, probably the Audumbara, was published by Rapson in *J.R.A.S.*, 1900, pp. 112–13, Pl. I. 12. The obverse has an uncertain symbol also found on the Mathurā coin in this Catalogue, Pl. XXIV. 17, and the reverse a figure holding a trident battle-axe. To the Audumbaras are also attributed the two coins from the same region illustrated in Pl. XV. 11 and 12. They have as types a stupa

[1] *A.S.R.*, xiv, 134.

and a tree with cobra and taurine symbol in the field. The inscriptions are too fragmentary to assist in the attribution.

§ 97. These coins come from a well-defined area in the Northern Panjab. To Cunningham's references to finds from Pathankot and Jwālamukhi we can now add the Irippal find, and point to the numerous coins now in the Museum from the collection of J. P. Rawlins, who collected in the Hoshiarpur district, which also gave Mr. Whitehead some of his coins. The Audumbaras should be located in the area formed by the eastern part of the modern Kangra district, the Gurdaspur district and Hoshiarpur district, that is to say, the valley of the Beas, or perhaps the wider region between the upper Sutlej and the Rāvi. Pliny (*Nat. Hist.*, v. 17) mentions a people, the *Odeonbares*, who lived in Kacch. These are certainly not the people who issued our coins. The *Mahābhārata* mentions the Audumbaras with the peoples of the north. The *Bṛhatsaṁhitā* (xiv. 3) puts them in the middle country. The *Gaṇapāṭha* on Pāṇini iv. 2, 5, 3, places them near the people of Jālandhara, a location which the coins support. For a full discussion of the place of the Audumbaras in ancient India and their commercial importance see J. Przyluski, *Un ancien peuple du Penjab: les Udumbara*, in *Journ. As.*, 1926, pp. 1–55.

§ 98. Ayodhyā (pp. 129–139). The coins here attributed to Ayodhyā, because most of them were found on the site[1] of that ancient city, are, with the exception of one class, presumably the currency of a somewhat wider area, the kingdom of Kosala, of which Ayodhyā was the capital. They fall into three classes. The first and earliest consists of a few rare cast pieces, of which three types are known. The first type is known from one piece only (Pl. XVI. 6); it has a flower on the obverse and a plain reverse, and may not be a coin at all, but an ornament. Type II is known only from a unique specimen in the Museum (Pl. XVI. 7); the obverse type is a svastika which connects it with type III, and the reverse 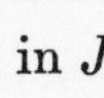 is well known from several series of punch-marked

[1] C., *C.A.I.*, p. 90. H. Rivett-Carnac, *J.A.S.B.*, 1880, p. 138.

coins. The square coin published by H. Rivett-Carnac,[1] *obv.* svastika, *rev.* bull, is probably also a coin of this series. Type III is the commonest of this class:[2] the obverse, a svastika over a fish, is connected by the former symbol with the preceding type; the roughness of the casting makes it difficult to break up the reverse type into its component symbols. These are probably a crescent or a taurine symbol above a steelyard, but might be a taurine symbol over an axe. The former is the more probable explanation, and the occurrence of the steelyard suggests that these are local coins of the city, as distinct from the dynastic issues; they may be compared with the Taxila pieces bearing a steelyard. Their date may be conjectured to be the third century B.C.

§ 99. The remaining coins of Ayodhyā are inscribed with the names of the rulers who issued them, and fall into two very distinct classes, issued by two separate dynasties, one of square cast coins showing no trace of foreign influence in their style and types, and one of round struck pieces which have types rather than symbols. The coins of the rulers of the first dynasty closely resemble one another in style and are connected by their types. The obverse is a bull, or rarely an elephant, before an elaborate symbol not always distinct, , which is replaced on the coins of the later dynasty by a ceremonial standard or spear. The reverse type consists of a group of five or six symbols. The characteristic symbols are a small 'Ujjain' symbol , a tree in railing , a group of four *nandipadas* in a square 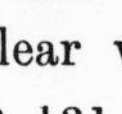, a svastika 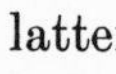, a symbol 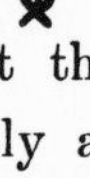, and a river or snake; it is not clear which the latter is, but the drawing 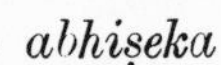 on pp. 130–131 is perhaps too definitely a snake; two rulers, Viśākhadeva and Śivadatta, have also the type of the *abhiṣeka* of Lakṣmī. The names of six rulers of this dynasty are known from their coins, which bear simply the Prākrit form of the name in the genitive. They are Mūladeva (*Mūladevasa*), Vāyudeva

[1] *J.A.S.B.*, 1880, Pl. XVII. 16 B.

[2] Cf. *J.A.S.B.*, 1880, Pl. XVII. 15A and B; *C.I.M.* i, p. 149, nos. 12–13.

(*Vāyudevasa*), Viśākhadeva (*Visakhadevasa*), Dhanadeva (*Dhanadevasa*), Śivadatta (*Sivadatasa*), and Naradatta (*Naradatasa*). At least one other ruler is represented by the uncertain coins on p. 135. The name on nos. 37, 38 is possibly Pāthadeva (*Pāthad*[– –]). The British Museum does not possess the type of Viśākhadeva first published by Rivett-Carnac and now in the Indian Museum,[1] in which the central symbol on the reverse is a buckler-like object, a solar symbol with a central boss surrounded by a circle of dots within rims. This came from Fyzabad, as did all the coins published by Rivett-Carnac. No attempt to arrange these rulers in chronological order is possible, nor have we any literary or inscriptional references to them. They probably cover the second century B.C.

§ 100. The third class of coins belongs to a later dynasty. From Rivett-Carnac and Cunningham we know that these come from the same site. They are round pieces struck from dies leaving the seal-like impression characteristic of early Indian struck coins, and very distinct from the coins of the earlier dynasty. The usual types are obverse:—a bull before a standard or spear [2] and reverse a bird, usually called a cock but probably a *haṁsa*, and a palm-tree with a river (or less probably a snake) below. These three elements are to be regarded as separate symbols and not as being combined to form a single type, as their proportions show. Another but rarer reverse type is an elaborate *nandipada* in a framework; the complete form of this type is probably something like the  found on the coins of Almorā. This occurs on the coins of Kumudasena, Ajavarman, Saṁghamitra, and Vijayamitra; Vijayamitra is the only ruler who coins both types. On the coins of Kumudasena and Ajavarma, the object in front of the bull is probably a form of that on the coins of the earlier dynasty, a kind of triangular standard with cross-bar in railing .

[1] *J.A.S.B.*, 1880, Pl. XVI. 1–2; *C.I.M.*, i, p. 148, nos. 1–2, Pl. XIX. 13.

[2] It closely resembles the ceremonial spear on the Aśvamedha coins of Samudragupta, *B.M.C. Gupta Coins*, Pl. V. 9.

Kumudasena[1] is the only member of the dynasty to call himself *rāja*; the others inscribe their coins with their names only. The rulers represented in the British Museum are Satyamitra (*Satyamitasa*), Āryamitra (*Ayyamitasa*), Saṁgha[mitra] (*Sa*[*ṁ*]*gha*[- -]), Vijayamitra (*Vijayamitasa*), Kumudasena (*Rājña Kumudasenasa*), to which may be added from the Indian Museum Collection the names of Ajavarman[2] (*Ajavarmaṇa*) and Devamitra (*Devamitasa*).[3] None of these rulers is otherwise known to history. Their reigns probably covered the first two centuries A.D.

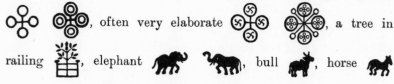

§ 101. ERAN (pp. 140–144). Eran, now a village in the Saugor district of the Central Provinces at the confluence of the rivers Bīna and Reutā, was in ancient times a place of great importance. This is evident from the historical inscriptions there:—of Samudragupta, Budhagupta, and Toramāṇa. The last of these preserves the old form of the name, Erakaina. Cunningham[4] procured many ancient coins from this site of which the most remarkable, a series of fine punch-marked copper coins, are here attributed to Eran. They have affinities with the punch-marked copper coins (p. 101 f.) and with the coins here catalogued under Ujjāyinī, and indeed a number previously attributed to Eran have been transferred to the latter city. These coins are possibly isolated survivors of the copper coinage of ancient India, which corresponded to the silver punch-marked coins. The general type is a large square coin with four or five punches on the obverse and a plain reverse; on the few specimens on which there is a reverse type, it is one that really belongs to the obverse series. The obverse punches may be arranged in groups, of which two or three are constant, as in the silver punch-marked series. The commonest symbols are the Ujjain symbol 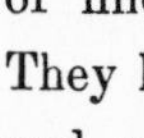 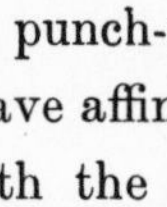, often very elaborate 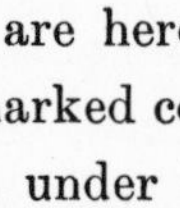 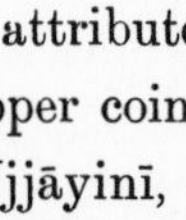, a tree in railing 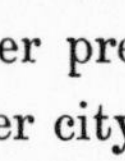, elephant 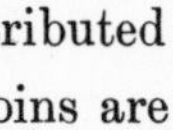 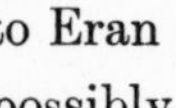, bull 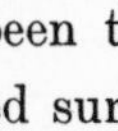, horse 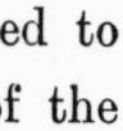

[1] On this coin see Rapson in *J.R.A.S.*, 1903, p. 287.
[2] *C.I.M.*, i, p. 150, no 16, Pl. XIX. 16.
[3] *Ibid.*, i, p. 151, Pl. XIX. 18.
[4] *A.S.R.*, x, pp. 76–81; xiv, pp. 148–149.

(very rare on early Indian coins), a river with fish (Pl. XVII. 9, 11), and a ribbon of svastikas and taurine symbols , a six-armed symbol , identical with that found on the punch-marked copper coins, a triangular-headed standard in railing  resembling one of the symbols on Khāravela's Hathigumphā inscription.[1] The general type of most of the symbols is found elsewhere, although the exact form is usually peculiar to Eran; some, however, are not found elsewhere, notably  and 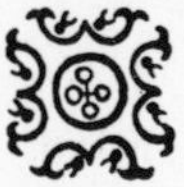. The characteristic coins of Eran are those described under var. *b* onwards. Var. *a* is retained here on the ground of provenance, but its place is rather with var. *l* of the uninscribed cast coins.

§ 102. The site of Eran also yielded the earliest inscribed Indian[2] coin—that of Dharmapāla; it bears simply the inscription *Dhamapālasa* read round the coin from right to left. The coin cannot be later than the third century and might even be earlier. I am unable to read *lajino*[3] or *raña*[4] in front of *Dhamapālasa*. In view of the deep striking of the other letters, the marks on the right are probably fortuitous, and the analogy of other early coins does not lead us to expect a title.

Cunningham possessed two other inscribed coins from Eran which are not in the Museum. They were published by him in the *A.S. Reports*.[5] The first of these may be described as follows:

Obv. An archway with crescent above, between two crosses; above, the inscription *Erakanya*. The last akṣara is not absolutely clear, but Cunningham's reading seems fairly certain in *A.S.R.* X., Pl. XXIV. 16.

Rev. Ujjain symbol, tree in railing with river above.

Æ 0·7. Wt. 24 (broken); sq.

[1] *Actes du Sixième Congrès des Orient.*, Leiden 1885, iii, 2, p. 136, Pl. I.

[2] *A.S.R.*, x, Pl. XXIV. 15; R., *I.C.*, Pl. IV. 7, Bühler; *Indian Studies*, iii, p. 43 (*Sitz.-ber. K. Ak.*, Wien, 1895).

[3] *A.S.R.*, x, p. 80.

[4] *C.H.I.*, i, p. 538.

[5] x, pp. 80, 81, Pl. XXIV. 16–17; xiv, p. 149, Pl. XXXI. 17, 18.

Cunningham's description of the second coin, which it is impossible to check from the poor autotype available, is:

Obv. Bull to r. with wheel below and inscription *Erakanya*.

Rev. Ujjain symbol. Æ 0·4. Wt. 23 grains; sq.

A fourth inscribed coin of Eran was in the White King collection;[1] it differs from the preceding in being round and cast.

Obv. Horse to l., Ujjain symbol above.

Rev. Between two trees in railings, the inscription reading vertically upwards *Erak* (-): the last akṣara is uncertain, but might be a *y* with a very long middle stroke or even *nya*. Æ 0·8.

The horse, like the Ujjain symbol, seems to have been a characteristic type of Eran. The occurrence of a place-name is very rare on early Indian coins, but is paralleled in the coins of the neighbouring Ujjāyinī.

§ 103. KĀḌA[2] (pp. 145–146). The very rude cast copper coins bearing a legend *Kāḍasa* in early Brāhmī characters, probably of the latter half of the third century or early second century B.C., have not yet been attributed. The legend is the genitive of *Kāḍa* which it has been suggested might be for a Sanskrit *Kāla*. Cunningham suggested *Kāḍa* = *Kādrava*, the descendant of Kadru.[3] It is probably a tribal name and not that of a ruler; the number of varieties also suggests this. No find-spots are recorded, but Cunningham mentions that he found one with coins of the Kuṇindas. The Museum has specimens from the Rodgers and Whitehead collections which fact also points to a Panjab provenance. Five varieties are distinguished here; var. *a* is a very crudely cast piece with obverse, a large sun, and reverse, a tree in railing such as we are familiar with on uninscribed cast coins. The inscription is placed perpendicularly on the right; on the left is an uncertain rectangular object (Pl. XIX. 14). Var. *b* has the same type on obverse and reverse, namely, an undulating line presumably representing a snake, below which is a taurine

[1] Rapson, *J.R.A.S.*, 1900, p. 108, Pl. 7.
[2] C., *C.A.I.*, Pl. II. 21–22; R., *I.C.* Pl. III. 7.
[3] *A.S.R.*, ii, 10.

symbol and the inscription (Pl. XIX. 15): var. *c* is similar on one side but the order is reversed, the inscription being uppermost. On the other side is a standing figure of a deity with a sceptre or spear in his left hand and a small bag in the right hand. He is possibly *Kārttikeya,* who is similarly represented on coins of Ujjāyinī. Beside him is a svastika and above it an uncertain object, probably a kalaśa with flowers (Pl. XIX. 17). Var. *d* differs in being square; one side is completely filled by an elephant and the other has the usual snake, taurine, and legend. Var. *e* is a small coin with the object we have called a kalaśa in var. *c* on the one side and the legend on the other (Pl. XIX. 20); var. *f*, which is anonymous, is connected with var. *a* by the obverse type sun; the reverse we have called a horse in the Catalogue (p. 146), but it may be meant for a deer (Pl. XLIII. 10, 11), which it is more natural to find on coins of this period.

§ 104. KANAUJ (p. 147). We have placed under this rather unsatisfactory heading coins of three kings who clearly belong to one dynasty. One of the coins is known to have come from the site of the ancient city of Kanyākubja. As we know nothing of the history of Kanauj in the first century B.C. to which these coins belong and the names of these kings do not occur in any inscriptions, one can only conjecture that these were coins of a dynasty which ruled here. The coins of two of these kings Brahmamitra and Sūryamitra have identical obverse types, three well-known symbols  arranged in a different order on each. The reverse of Brahmamitra's coin has a *nandipada* symbol on a pillar within a railing on the left and another quite illegible on the right. The reverse of Sūryamitra's coin is quite illegible. The obverse of the coin of the third king Viṣṇudeva is connected with the preceding by the symbol tree in railing, but the other two symbols are different; one of these is a hare in the crescent moon found on a rare variety of the punch-marked silver (Class 2, Group V, var. *b*) and a symbol 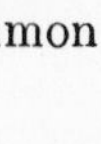 not found elsewhere, which may be connected with the common on punch-marked coins. The reverse has a horse apparently before a sacrificial post (yūpa) and may commemorate an aśvamedha sacrifice. This last coin which was in the Prinsep collection came from Kanauj.[1] The legends are in Prākrit, *Brahmamitasa*, *Sūyamitasa*, and *Viṣṇudevasa*.

§ 105. KAUŚĀMBĪ (pp. 148–155). Cunningham's identification of the ancient Kauśāmbī (Kosambi) with the modern Kosam, thirty miles SW. of Allahabad in the Manjhanpur tahsil of the Allahabad district has now been amply confirmed,[2] and the coins from that site can be associated with one of the most important cities of ancient India, the old capital of the Vatsas (Vaṁsas). The coins, however, belong to a period upon which neither Sanskrit nor Pāli literature throws any light. Almost all the coins here catalogued came from the Cunningham collection, and were procured at Kosam.[3] Clive-Bailey's coins[4] of Kauśāmbī also came from this site, as did coins found by Führer,[5] and now in the Lucknow Museum. The coins given to the British Museum by Mr. H. Nelson Wright also came from Kosam. Setting aside 'no less than 100 common square cast coins with elephant and Buddhist symbols',[6] which are common on other sites, the coins found at Kosam form a very definite local group linked together by common types.

§ 106. The coins of Kauśāmbī are all of bronze and, like those of Ayodhyā and the Audumbaras, fall into two classes, an earlier one of round cast pieces of purely Indian type quite free from any foreign influence, and a later of struck coins. The characteristic types of Kauśāmbī which prevail throughout the series are a bull and a tree in railing.

The majority of the cast pieces are uninscribed, and of these four

[1] *J.A.S.B.*, iii, p. 434, Pl. XXV. 1; *P.E.*, i, p. 115, Pl. VII. 1; ii, p. 2; Lassen, *I.A.*, ii, pp. 923-925; Smith, *J.R.A.S.*, 1893, Pl. III. i, p. 27. The characters in the inscription are not so early as Smith suggests.

[2] C., *A.S.R.*, i, pp. 361–362; *E.I.*, ii, p. 244; *A.S.R.*, 1921–2, pp. 120-121; *ibid.*, 1923-4, pp. 172–174; *C.H.I.*, i, pp. 524–525.

[3] C., *A.S.R.*, x, 4–5.

[4] *J.A.S.B.*, 1873, pp. 109–111, 191.

[5] *E.I.*, ii, p. 244.

[6] *A.S.R.*, x, p. 4

varieties may be distinguished. The first and largest, var. *a*,[1] has as its obverse type a bull to left before a triangle-headed standard  ; above the bull on the right is the symbol  which we know from a series of punch-marked silver coins. The bull closely resembles that on a group of cast copper coins (cf. vars. *d–k*). The reverse type has a leafy tree in railings, perhaps with birds on the upper branches (cf. p. 92, var. *l*); below is the symbol  and on l. a *nandipada* symbol  above a wheel, and on r. an Ujjain symbol  above a svastika . Var. *b* is so far known from one specimen only (p. 149, no. 12, Pl. XXI. 3). The obverse is as on var. *a*, except that the symbol above the bull is a four-spoked wheel. The reverse has a bull to r. before a tree in railing. Var. *c*[2] is also unique; the obverse type is the *abhiṣeka* of Lakṣmī, and the reverse has a tree in railings of a type different from that of var. *a*, on the left of which is the triangle-headed standard found on the obverse of var. *a*, while on the right is an Ujjain symbol  over what is probably a hollow cross , and not a svastika as stated in the Catalogue (no. 13). Var. *d* is a recent gift to the Museum from Mr. Philip Thorburn, and is not described in the Catalogue. It is as follows:

13 *a*. *Obv.* Elephant before  ; Ujjain symbol above.

Rev. Tree in railings of type of var. *c*; on l.  ; on r. *nandipada* above a wheel. Æ 0·8. Wt. 45·5.

The occurrence of the majority of the symbols on these coins, elephant,  , , the trees found on vars. *l* and *o* (pp. 92, 93), on varieties of early cast copper coins, suggests that some of the latter may also be connected with Kauśāmbī.

[1] *P.E.*, ii, Pl. XLIV. 6; C., *A.S.R.*, x, Pl. II. 8; R., *I.C.*, Pl. III. 12; C., *C.A.I.*, Pl. V. 7.

[2] C., *A.S.R.*, x, Pl. II. 7; C., *C.A.I.*, Pl. V. 9.

§ 107. Closely connected with the preceding in style, types, and date are two inscribed coins bearing the names of Sudeva[1] (*Sudevasa*) (no. 14) and Bṛhaspatimitra ([*Baha*]*satimitasa*)[2] (no. 15), which cannot be later than the first half of the second century B.C., and might even be as early as the third century. This Bṛhaspatimitra is a different ruler from the Bṛhaspatimitra who issued the struck coins (nos. 16–25), which are comparatively common. Apart from the striking differences in the fabric and type, the epigraphy is quite different and earlier; compare, for example, the form of *m*, *s*, and *t* in the two. The epigraphy of the former is still, roughly speaking, 'Aśokan', while that of the latter is Śuṅga.

The coin of Bṛhaspatimitra has now been cleaned and can be described more fully. The object in front of the horse is the symbol  in a square; there is an Ujjain symbol above. The elephant on the rev. is standing to r. with uplifted trunk; there is an Ujjain symbol above it and a tree in railing in a square behind it. There is an uncertain -shaped object in front.

§ 108. Of the struck coins, all of which are connected by types, those of Aśvaghoṣa[3] (*Aśvagoṣasa*) (no. 17) and Parvata (*Pavatasa*) (nos. 16–16 a) are perhaps the earliest. They are connected by their thin fabric and square shape. The larger round coins of Parvata, which resemble those of Bṛhaspatimitra II, are not represented in the Museum. There is one in the Indian Museum[4] and another in the Bibliothèque Nationale (formerly Vincent Smith). The types are probably the same as those of Bṛhaspatimitra II, although the object in front of the bull is not clear. The reverse is the same as on the smaller pieces. The coins of Bṛhaspatimitra II[5] (*Bahasatimitasa*), Agnimitra (*Agimitasa*), and Jyeṣṭhamitra (*Jeṭhamitasa*) form the next group and are closely connected. They are of the end of the second and first century B.C. The form of tree is that of var. *c* of the cast coins. Three varieties are known of the coins

[1] C., *C.A.I.*, Pl. V. 10.
[2] *Ibid.*, Pl. V. 8.
[3] *Ibid.*, Pl. V. 14.
[4] *C.I.M.*, i, Pl. XX. 4.
[5] C., *C.A.I.*, Pl. V. 1.

of Jyeṣṭhamitra, of which the third (no. 37) bears the deity with whom we are familiar on coins of Mathurā. The symbol  in front of the bull on these coins may be compared with  which appears on the coins of the Kuṇindas, and the snake-like  or object on the right may be compared with that on the coins of Ayodhyā, the Audumbaras, Kāḍa, and the Kuṇindas. A series of much-worn coins of Bṛhaspatimitra II and of Agnimitra is known, countermarked with a triangle-headed standard (not a tree as stated on p. 152) in a railing  or with a nandipada.

The remaining coin with a ruler's name, that of Dhanadeva[1] (*Rāja* (for *jño*) *dhanadevasya*), is later than the preceding, as the epigraphy and the use of Sanskrit shows. The very common coins with the types of Dhanadeva with incomplete and apparently meaningless legends[2] represent the last stage of the coinage of Kauśāmbī, and must belong to the early centuries A.D.

§ 109. The name of a king Bṛhaspatimitra (*Bṛhāsvātimita*) occurs on inscribed bricks found at Morā,[3] seven miles west of Mathurā commemorating the erection of a temple by his daughter, and in one of the inscriptions at Pabhosā[4] (*Bahasatimittra*) near Kosam commemorating the excavation of a cave by his uncle. These have been assumed[5] to be the same individual and to be identical with the Bṛhaspatimitra of the coins, of whom we have just seen that there are really two.

Comparing the epigraphy of the two inscriptions, we see that the Morā inscription is much the earlier in date; when we remember that the Morā inscription is put up by his daughter and the Pabhosā by his uncle—although the difference in date may not have been

[1] C., *C.A.I.*, Pl. V. 18.

[2] C., *A.S.R.*, x, Pl. II. 6; C., *C.A.I.*, Pl. V. 12–13; *P.E.*, Pl. VIII. 12–15.

[3] Vogel, *J.R.A.S.*, 1912, p. 120, Pl. II. 1.

[4] *E.I.*, ii, p. 241 and plate.

[5] Vogel, *l. c.*; Jayaswal, *J.B.O.R.S.*, 1917, pp. 473–480; *C.H.I.*, i, pp. 524–525.

great—it is still more unlikely that the king referred to should be the same in both. The epigraphy of the Pabhosā inscription agrees very well with that of Bṛhaspatimitra II's coins, and although the doubling of the *t* before *r* (*mittra*) is not found on the coins, the two may well be identical, especially as Pabhosā may be presumed to be within the territory of a king of Kauśāmbī. The inscription is dated in the tenth year of a king Ūdāka,[1] who has been identified by Jayaswal[2] with the fifth king of the Śuṅga dynasty whose name appears in various forms—Odraka, Andhraka, &c.—in the Puranic lists. According to the Puranic chronology, the date in question could be 120 B.C., and a date of *c.* 125 to 100 B.C. would suit Bṛhaspatimitra II's coins. As to the Morā inscription there is no palaeographical objection to identifying the Bṛhaspatimitra mentioned there, whose daughter married the king of Mathurā, with Bṛhaspatimitra I of the coins. We cannot agree that Bṛhaspatimitra[3] is mentioned in the Hathigumphā inscription. The word in question begins *bahu*, the certain elements in it seem to be *bahu(s - -)idita*; it is very probably not a proper name at all, for the suggested reading of the preceding words as *Magadhā ca rājānaṁ* is extremely improbable, philologically as well as palaeographically. It is quite impossible to identify the Bṛhaspatimitra of the coins with the Śuṅga Puṣyamitra—quite apart from the improbability of this use of synonyms—for the coins cannot be removed from Kauśāmbī, the coins of which are a very homogeneous series.

§ 110. While these pages are going to press the Museum has acquired an interesting coin of Kauśāmbī formerly in the Sutcliffe collection.

Obv. Elephant l. on  ;  in front of it and six-armed whorl behind with  above;  below; above legend  (*K*[*o*]*sa*[*ṁ*]*bi*).

[1] This is, I think, the correct reading. [2] Jayaswal, *l. c.*

[3] Jayaswal, *J.B.O.R.S.*, 1917, pp. 457 and 472-483.

Rev. Tree in railing, above, on l., on r.; on either side of railing.

Æ (cast). Wt. 76.

The general types of this coin are those of the early cast uninscribed coins attributed to Kauśāmbī (§ 106), and to Bṛhaspatimitra I (§ 107). The legend now confirms the attribution of these

pieces. For the use of a place-name as a coin legend we may compare the coins, all very rare, of Ujjayinī and Eran which also bear the name of the place of issue in the nominative. The coin mentioned in *A.S.R.* 1924–1925, p. 131, Pl. XXXVIII *d* 3, as lent to the Indian Museum, is probably similar.

A new variety of the cast copper coins has recently been presented to the British Museum by Mr. H. Nelson Wright

Obv. Elephant on to l. before ; above; other symbols, or possibly inscriptions, illegible.

Rev. Three symbols; and tree in railing.

Æ ·8. Wt. 61.

This coin bears a symbol new to this series and otherwise only known from the coin of Viṣṇudeva described on p. 147. The fact that the three coins there described all have a tree in a railing and two of them have the symbols and also found at, but not, however, peculiar to, Kauśāmbī, may give a clue to their ultimate attribution.

§ 111. Kulūta (p. 158).[1] All available information about the Kulūtas has been collected by Rapson in *J.R.A.S.*, 1900, pp. 530 ff. They were the ancient inhabitants of the Kulū valley in the Kangra district of the Panjab. The earliest literary reference to the Kulūtas is in Varāhamihira's *Bṛhat-Saṁhitā*[2] where they appear in the peoples of the north-east and also of the north-west divisions; the former are the Kulūtas with whom we are here concerned. Hiuen Thsang visited them in the second quarter of the seventh century. About the same time or somewhat earlier the author of the *Mudrā-rākṣasa*[3] mentions them as Mlecchas or foreigners in similar company to Varāhamihira. The only known coin (p. 158, Pl. XVI. 4), however, is of much earlier date, probably the first or early second century A.D. The legend, *Vīrayaśasya rājña Kulūtasya* 'of the Kulūta king Vīrayaśa (= Vīrayaśas)' is practically Sanskrit, which shows the coin is not early; the survival of the Prākrit *raña* in Kharoṣṭhi on the reverse shows that it cannot be very late. A date round about A.D. 100 seems to be indicated. The types are purely Indian. The *obv.*, a wheel surrounded by a circle of dots, probably represents an elaborate dharmacakra; a similar type is found on the unique coin bearing the name Vṛṣṇi (Pl. XVI. 5, p. 281). The reverse type is made up of a number of symbols all well known, a mountain with a river below , and a svastika , a nāga symbol  and an elaborate nandipada symbol ; four of these are also found in slightly different forms on the silver coins of the Kuṇindas, who were neighbours of the Kulūtas. Like the Audumbaras and Kuṇindas they use both the Kharoṣṭhi and the Brāhmī alphabets. On linguistic grounds one would put the coins of Amoghabhūti earlier than those of Vīrayaśas. Cunningham classed this Kulūta coin with those of the Audumbaras, probably on grounds of provenance. The weight we may notice is an unusual one (75·7 gr.). The coin is a didrachm of the standard of the later Greek and Parthian kings of India, who do not, however, strike this denomination.

[1] *C.A.I.*, Pl. IV. 14; Bergny, *J.R.A.S.*, 1900, p. 420.

[2] xiv, 22; xiv, 29.

[3] Ed. Kale, p. 34.

§ 112. Kuṇinda or Kulinda (pp. 159–168 and 288). The form Kulinda is commoner in literature but does not occur on the coins. The coins of the Kuṇindas fall into two main groups, one issued about the end of the first century B.C. and the other about three centuries later.

The former bear the name of Amoghabhūti and the latter are anonymous, with the titles of Śiva only. The first group consists of silver and copper coins similar in type. The module of the silver coins was suggested by the hemidrachms of the later Greek kings but the types are purely Indian. The obverse bears a deer to r. and a figure of Lakṣmī standing facing on a lotus and holding a lotus in her uplifted r. hand. Between the horns of the deer is the cobra symbol  and above its back the symbol . Four variants are distinguished by the additional symbols or symbol in the field, usually between the deer's legs. Var. &c. (*a*) ; (*b*)  and ; (*c*) no symbol; (*d*) . The reverse type recalls that of the Kulūta coinage. In the centre is the symbol  surmounted by a nandipada symbol , on the right is a tree in a railing, and on the left two symbols ; below is a representation of a river .

§ 113. The legends are in Prākrit, the obverse being in Brāhmī and the reverse in Kharoṣṭhī. The dialect of the obverse is more closely allied to Sanskrit than that of the reverse. A curious feature is the indiscriminate use of -*sa* and -*sya* in the genitive of the obverse legend. The use of the genitive of the -*a* stem in a stem in -*i* (*Amoghabhūtisya*) has already been mentioned as a usual feature of the language of this period (cf. § 93, and note 2). On the copper coins a border of dots replaces the Kharoṣṭhī legend and there are no symbols in the field of the obverse. Cunningham[1] says that the copper coins are occasionally inscribed on both sides, but the British Museum possesses none of this type. The legend on the silver and neater copper coins is:

Rājñaḥ (*raña*) *Kuṇiṁdasa* (or -*sya*) *Amoghabhūtisa* (or -*sya*) *mahārājasa* or (-*sya*).

[1] *A.S.R.*, xiv, p. 138.

The Brāhmī legend runs continuously round the coin; on the reverse in the Kharoṣṭhī inscription *maharajasa* is written independently in the exergue while the remainder runs round the coin. This latter arrangement is a little remarkable and suggests that some importance is given to the word *maharaja* by giving it the place occupied by the king's name on Greek and Śaka coins. Nothing similar is found on the obverse however. In any case, we see no reason to doubt that Amoghabhūti is the name of a ruler and that the legend means 'of king Amoghabhūti the Kuṇinda king'. Mr. K. P. Jayaswal[1] has suggested that Amoghabhūti is an official title meaning 'of unfailing prosperity' and that the coins are anonymous, but there is no need to interpret the legend in this way, particularly as the word 'king' occurs not once but twice in it. Nor can we agree that 'the same appellation appears for centuries'.[2] The silver coins are all of the same style and fabric and there is no reason to think they cover a longer period than one reign. Class I of the copper of neat fabric with good legends are contemporary. It is presumably Class II of coarse fabric with incomplete legends which has given rise to the suggestion that this coinage was continued long after the death of Amoghabhūti. There is, however, a strong resemblance among all these pieces, and no signs of a progressive degeneration or evidence that they were issued over a long period. In view of the exceptional neatness of the finely struck copper coins and their comparative scarcity it is probable that Class II represents the ordinary copper coinage of the reign. There is just the probability that they are imitations made by early Kushān invaders like the imitations of coins of Hermaeus. Class III (p. 288), consists of two coins of a larger diameter. They are rudely made but have the same types as the other coins bearing the name Amoghabhūti. The legend in two lines on the obverse occupies a disproportionate amount of space.

§ 114. Economically the silver coins of the Kuṇindas represent

[1] *Hindu Polity*, p. 82 note.

[2] Jayaswal, *l. c.*; cf. Smith, *C.C.I.M.*, p. 161:—'They vary much in execution, and probably extend over a considerable period.'

an attempt of an Indian ruler to issue a native silver coinage which would compete in the market with the later Indo-Greek silver. It is probable that Amoghabhūti's political history was similar. He was probably an Indian chief who founded a short-lived kingdom at the close of the periods of Greek dominion in the Panjab in the last half of the first century B.C. which was soon swept away by the Śaka and Kushān invaders. The coinage of the Kuṇindas then disappears for nearly three centuries till at the end of the second or in the third century A.D. we find coins again issued by a Kuṇinda republic. These are large pieces the module of which is suggested by the Kushān copper coins. The reverse revives the old Kuṇinda type of deer, tree, river, &c., and the obverse bears a figure of Śiva holding a trident and the legend:

Bhāgavata-catreśvara-mahātmanaḥ.

The last word is not *Mahātraṇa* as given on p. 117. The *m* in *tm* is often omitted and the *n* and *ṇ* are often difficult to distinguish, but on Pl. XXIII. 13 and 16, however, the last word is clearly *mahātmanaḥ*.

§ 115. Some evidence is available regarding the provenance of the coins of the Kuṇindas. 54 silver pieces were found with 21 silver coins of Apollodotos at Tappa Mewa[1] in the Hamirpur district of the Panjab. Two coins, presumably copper, were found on a site, which also yielded some 400 Śaka and Kushān copper coins, at Sunit[2] four miles west of Ludhiana. Three silver coins were found with 30 of Apollodotos at Jvālamukhī,[3] also in the Panjab: one was found at Karnāḷ.[4] Several were among the coins described by Prinsep[5] from Behat near Sahāranpur. Cunningham says that the Kuṇinda coins are found mainly between Ambāla and Sahāranpur.[6] The distribution of these coins therefore suggests that the Kuṇindas occupied a narrow strip of land at the foot of the Siwālik hills between the Jumnā and the Sutlej and the territory between the upper courses of the Beas and Sutlej. This agrees

[1] *Proc. A.S.B.*, 1893, pp. 11–12.
[2] *A.S.R.*, xiv, p. 65. [3] *Ibid.*, xiv, p. 134. [4] *Proc. A.S.B.*, 1875, p. 85.
[5] *P.E.*, i, Pl. IV, 1, 3, 6. [6] *C.A.I.*, p. 71.

very well with the few literary references to the Kuṇindas. In the *Bṛhat-saṁhitā*, Varāhamihira places the Kauṇindas[1] in the north-east division with the Kashmirians, Kulūtas, and Sairindhas, and also refers to the fate of a king of the Kuṇindas.[2] The form Kulinda is found in the same source (ch. iv. 24) and in the *Viṣṇu-Purāṇa*, and *Mahābhārata*; in the epic, the Kulindas live in the region indicated by the provenance of the coins. The name is known to Ptolemy who gives the name *Kulindrine* to the country in which the Beas, Sutlej, and Jumnā rise.

§ 116. Mahārāja Janapada. There are no coins bearing the legend *maharaja-janapadasa,* and the existence of the Mahārāja state, which has been based on this reading,[3] still awaits proof. The coins in question really have the inscription *Rajañajanapadasa* and are those catalogued here on pp. 211–12, nos. 12–16. The first coin of this class was published in *P.E.*, Pl. XLIV. 19, and reproduced by Cunningham in *C.A.I.*, Pl. IV. 11. There are no letters before the *r*, for Prinsep, who drew the coin himself, read the inscription (p. 223) *Rajñapadasa,* showing that it began as all the specimens here given do.

Cunningham (p. 69), taking some fortuitous marks as letters and forgetting that he had already read it almost correctly in *A.S.R.*, xiv, p. 150, read the inscription from the drawing as *Maharajasa-janapasada* but, with the number of specimens now available, we have no doubt that this is wrong and that the coin is one of the well-known Rājañya-janapada series.

§ 117. Mālavas. The coins of the Mālavas were unrepresented in the British Museum until 1935, when Mr. T. B. Horwood, I.C.S. (retired) presented the following six specimens.

Class 1 (*I.M.C.*, Class A, Group III)

1. *Obv.* X2JΔ (l.) IEɷ (r.)
(*Malavaṇa-jaya*)
Rev. Vase in dotted circle. Æ 25. Wt. 8·5.

[1] Ch. xiv. 31. [2] Ch. xiv. 33.
[3] Jayaswal, *Hindu Polity*, i, p. 159.

2. Similar 

Æ 2. Wt. 4·2.

3. Similar 

Æ 2. Wt. 5·2.

Class 2 (*I.M.C.*, Group V, var. *b*)

4. *Obv.* Tree in railing. Inscription as in 1.

Rev. Recumbent bull r. in border of dots.

Æ 3. Wt. 7·7.

Class 3.

5. *Obv.* 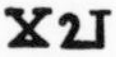

Rev. 

Æ 2. Wt. 6·5.

Class 5 (*I.M.C.*, Class B (no. 98))

6. *Obv.* 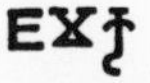 (*Jamaku.*)

Rev. Illegible.

Æ 25. Wt. 12.

§ 118. This small series is representative of the two great groups of Mālava coins so well represented in the Indian Museum:—those with the legend *Mālavānāṁ jayaḥ* and those with what are said to be the names of chiefs. The known coins of the Mālavas seem all to have come from the finds made in 1871–3 by A. C. L. Carlleyle at Nagar or Karkota Nagar in Jaipur State, some 25 miles SSE. by S. of Tonk and 45 miles NNE. of Bundi.[1] They have been discussed by Cunningham,[2] Vincent Smith,[3] and more recently by Mr. R. O. Douglas[4] and Mr. Jayasval.[5]

§ 119. The legend on the first series of coins is evidently for a Sanskrit *Mālavānāṁ jayaḥ,* a formula which can be paralleled on the coins of the Ārjunāyanas and Yaudheyas. The form found on the coins appears to be a Prākrit *Malavaṇa jaya* or *Malavahṇa*

[1] *A.S.R.*, vi, pp. 162 ff., esp. 173–183; xiv, 149–150.

[2] *A.S.R.*, xiv, pp. 149–151.

[3] *C.I.M.*, i, p. 160–164.

[4] *J.A.S.B.*, 1923, *Num. Suppl.*, xxxvii, § 237.

[5] *Hindu Polity*, i, 218.

jaya,[1] but it is difficult to know how far the absence of long vowels, &c., is deliberate, and too much stress need not be laid on the use of the lingual for the dental form of *n*. The date on these coins seems to be the second to the early fourth century A.D. I am unwilling to put any of the few coins I have seen much earlier. The Brāhmī characters may be described as early Gupta. The **X** is common as late as the fourth century, but the **I** belongs to the second and third. The coins cannot therefore be later than the early fourth century. We know that the Mālavas were defeated by Samudragupta and they probably lost their independence in Candragupta II's western campaign. The small copper coins[2] of the latter monarch bearing a vase as type were probably struck by him in the Mālava territory, where he took over the very common local type, just as he did with the silver coins of the Western Kṣatrapas. The Mālavas were probably under Kushān or Śaka domination in the first and second centuries A.D., and they are not likely to have become independent again before the end of the second century.

§ 120. The second class[3] of coins bear short legends which have been said to be names of chiefs and have as a rule similar types—tree in railing and bull—to the preceding. They are found with the coins bearing the name of the Mālavas and closely resemble them. I see no reason for dating them so early as the second century B.C. The epigraphy of those illustrated in the *I.M.C.* again suggests the second and third centuries A.D. The inscriptions Bhapaṁyana, Majupa, Mapojaya, Mapaya, Magajaśa, Magojaya, Mapaka, Pacha, Gajava, Maraja, Jamaku, &c., are puzzling. They are taken to be names of chiefs. Mr. Vincent Smith suggests they are of foreign origin.[4] They certainly do not look Indian, but it is difficult to think what invaders could have struck them. They are too late for the Śakas and too early for the Hūṇas; in addition, out of over twenty names not one bears any resemblance to any known Śaka or Hūṇa name. Mr. Jayaswal, noting that so many of them begin with *Ma*,

[1] *I.M.C.*, i, Pl. XX. 17.
[2] *B.M.C.*, Type IX, p. 60.
[3] *I.M.C.*, i, p. 174–177.
[4] *I.M.C.*, i, p. 163.

has suggested that this is a contraction for Mahārāja.[1] If this left the remainder an intelligible name the suggestion might be worth considering, but it does not help us. There are besides no parallels for such a contraction. The great objection to these inscriptions being names of rulers is that in not one is there any trace of a genitive. I am inclined to think they are not names but in most cases meaningless attempts to reproduce parts of *Mālavānāṁ jayaḥ*. This accounts for so many of them beginning with *ma* and for the frequency of *ja* as another letter of the inscription, and indeed for the limited number of consonants which form these inscriptions.

§ 121. The provenance and epigraphy of the coins of the Mālavas show them occupying a limited area in Eastern Rajputana from the second to the fourth century A.D. This agrees with the reference to them in the Allahabad inscription of Samudragupta. The later Mālava (*Mo-lo-po*) of Hiuen Thsang seems to be farther west than the find-spots of the coins. The similarity of the coin-legends to those of the Ārjunāyanas and Yaudheyas suggests that these were not very remote from them and were probably their neighbours on the north while the resemblance of their coins to those of the Nāgas suggests that the latter were their neighbours on the east. Varāhamihira [2] regularly classes the Mālavas with peoples of the north but, as Fleet has pointed out,[3] this cannot be correct of the Mālavas with whom we are dealing here. The *Mahābhārata* [4] also puts them in the Panjab with the Śibis and Trigartas. If the *Μαλλοί* of Alexander's time who were located in the Upper Panjab in the valley of the Ravi are identified as Mālavas, it may be to them that Varāhamihira refers. It is curious, however, that he should not mention a people who were powerful enough to give their name to a region and oust its ancient name of Avanti. It is possible that the Mālavas of the Panjab gradually retired southward from the second century B.C., before the Greek and Kushān invaders, and eventually settled where we find them in the Christian era. This can only be a conjecture, however, and as Rapson has

[1] *Hindu Polity*, i, p. 218.
[2] Cf. *Bṛhatsaṁhitā*, xiv. 27.
[3] *I.A.*, xxii, p. 184.
[4] *Sabhāparvan*, xxxii. 7.

suggested, there may have been two peoples[1] of the name. It is difficult, however, to follow him in giving to the *Μαλλοί* the coins which are undoubtedly of the later Mālavas of eastern Rajputana.

§ 122. Mathurā, pp. 169–191. The coins from the site and region of the ancient city of Mathurā, 'one of the most prolific fields in Northern India',[2] and attributed to its rulers, fall into two main series: those struck by local Hindu dynasties in the second and first centuries B.C., and those struck by their successors, a dynasty or dynasties of Śaka satraps. The types of the former, with the exception of a few coins to be specially mentioned, the different types of which may be evidence that they do not belong to this dynasty, are singularly uniform: *Obv.* figure of Lakṣmī holding a lotus in her uplifted hand.[3] *Rev.* Three elephants facing, each with a rider. The latter type is crudely represented and degenerates until it is almost irrecognizable. Its progressive degeneration is illustrated on Pl. XLIV, 8–12.

The coins attributed to Mathurā which epigraphy suggests to be the earliest are not of this type or fabric. They are square and have the four symbols 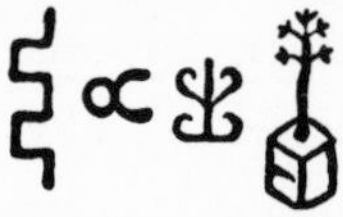 on obverse, and a tree in railing on the reverse. Unlike any of the later coins which bear a name with or without regal title, they bear in addition to the name Gomitra (*Gomitasa*), an additional word which, since Cunningham's time, has been read *Bārāṇāye*. Cunningham obtained these coins at Bulandshahr.[4] The reading, however, is very doubtful. What Cunningham read as □ *Ba* is really part of the symbol 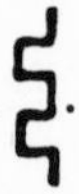. In the catalogue, p. 169, I have suggested *ya* as the reading of the first letter but this is improbable. I now think it

[1] *J.R.A.S.*, 1900, p. 542. [2] *A.S.R.*, xx, 37.

[3] This has sometimes been described as Kṛṣṇa, but the figure is certainly female. It is the same as appears in front of the deer on the Kuṇinda coins for example. Cf. A. K. Coomaraswamy in *Eastern Art*, 1929, pp. 175–189.

[4] *A.S.R.*, xiv, p. 147.

most probable that the legend begins with the syllable *rā* and reads *rāṇāyā* or *rāṇāye*.[1]

Coin no. 5 with a rude figure on the obverse and the legend *Gomitasa* is connected with the preceding by its reverse type of tree in railing, but the latter is of a different and unconventional type. The coin most probably belongs to a Gomitra of another dynasty. It may be compared with the two coins, nos. 58, 59, of Balabhūti.

§ 123. Of the coins of the regular Mathurā type we put first those bearing the name of another Gomitra, as one type is square, which may be evidence of an early date and just possibly indicates a connexion with the coins discussed in the preceding paragraph. The obverse type of var. *a* is Lakṣmī standing facing holding a lotus; on her left is a conventional tree , and on right the two symbols , with a river with fishes below  — that is to say five symbols in all. The name is above. The square and round pieces seem to have been struck from the same dies. The reverse is the three elephants type, well seen on Pl. XXV, 6. Var. *b* differs in having the king's name in place of the tree on the left, and has as reverse type an elephant or a horse. Var. *c* is of different style and has a different type; goddess on l. standing on a lotus: tree in railing above Ujjain symbol on l. and legend perpendicular on l. arranged in a square die. Two of the three symbols are variants of the usual Mathurā type, and one is a regular one. The other two symbols of var. *a* do not appear. The coin is possibly not of the Gomitra of var. *a*. We have classed here as var. *d* a number of small base-metal (potin) coins with type bull, tree in railing and Ujjain symbol: legend *Gomitasa*, and reverse plain, but it is doubtful whether they belong to the same Gomitra or even to Mathurā. It may be noted in this connexion that out of seven specimens not one comes from the Cunningham collection.

§ 124. The coins that follow are all round pieces of the regular

[1] Or with short vowels; the *n* is actually the dental form, but *ṇ* and *n* are not always distinguished.

Mathurā type. They bear the names of Brahmamitra (*Brahmamitasa*), Dṛdhamitra (*Dadhamitasa*), Sūryamitra (*Suryamitasa*), Viṣṇumitra (*Viṣṇumitasa*), Puruṣadatta (*Puruṣadatasa*), Uttamadatta (*Utamadatasa*), and Rāmadatta (*Rāmadatasa*).

The coins of Brahmamitra, Dṛdhamitra, Sūryamitra, and Viṣṇumitra are identical in type with those of Gomitra (II). Puruṣadatta, Uttamadatta, and Rāmadatta I (vars. *a–b*) replace the Ujjain symbol by the symbol . Next may be placed a group of rulers who add the title rājan to the king's name: Rāmadatta (II) (*Rajño Rāmadatasa*), Kāmadatta (*Rajño*[1] *Kāmadatasa*), Śeṣadatta (*Rājño Śeṣadatta*), Bhāvadatta (*Rajño*[1] *Bhāvadatasa*), Uttamadatta (*Rajño Uttamadatta*), and Balabhūti (*Rajño*[1] *Balabhutisa*). It is probable that two Rāmadatta's are to be distinguished: vars. *a* and *b* belong to an earlier one, and *c* probably and *d* certainly to a later one. In addition to the usual symbols, the coins of the later Rāmadatta and of Kāmadatta have a bull on the right and a star on the left. Balabhūti's var. *b* recalls var. *b* of Gomitra I and these coins may be of another dynasty. The British Museum has no coins of Uttamadatta with the title of king; these are known from the Indian Museum specimen, *C.I.M.*, i, Pl. XXII, 11, p. 193. The latter may be of a later ruler than the one without the regal title, but as all have the usual reverse type of an elephant, they are probably all of one ruler. One of the British Museum coins of Uttamadatta is countermarked with a symbol that appears as the type of a coin of the Audumbara Mahādeva (cf. § 96). As already mentioned under Aparānta (§ 91) the uncertain coins on p. 182 (nos. 80–84) are probably of Mahārāja Aparānta, e.g. Pl. XXIX, 24,[2] and to be attributed to Mathurā. Rapson published three specimens of Śeṣadatta's coins from the White King collection in *J.R.A.S.*, 1900, p. 110, nos. 9–11, of which the following type (nos. 9–10) is certainly of this series:

Obv. Lakṣmī, &c. standing facing: tree on r. 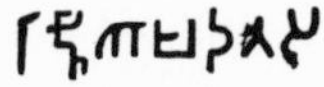
Rev. Three elephants type.

[1] Not *a*[*ḥ*] as in the text. The rules of *sandhi* are not observed.
[2] As are also *C.I.M.*, i, p. 104, nos. 4–6.

Sir Richard Burn has three specimens of this coin. In view of the regularity of type of this series it is very doubtful if the coin *ibid.*, no. 11 *obv.* wheel on chaitya, *rev.* (*Śe*)*ṣadata*(*sa*) with upper part of a standing figure, is to be attributed to Mathurā.

The B.M.C. coin, no. 31 a, on being cleaned proved to be of Śeṣadatta and the name—an improbable one in any case—Goṣa-datta, is to be removed from the series.

The Museum has no coins of Bhāvadatta of whom three specimens are known, none in very good condition; one is in the Indian Museum (*C.I.M.*, i, p. 193); another was published by Rapson[1] (*J.R.A.S.*, 1900, p. 113, no. 13, from the White King collection), and there is a third in Sir Richard Burn's collection. These coins differ from the usual type in having the legend in two lines above the figure of Lakṣmī.

Obv. Conventional tree; upper part of Lakṣmī; above in two lines 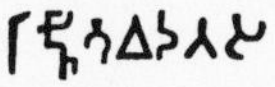 (*Rājño Bhavadatasa*).

Rev. Elephant r. (I.M.); l. (W. K. and R. B.).

The coins bearing the names of Śaśachandrāta and Vīrasena have been attributed to Mathurā.[2] They are in any case of much later date and we have preferred to class them as uncertain here (p. 280).

§ 125. The coins above described cover the period from the end of the third to the middle of the first century B.C., when we find these Hindu rulers succeeded by a dynasty of Śakas who bear the title Kṣatrapa or Mahākṣatrapa. These fall into two groups, (*a*) the Kṣatrapas Śivaghoṣa, Śivadatta, Hagāmaṣa, and Hagāna, (*b*) the Mahākṣatrapas Rājuvula (Rājula), and his son Śoḍāsa. The coins of the first group, of which only those of Hagāmaṣa and of Hagā-maṣa and Hagāna are common, retain the local obverse type of Lakṣmī. The  on the right is probably not a separate symbol but

[1] Rapson tentatively proposed the reading *Bhīma-* or *Bhūmi-* for the first part of the name: the coin seems, however, to be identical with Sir Richard Burn's coin and the reading is probably *Bhāva*.

[2] Rapson, *J.R.A.S.*, 1900, pp. 114–115, *C.I.M.*, i, pp. 190–191.

the stalk of the lotus which she holds. The conventional tree remains, but the other symbols disappear, and the river below is replaced by , a symbol which distinguishes these coins from those of the Hindu rulers. The reverse type on all this group is a horse. The legends are *Khatapasa Śivaghoṣasa*, *Khatapasa Śivadatasa*, and *Khatapasa Hagāmaṣasa*. The joint issue of the satraps Hagāmaṣa and Hagāna bears the legend *Khatapāna Hagānasa Hagāmaṣasa* and the characteristic symbol  on obverse and the usual horse on the reverse.

The coin of Śivadatta in the Museum appears to be unique. Śivaghoṣa is known only from a unique specimen in Sir Richard Burn's collection:

Obv. Lakṣmī and tree, 𑀔𑀢𑀧𑀲𑀰𑀺𑀯𑀖𑁄𑀱𑀲 (*Khatapasa Śivaghoṣasa*) around.

Rev. Horse l. Æ 0·75. Wt. 81·4.

§ 126. A coin in Sir Richard Burn's collection belongs to a hitherto unknown satrap, probably another son of Rājuvula. It closely resembles the coins of Śoḍāsa, var. *c.*:

Obv. Lakṣmī stands facing holding lotus in r. hand: conventional tree on l.

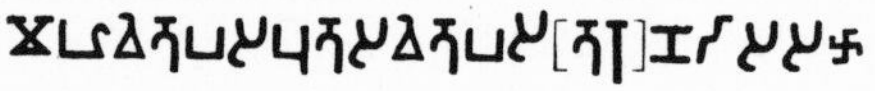

𑀫𑀳𑀔𑀢𑀧𑀲𑀧𑀼𑀢𑀲𑀔𑀢𑀧𑀲[𑀢𑁄𑀭]𑀡𑀟𑀲𑀲

Mahakhatapasa putasa khatapasa [T(o)ra]ṇaḍāsasa.

Rev. Abhiṣeka of Lakṣmī of usual type.

Æ 0·65. Wt. 78.

The reading of the name is unfortunately uncertain. It ends -*ḍasasa* and is not *Śoḍasasa*, for the lingual *ṇ* is certain. The two preceding consonants seem to be *T*[*o*]*ra* or *Bhara*, but *Ś*[*o*] is not impossible. In view of the mention of an unnamed son of Rājuvula in the Morā inscription[1] this coin should be borne in mind. The initial letter on the coin is certainly open at the bottom, which does not agree with Cunningham's suggestion of *Va* or *Vi*.

[1] See § 127.

§ 127. With the possible exception of Brahmamitra, who has been identified as the Brahmamitra mentioned in an inscription on a pillar at Bodh Gayā,[1] none of the rulers so far mentioned is known from inscriptions or literature. The identification of the two Brahmamitras is very problematical, however, as is that of Indramitra mentioned on another pillar with Indramitra of the Pañcāla dynasty. Both names are very common, and the probability is that the two kings were members of a local dynasty. The actual donors are, however, their respective queens, which does not make it quite so certain that their husbands were related.

These later rulers of Mathurā do not appear in the Puranic lists, perhaps because they were vassals of the Śuṅgas. The last two rulers of whom coins are known, Rājuvula and his son Śoḍāsa are also known from inscriptions, one of which enables us to say that they were Śakas and not Pahlavas. Rājuvula is the *Mahakṣatrava Rajula* of the Mathurā Lion Capital,[2] which commemorates an endowment by his chief queen and the *mahākṣatrapa Rājuvula* of an inscription from Morā [3] of the time of a son of his whose name is no longer legible. The name is Rajuvula [4] in the Kharoṣṭhī legend of his coins of Class I (Strato type) and abbreviated to **PAIY** in the corrupt Greek legend of the obverse. It is Rājuvula on the Brahmī inscriptions on his coins of Class II and on the coins of his son Śoḍāsa which give the patronymic (var. *b*), and in the Morā inscription. It is Rajula in the Kharoṣṭhī inscription of his Class III and on the Mathurā Lion Capital. The forms Rañjabula, Rañjubula, and other variants with *b* are due to reading the Kharoṣṭhī *v* as *b*—a mistake easily made—and should be discarded. There is some doubt about the nasal in the first syllable. In most of the Kharoṣṭhī legends on the coins the first syllable is *Ra*, but on some there is a hook below the *r*, which can be read *Raṁ*. While it is not always certain that emphasis is to be

[1] J. H. Marshall, *J.R.A.S.*, 1908, p. 1096; *A.S.R.*, 1907–8, p. 4; *C.H.I.*, i, p. 526.

[2] S. Konow, *C.I.I.*[2], II, i, pp. 30–48: Thomas, *E.I.*, ix, 135 ff.

[3] *A.S.R.*, xx, p. 49, Pl. V, 4; *A.S.R.*, 1911–12, p. 127.

[4] i.e. Rājuvula: the long *a* is not distinguished in the Kharoṣṭhī.

laid on such a hook at the foot of a Kharoṣṭhī letter, Rañjuvula seems a possibility, but the bulk of the evidence is in favour of Rājuvula.[1] On the Lion Capital, A. l. 1,[2] the first *akṣara* is clearly *Ra*, and there is no **N** in the Greek legend on the coins. Rajula in Kharoṣṭhī is of course for Rājūla, a natural contraction of Rājuvula, which we could not easily get from a form with *b*.

§ 128. The Greek legend on the coins is quite meaningless on most specimens, and it is difficult to recognize letters, much less words. On one coin, no. 1, it is possible to read every letter, and the legend is **BACIΛЄI BACIΛЄШC CШTHPOC PAIY**. The first two words are for the Śaka title **BACIΛЄШN BACIΛЄШC**, more commonly **BACIΛЄШC BACIΛЄШN**, the former order being here followed because **BACIΛЄШC CШTHPOC** are found together on coins of Strato and other Greek kings. It has been suggested[3] that the order is **BACIΛЄШC CШTHPOC PAIY BACIΛЄI** and that *Razubasilei* is the Greek form of the king's name. The usual interpretation which takes **PAIY** as all of the king's name that appears on the coins is preferable.

The reverse Kharoṣṭhī legend is *apratihatacakrasa Rajuvulasa* 'of the Kṣatrapa Rajuvula, whose *cakra* is irresistible'; the epithet is not found elsewhere, but Gondophares calls himself *apratihata*. On Class III the legend is *Mahakhatapasa apraticakrasa Rajulasa*, with an obverse inscription which appears to be very corrupt Greek.

Śoḍāsa's name is found in Brāhmī on his coins, in the dedicatory inscription by Āmohinī at Mathurā,[4] and in the Jail Mound inscription at Mathurā,[5] as Śoḍāsa; on the Mathurā Lion Capital it is written in Kharoṣṭhī as Śuḍasa. Cunningham's suggestion that Śoḍāsa was the son of Rājuvula[6] has been confirmed by coins and inscriptions. The name Mewaku was read on a coin by Bhagvanlal

[1] There is no authority for forms with *ū*.

[2] *C.I.I.*, II, i, Pl. VII.

[3] S. Konow, *C.I.I.*, II, i, p. xxxiii: Lüders in *S.B.A.W.*, 1913, p. 425.

[4] *E.I.*, ii, p. 199, *Vienna Oriental Journal*, v, 177.

[5] *A.S.R.*, iii, p. 30, Pl. XIII, 1.

[6] *A.S.R.*, iii, p. 40.

Indraji,[1] and its issuer identified with the Mevaki Miyika of the Mathurā Lion Capital.[2] The coin, however, is really one of Śoḍāsa, being the Museum specimen no. 142, Pl. XXV. 25.

§ 129. The coins show that Rājuvula ruled a much wider area than Mathurā for he imitated coinages other than the local type of his predecessors here. His commonest coins are drachms of light weight and very base metal copied from the coins of Strato I and II, one of the last Greek coinages. The bust on the obverse is very well done and shows a typical Śaka portrait such as we find on the coins of Miaus and Nahapāna. These coins were struck over a wide area and their find-spots range from the valleys of the rivers forming the Indus to the Gangetic Doab. Finds are recorded from Sultānpur,[3] and Nūrmahal in the Jullundar Doab,[4] from Pāḍham between Etah and Shikohābād and Sankīsā[5] in the Farrukhābād district in the U.P. His coins of Class I were found with coins of Strato at Mathurā[6] and in the Eastern Panjab.[7] Class III also has types taken from his predecessors in the Eastern Panjab, Hercules and a lion, a combination previously used by Maues. They are of lead, like some of the coins of Strato, and belong to the Panjab, as their Kharoṣṭhī legends and types show. The British Museum has no coins of this type from the Cunningham Collection, but Talbot, Rodgers, Rawlins, and Whitehead, all Panjab collectors, are represented. They have been found at Sirkap (Taxila).[8] Class II is the scarcest of Rājuvula's types, his issue at Mathurā in which he copies on the obverse the local type of Lakṣmī and tree: the reverse, abhiṣeka of Lakṣmī, is too characteristic a Hindu type to have been taken, as has been suggested, from the rare coins of Azilises which also bear it. The scarcity of these coins suggests that Rājuvula only occupied Mathurā late in his reign. The facts that Śoḍāsa only issues coins of Mathurā type, and that his coins have been found with those of his father at Mathurā, Pāḍham,

[1] *J.R.A.S.*, 1894, p. 548.

[2] Rapson, *ibid.*, and Sten Konow, *C.I.I.*, II, i, p. xxxiii.

[3] *A.S.R.*, xiv, 57. [4] *Ibid.*, p. 62. [5] *A.S.R.*, xi, 38; *ibid.*, xi, 25.

[6] *A.S.R.*, iii, p. 40; *J.A.S.B.*, 1854, p. 691. [7] *C.A.I.*, p. 86.

[8] *A.S.R.*, 1912-13, p. 49; 1914-15, p. 33; 1915-16, p. 33.

and Sankīsā, but not in the Panjab finds above mentioned, show that he ruled a much more limited area. His coin-types are those of his father's Mathurā issues; three forms of legend distinguish them: Śoḍāsa describes himself as (*a*) 'kṣatrapa, son of the Mahākṣatrapa', (*b*) 'kṣatrapa, son of Rājuvula', and (*c*) 'Mahākṣatrapa'. The first two types were perhaps issued in his father's life-time, and the last when he succeeded him as great satrap. In this case the scarcity of the third type would indicate a short sole reign. The title *svāmin* given in the Mathurā inscription is not found on the coins. It is also borne by the unnamed son of Rājuvula in the Morā inscription but is not known to be borne by Rājuvula. It is very familiar in the line of the Western Kṣatrapas.

§ 130. The coins of the Hindu kings of Mathurā cover the period from the beginning of the second century to the middle of the first century B.C. Next come the Śivadatta–Hagāmaṣa group of Śaka satraps, who may be put in the period of about 60–40 B.C. Some of them may be contemporary at Mathurā with Rājuvula's rule farther north. Rājuvula, whose Mathurā type coins are very scarce, may have only ruled there in the latter part of his reign, which we may put in the period 40–20 B.C. Śodaṣa we would put to 20–10 B.C., or a little later. The disputed date 72 or 42 in the Amohinī inscription has been finally proved to be 42 by Rapson.[1]

§ 131. PAÑCĀLA (pp. 192–204). The coins attributed by Cunningham[2] to a local dynasty ruling in Pañcāla form one of the longest and most uniform series of ancient Indian coins. The obverse type is the same throughout, the three symbols 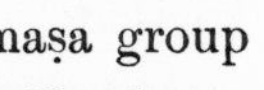 with the king's name below in the genitive in a square die impressed on a round coin, in the incuse characteristic of a number of early Indian coins. The reverse type is a deity or symbol of a deity on a kind of platform with a railing in front and pillars or posts

[1] *Indian Studies in honour of C. R. Lanman*, Cambridge, Mass., 1929, 49–52; *C.H.I.*, i, p. 575. See also Sten Konow, *C.I.I.*, II, i, p. xxxiv, and Lüders, *E.I.*, ix, pp. 243 ff.

[2] *C.A.I.*, pp. 79–84.

on either side. In the Catalogue an attempt is made to arrange the coins in a chronological order on palaeographical grounds. The result can only be correct in its main lines, and the exact order of the individual rulers cannot be guaranteed. We shall therefore for convenience deal with the rulers here in alphabetical order.

§ 132. The following rulers are known from coins in the British Museum:—

Agnimitra (*Agimitrasa*), Bhadraghoṣa (*Bhadraghoṣasa*), Bhānumitra (*Bhānumitrasa*), Bhūmimitra (*Bhūmimitrasa*), Dhruvamitra (*Dhruvamitrasa*), Indramitra (*Indramitrasa*), Jayagupta (*Jayaguptasa*), Jayamitra (*Jayamitrasa*), Phalgunīmitra (*Phagunimitrasa*), Rudragupta (*Rudraguptasa*), Sūryamitra (*Sūyamitrasa*), Viṣṇumitra (*Viṣṇumitrasa*), and Viśvapāla (*Viśvapalasa*). To these we have to add Bṛhaspatimitra from a coin in the Lucknow Museum.[1] The word *-mitra*, which is found in the majority of these rulers' names, seems to be written *-mitra* on all these coins, and not *-mita* as in the dialect of other series of coins. The title king is not found on any of the coins.

§ 133. The reverses are of special interest to the student of Hindu iconography, as we have nothing similar elsewhere of so early a date. Unfortunately the small scale of the types and the condition of the coins prevents us from learning as much as we might have done from these pieces. The reverse type is a deity—or his symbol, in most cases the former—whose name forms as a rule a component of the issuer's name and who was his patron deity.

The reverse of Agnimitra's coins represents a deity standing on a railed platform between two pillars. His hair is represented as five flames. His right hand is raised and the left rests on his hip. He is to be identified as Agni, the god of fire. On the reverse of Bhadraghoṣa's coins is a female deity standing on a lotus, whom we may identify as Bhadrā in allusion to the name of Bhadraghoṣa, but with which of the goddesses who bear this epithet it is difficult

[1] *C.I.M.*, i, p. 185; *Progr. Rep. N.W.P. and O*, 1891–2, pp. 2 and 4.

to say. The type suggests Lakṣmī. Bhānumitra has on his reverse a radiate globe representing the sun (*bhānu*) on a similar platform, the details of which are not visible on any of the Museum specimens but can be well seen in *C.I.M.*, i, Pl. XXII. 4. Bhūmimitra has a deity standing facing on a platform between two pillars each with three cross-bars at the top, His attitude is similar to that of Agni, but his hair is represented by five snakes (*nāgas*). He holds a snake in his hands. One would expect a personification of the earth goddess Bhūmi but, as the figure is male, it is probably the king of the *nāgas* representing the earth.

§ 134. The coins of Dhruvamitra do not bear a deity but an object described by Cunningham [1] as a trident, the emblem of Śiva, also known as Dhruva. The object in question, which stands on a platform in the position usually occupied by the deity between two pillars with cross-bars at top is, however, not a trident. On no. 53 (Pl. XXVII. 5) it looks like a battle-axe, but on no. 55 (Pl. XXVII. 6) and others the shaft is clearly bent. It must be a symbol of Dhruva, the pole-star. The known coins of Indramitra are all small, and Indra is only crudely represented on them by a standing figure in the usual attitude upon a platform without pillars. On the smallest type he is in an archway, and the symbol  found on the obverse is put in the field. The reverse of Jayagupta's coins is exactly similar to that of the last-named coins. The reverse of Jayamitra's coins shows a male deity in the usual attitude on a platform between two pillars; that in his right is crowned by a spear-head, that in his left by two cross-bars. The reverse of Phalgunīmitra's coins shows a female deity standing on a lotus holding a lotus bud in her right hand; behind her head is a star represented like the sun on Bhānumitra's coins; on the left is the symbol . Her hair is represented by five flames. She is to be identified as a personification of the *nakṣatra* Phalgunī. Rudragupta has on his reverse a trident between two pillars (e.g. Pl. XXVII. 2), the emblem of Rudra-Śiva. On other coins (e.g.

[1] *C.A.I.*, p. 81.

Pl. XXVII. 1) the object appears to be a star or a kind of double trident with prongs below as well as above. Sūryamitra, like Bhānumitra, has the sun as his main reverse type. It is represented as a ball from which rays radiate; below it is the symbol , and the whole is placed on a platform, as usual between two pillars with cross-bars.

§ 135. The coins of Viṣṇumitra are unfortunately all small, but the deity on the reverse, who may be identified as Viṣṇu, differs from the usual type in having both arms raised; in his left arm he holds a circular object (? a discus). He is not represented as four-armed, as has been suggested.[1] His robes hanging down give this effect, which is found in other representations of deities with up-lifted arm, e.g. Agni and Indra, also. Four arms would come from the shoulders and not from the elbows. It is possible that he is represented as grasping on the left a pole surmounted by a discus and another on the right surmounted by a trident. The reverse of the unique coin of Viśvapāla is illegible, but it seems to include the symbol  found on Phalgunīmitra's reverse. Before leaving the types of these coins we may note that coins of Bhānumitra and of Bhadraghoṣa are found counter-marked with the symbol  obliterating the central symbol—and of Agnimitra with the local symbols obliterated by a female figure (Pl. XLVI. 16), also counter-marked on a coin of Bhānumitra in the Indian Museum (*C. I. M.*, i, Pl. XXII. 3) and by a lion ? (Pl. XLVI. 15).

§ 136. Cunningham found these coins in 'Rohilkhand and chiefly at Ahichhatra, Aonla and Badaon',[2] that is, the ancient northern Pañcāla. Ahichhatra was the old capital of this region. Cunningham goes on to say they are very rarely found beyond the limits of North Pañcāla. Vincent Smith[3] found them 'common in Eastern Oudh and in the Basti district'. Carlleyle obtained about a hundred at Bhuila in the Basti[4] district, mostly Agnimitra and Indramitra.

[1] Coomaraswamy in *Eastern Art*, 1928, p. 35.
[2] *C.A.I.*, p. 75.
[3] *C.I.M.*, i, p. 184.
[4] *J.A.S.B.*, 1880, p. 21.

Several coins of the 'Mitra' dynasty were found at Pindari about $1\frac{1}{3}$ miles south-east of Bhuila Tal.[1] A coin of Indramitra was found at Kumrahar (Pāṭaliputra).[2] Col. C. E. Shepherd's coins of Rudragupta and Dhruvamitra came from Rāmnagar (Ahicchatra).[3] While the coins are found over a wider area than Cunningham first stated, there is no doubt that the main source for them is Ahichhatra, from which Rivett-Carnac also obtained a considerable number and variety of coins.[4]

§ 137. None of the kings of this dynasty, the coins of which cover a period of from about 200 B.C. to the end of the first century B.C., is known from inscriptions or literature. The identity of name is not sufficient to identify Indramitra confidently with the Indramitra whose queen dedicated a railing at Bodh Gayā (cf. § 127). Attempts have from time to time been made to identify rulers of this dynasty with names in the Puranic lists of the Śuṅga dynasty,[5] but without success. The only name found in both lists is Agnimitra, which is too common a name for any deduction to be made from it. Sujyeṣṭha or Vasujyeṣṭha has been identified with Jyeṣṭhamitra (Jeṭhamitra), but the latter has no connexion with the Pañcāla series, even if we accept the possibility of this contraction. Bhadraghoṣa is identified with Ghoṣa of the Puranic lists, which is very unlikely. Bhūmimitra is identified with the Kānva king of the same name, but his coins cannot be removed from the middle of the Pañcāla series, while the Kānva was the second of the successors of the Śuṅgas.

§ 138. The evidence of the uniformity of the coins and of their find-spots show that this 'Mitra' dynasty ruled in Northern Pañcāla, and perhaps also in part of Southern Pañcāla. The capital was Ahichhatra. They cannot be identified with the Śuṅgas. The

[1] *A.S.R.*, xii. 153.

[2] *A.S.R.*, 1912–13, p. 85.

[3] *J.A.S.B.*, 1902, pp. 42–43.

[4] *J.A.S.B.*, 1880, pp. 21–28, Pl. II; pp. 87–90, Pls. VII–IX.

[5] Rivett-Carnac, *J.A.S.B.*, 1880, pp. 21–23; Jayaswal, *J.B.O.R.S.*, 1917, p. 476 f.; Hemchandra Raychaudhuri, *Political History of Ancient India*, 1923, pp. 211 ff.; de la Vallée-Poussin, *L'Inde aux Temps des Mauryas*, pp. 175–176.

dynasty was in existence before the Śuṅgas, if we date the accession of Puṣyamitra about 184 B.C., and survived not only the Śuṅgas but also the Kānvas, probably disappearing with the latter before the Śakas.

§ 139. Purī (pp 205–209). The very crude imitations of Kushān copper coins here attributed to the Purī district of Bihar and Orissa, because a find of them was made at Manikaratna in Purī in 1893, and described in some detail by Hoernle in the *Proc. A.S.B.*, 1895, pp. 61–65, may have circulated over a wider area, probably the whole of the ancient Kaliṅga. Two much worn coins of Kanishka were found with this hoard. More recently a find of 363 similar pieces was made on the northern slopes of the Rakha hills in the Singbhum district of Bihar and Orissa.[1] The Balasore find of 1912 contained 910 coins.[2] Sir Walter Elliot[3] in 1858 described a find made four miles west of Purushottampur in the Ganjam district and noted the striking resemblance to the coins of Kanishka. In 1927 the Maharaja of Mayurbhanj presented a number of these coins and two Kushān pieces from a find at Bhanjakia in his territory; these coins were smaller pieces than those previously known, being roughly half the usual weight. This find included two inscribed pieces and many coins of Kanishka or Huvishka.[4] To this class no doubt belonged the finds mentioned by Beglar from Gulka[5] and Jaugada.[6] The specimens he saw he described as 'probably Indo-Scythic'.

§ 140. The coins of this class, which are rudely cast and quite untrimmed, are of the simplest type; the obverse is a very primitive copy of the standing Kushān king, and the reverse a copy of one of the deities on the reverse of Kushān coins, probably the moon-god Mao as the exaggerated crescent suggests. Two main types may be

[1] E. H. C. Walsh, *Journal of the Bihar and Orissa Research Society*, 1919, pp. 73-81, with a plate.

[2] *A.S.R.*, 1924–5, p. 130.

[3] *Madras Journal of Literature and Science*, 1858, pp. 75–6. *Num. Glean.*, pp. 33-4.

[4] *A.S.R.*, 1924–5, p. 132.

[5] *Ibid.*, xiii 72.

[6] *Ibid.*, 116.

distinguished: one showing a fairly full figure of the king, readily betraying its prototype, and the other a small dumpy figure with exaggerated feet; even on the latter the Kushān dress is still recognizable. Varieties may be distinguished according to the position of the arms, and the presence or absence and position of the crescent. There is no reason to believe from the unfinished appearance of these coins that, as has been suggested, the Rakha find indicated a minting-place. The coins from other finds are equally rude and untrimmed. The fact that they occur in regular hoards leaves no doubt that they are really coins.

It is clear from the finds that the people of this region, the ancient Kaliṅga, when the supply of Kushān copper coins which they had been using began to fail them, took to copying them, having plenty of copper available in the copper mines of their country. These pieces probably belong to the end of the third or early fourth century. This date is also suggested by the inscribed coin first found in the Rakha hills find.[1] The reverse has the usual 'Mao' type, but the obverse is quite a remarkable one. It bears three cones or mountain peaks, below which is the legend usually read *ṭaṅka* in characters of the fourth century A.D.[2] This inscription is a remarkable one; it is not in the genitive, so that it cannot be a tribal name or that of a ruler. It has been taken to be a denomination, but this seems very unlikely. One expects a geographical name (cf. Tripuri, Kauśambī, &c.). The first character is not certain. It is *t* rather than *ṭ*, and has a vowel *e*. Teṅka or Laṅka are possible readings. There were 63 specimens of this variety in the find of these coins from Balasore district, and 2 in that from Bhanjakia.[3]

§ 141. Rājanya (pp. 210–212). These coins have long been known,[4] but the correct reading of the first part of the legend

[1] *Journ. Bih. Or. Res. Soc.*, 1919, p. 80, Pl. no. 2.

[2] It is hardly possible that these coins are as late as the seventh or possibly the sixth century, to which R. D. Banerji (*Journ. Bih. Or. Res. Soc.*, 1919, p. 83) would put them. The epigraphy can be paralleled in Samudragupta's Allahabad inscription.

[3] *A.S.R.*, 1924–5, p. 131.

[4] *P.E.*, Pl. XLIX. 18; *A.S.R.*, xiv, p. 151; Rapson, *I.C.*, § 47.

Rajaña—previously read *rajña*—was only given by Vincent Smith in *C.I.M.*, i, p. 164. This corresponds to a Sanskrit Rājanya, a synonym of Kṣatriya, but as Mr. Jayaswal[1] has pointed out, it is here the name of a people and the inscription *Rajaña-janapadasa* means 'of the Rājanya tribe'. Varāhamihira[2] mentions the Rājanyas among the peoples of the north; the name has been taken as a synonym of Kṣatriya and the people identified with the Kathaioi of the Greeks. It is probable, however, that the Rājanyas only formed one of the Kṣatriya tribes. They are also mentioned in the Sabhāparvan of the *Mahābhārata*. The coins of the first and common type are of two classes, one with Brāhmī and the other with Kharoṣṭhī legends; the types are the same on both classes: *obv.* Lakṣmī and *rev.* a bull. The Lakṣmī resembles that on the coins of Mathurā, but there is no close similarity of fabric. The provenance of the two classes seems to be the same, so that one probably succeeded the other. Those with Kharoṣṭhī inscriptions may be put in the second century B.C., and those with Brāhmī in the first century B.C. A second and rare type (no. 17) has *rev.* a tree in railing which links it with the third type (no. 18) *obv.* stupa, and justifies the attribution of the latter on which the inscription cannot be read. Most of the coins in the Museum came through the late Mr. J. C. Rawlins from the Hoshiārpur district of the Panjab, and the Rājanya country may be located here.

§ 142. Śibi (p. 213, nos. 21–22). A definite attribution of these two coins is not given in the text of the Catalogue as I hesitated to read the first surviving character of the legend on both as *Śi* (𑀰𑀺); it seemed to be *gi* (𑀕𑀺). Although I have not yet seen a specimen with the usual form of ś on it, I have now no doubt about the attribution of these coins to the tribe of the Śibis. In addition to the two coins here described the Museum has a third, here wrongly attributed to the Ārjunayānas (p. 121, no. 3), which a comparison with a better specimen in Sir Richard Burn's collection showed to be also of the Śibis.

[1] *Hindu Polity*, i, pp. 158–159.

[2] *Bṛhatsaṁhitā*, xiv. 28; Fleet, *I.A.*, xxii., p. 182.

These coins were first published by Prinsep[1] from Stacy's specimen from Chitor. His excellent drawings supply the character *ya* before Śibi and show the elaborate *nandipada* on the top of the mountain symbol on the reverse which is not visible on the very worn specimens I have seen. The reverse type recalls that of the Kulūtas and Kuṇindas. Carlleyle[2] obtained seven specimens at Tambavati Nāgari, eleven miles north of Chitor, and two in Chitor. He gives (p. 200) a careful drawing of the complete inscription made up from his specimens, which shows that Cunningham's reading *Majhamikāya-Śibi-janapadasa* is the correct one. Cunningham[3] himself later published these coins and pointed out that *Majhamikāya* is for a Sanskrit *Madhyamikāya*. From the published specimens we can now give a full description of the type:

Obv. 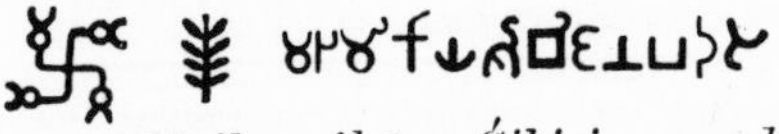

Majhamikāya-Śibi-janapadasa.

Rev. 

The legend means 'of the tribe of the Śibis of the Middle Country'.

§ 143. Varāhamihira puts the Śibis in the north with the Mālavas and the people of Taxila[4] and with the Ārjunayānas and Yaudheyas.[5] The *Mahābhārata* puts them with the Trigartas and Mālavas as conquered by Nakula,[6] and as paying tribute to Yudhiṣṭhira along with the Trigartas and Yaudheyas.[7] A king of the Śibis is mentioned in the *Aitareya Brāhmaṇa*, and they may be the Śivas[8] of the *Ṛg-veda*. A Śibi king has become the ideal of self-sacrifice in Buddhist legend. Śibipura mentioned in the Shorkot inscription of the year 83 (= A.D. 403) probably preserves their name.[9]

1 *P.E.*, Pl. VIII. 2–3, pp. 112–114.
2 *A.S.R*, vi, pp. 200 ff.
3 *Ibid.*, xiv, pp. 145–147, Pl. XXX. 13, 14.
4 *Bṛhatsaṁhitā*, xvi. 26.
5 *Ibid.*, xvii. 19.
6 *Sabhāparvan*, xxxii. 7.
7 *Ibid.*, lii, 11: for other references in the *Mbh.* see Sörensen's Index.
8 Cf. Keith in *C.H.I.*, i, p. 82, and the index *s.v.* Śivas.
9 *E.I.*, xvi, pp. 15–17.

The Śibis are identified with the *Siboi*[1] of the Greek accounts of Alexander's campaign, who are to be located between the Indus and Chināb. As already mentioned, these coins have been found at Chitor and Tambavati Nāgari; Bhandarkar also found them in his excavations in Nāgari on the Hathibada site, that is, they come only from a limited area in western Rajputana.[2]

Here we have the same problem as in the case of the Mālavas: literary references indicating a people in the upper Panjab and coins from Rajputana only. The date of the coins is the second century B.C. The coins, which are later than the literary references to the Śibis of the Panjab, cannot from their provenance be attributed to them—unless we assume they had been driven south—but to another branch who distinguish themselves as 'Śibis of the Middle Country', which is not here Madhyadeśa.

§ 144. TAXILA (pp. 214–238). The identification of the ruins near the modern Shāh-Dheri, in the valley of the Haro river, some twenty miles north-west of Rāwalpindī, with the ancient city of Taxila (Takṣaśilā), the capital of the kingdom of the same name, is due to Cunningham,[3] who says that thousands upon thousands of coins are found there.[4] It is on Cunningham's authority that most of these coins in the Museum collection are attributed to Taxila. The majority of the Museum specimens, including all the rarer pieces, were obtained by him on the site. Of the three main sites corresponding to three stages in the history of the city in ancient times—the Bhir Mound, Sirkap, and Sirsukh—Cunningham was mainly concerned with Sirkap.[5]

§ 145. In the Catalogue the coins are divided into two main series—inscribed and uninscribed. The inscribed coins are of three

[1] J. W. McCrindle, *The Invasion of India by Alexander the Great*, Westminster, 1893, p. 366.

[2] *A.S.R.*, 1915–16, Pt. 1, p. 15.

[3] *A.S.R.*, ii, pp. 111–35; v, pp 66–75; xiv, 8–24; Sylvain Lévi in *J.A.*, Series VIII, vol. xv, pp. 236–7.

[4] *A.S.R.*, xiv, p. 16.

[5] On the history of Taxila in ancient times and its excavation in modern times, see Sir John Marshall, *Guide to Taxila*, Calcutta, 1918.

classes: (1) the *negama* series, (2) the *paṁcanekame* series, and (3) the *Hirañasame* series. Of these, Class I are oblong struck copper pieces with the characteristic Indian incuse on one side. They all bear the inscription *negamā*, a nominative plural corresponding to a Sanskrit *naigāmah*, 'the traders', or possibly an adjective (fem.) from *nigama*, 'market merchant gild, quarter of a city'. The word is either the name of the issuers or an adjective from it. In any case it indicates 'mercantile money token issued by traders',[1] or 'trade token', 'coin of commerce'.[2]

§ 146. The reverse legends, according to which the varieties are distinguished here, have not been explained. That of var. *a* was read *Tālimata* by Bühler,[3] and *Rālimata* by Cunningham.[4] I think the latter is the correct reading of the initial consonant, while the last letter is not *ta* but *sa*, so that we have *Rālimasa*. Var. *b* has the legend *Dojaka* in Kharoṣṭhī, and *c* the same in Brāhmī. Var. *b* is distinguished from the others in having a horizontal stroke above the *ga* of the obverse legend which Cunningham explained as the numeral one.[5] The reverse has the type of a steelyard also found in var. *e*. The word *dojaka* has not been explained. *Do* suggests Sanskrit *dvi*, but the word, in view of the variations in weight, can hardly be a denomination as Cunningham very tentatively suggested.[6] Var. *d* has the legend in Brāhmī *At*[-]*takā*. The third *akṣara* is almost certainly *ka*, which gives *Atakatakā*. It is not -*ra* as suggested by Cunningham, who hoped to identify the legend with the Kharoṣṭhī one of var. *f*. Var. *e* has on the obverse above the inscription a steelyard shorter than that on var. *b*. The reverse has an almost illegible inscription of the form (-)*ra*(-)*ma*(- -). The thick square dumpy fabric of this variety contrasts it with all the others.

[1] Bühler, *Indian Studies*, iii, 2nd ed., Strassburg, 1898, p. 49.
[2] Cunningham, *A.S.R.*, xiv, p. 20.
[3] *Ibid.*
[4] *C.A.I.*, p. 64.
[5] *A.S.R.*, xiv, p. 20; *C.A.I.*, p. 65.
[6] *A.S.R.*, xiv, p. 20.

§ 147. Var. *f* reads on the obverse [-]*dare*[-]*kame* in Kharoṣṭhī. The surviving fragment of the *n* justifies us in reading the last word, as one would expect, as *nekame*. The first letter might be *K* or *E*—not, I think, *A* as Cunningham suggested, so that we have *Kadare-nekame*. The reverse type is almost illegible, but it undoubtedly is a female figure as represented in the drawing in Cunningham's plate.[1] Cunningham calls her a 'Maenad moving to left rudely copied from the coins of Pantaleon and Agathocles'. It is more correct to say that she is the same deity as appears on these coins.[2] She probably occurs again on Class I, var. *h* (see p. 221), of the uninscribed coins of Taxila. She is best seen on the coins of the two Greek kings, where we have a representation of an Indian deity by a Greek artist. The figure is dressed in Indian fashion, and wears ear-rings and a kind of egret in her hair on the right side of her head such as we see on the third of the group of three deities on certain punch-marked coins (Class 2, Group II, vars. *c*, *e*, and *f*). She holds a lotus in her right hand, and the pose generally is that with which we are familiar in Lakṣmī on the coins of Mathurā and elsewhere. She does not, however, stand on a lotus like the usual Lakṣmī or the similar deity who may be recognized as Lakṣmī on certain coins of Maues.[3] For the present we may call her Lakṣmī, but it is tempting to think of her as the city goddess of Taxila, for which we would have a parallel in the figure of the patron divinity of the city of Puṣkalavatī.[4]

§ 148. These *negama* coins are exceedingly rare; indeed, they seem to be known only from the Cunningham specimens in the Museum. The epigraphy has been described as Aśokan, but when we see how closely the Brāhmī inscriptions of the coins of Agathocles resemble the Brāhmī of Aśoka, we realize how difficult it is to date these coins within fifty years. I am inclined to put them in the first quarter of the second century B.C. If any deduction is to be

[1] *A.S.R.*, xiv, Pl. X. 21.
[2] i.e. *B.M.C.*, *Greek and Scyth. Kings*, Pl. III. 9; IV. 9.
[3] *Ibid.*, Pl. XIX. 5.
[4] *Ibid.*, Pl. XXIX. 15; Rapson in *J.R.A.S.*, 1905, p. 787.

made from their absence from the well-known hoard of coins of Taxila, Pantaleon, and Agathocles,[1] it is that they are later than these Greek rulers and not earlier. As to the interpretation of the legends I do not think the names Ralimasa, Atakatakā, Dojaka are, as has been suggested, names of cities.[2] These pieces are too closely associated with one another and with Taxila to be separated from this city. It is more likely that they are the names of quarters or wards. In any case they are the names of the Naigamas; none of them seems to be the name of a trade, nor indeed to have an obvious Sanskrit etymology, which makes the suggestion that they are topographical names, i.e. of quarters of the city, a more probable one.

§ 149. Class II, which in comparison with Class I may be described as common, bears the legend *Paṁcanekame*, 'the five gilds'. The type is a 16-spoked wheel with  above on the obverse, and on the reverse a svastika between two *nandipadas*  [3] with the inscription below. These coins are cast and square, quite different in fabric from Class I. They are commoner than the preceding class, and probably circulated over a wide area. It is curious that Cunningham does not mention them in his account of the coins of Taxila in *A.S.R.*, xiv, as if he had not found specimens there. In *C.A.I.* he includes them under Taxila without comment. The symbols on them are found on uninscribed coins of Taxila. The legend indicates that the coin is a joint issue of the 'Five Naigamas', a kind of Pentapolis. It is curious that Class I represents the issues of five separate *naigamas*, but it is hardly safe to assume they were the five *naigamas* which combined to issue Class II. We have placed here as var. 2 of Class II, the coin illustrated by Cunningham, *C.A.I.*, Pl. III. 14. The types include a wheel and a bow and arrow, but it is impossible to read any of the legends.

[1] *A.S.R.*, xiv, p. 21.

[2] D. R. Bhandarkar, *Lectures on Ancient Indian Numismatics*, 1921, p. 6.

[3] A form found in the Jaugada inscription of Aśoka, *C.I.I.*, I, p. 116.

§ 150. We have already seen that, in cases where coins have the same inscription in Kharoṣṭhī and Brāhmī, there are slight differences of dialect, i.e. the coins are really bilingual; for example, on the coins of the Audumbaras and Kuṇindas, we have in Brāhmī *rajña* and in Kharoṣṭhī *raña*. At Taxila we have in Brāhmī *negama*, in Kharoṣṭhī (var. *f*) *nekame*. This interchange of *k* and *g* is paralleled in this region on the coins of Agathocles, which have in Brāhmī the name *Agathuklayaṣa* [1] and in Kharoṣṭhī [2] *Akathukrayasa*. The Mānsehrā Edict [3] transliterates the γ of Antigonos by *g* and the Shāhbāzgarhī version by *k*.[4] There were, therefore, two slightly different dialects in use in the Taxila country at the time of the issue of these coins. In this connexion we may note the brief bilingual inscriptions in Brāhmī and Kharoṣṭhī from Kanhiāra and Paṭhyār in the Kāngra district published by Vogel.[5] In view of the similarity of the dialects on the coins and the inscriptions just mentioned, we may assume that the reason for duplicating the inscriptions was that the people of one district were familiar with only one alphabet.

§ 151. The final syllable in *negama* in the Brāhmī is *ma* or *mā*; in the Kharoṣṭhī it is *me*; on no. 13, which has a Kharoṣṭhī inscription, *me* is clear; on most of the coins of Class 2 the last *akṣara* is very indistinct, and might be *ma*, but on nos. 17 and 24 it is clearly *me*; *negama* in the dialect which used Brāhmī corresponds to *nekame* in that which used Kharoṣṭhī. -*e* is a nominative termination of the *a* stem in Māgadhī,[6] but it is also found in the Prākrits of the North-West; for example, in the Shāhbāzgarhī Edicts.[7] Another clear example from the North-West of the nominative in -*e* is found on the curious gold piece of Puṣkālavatī published by Rapson [8] with the legend ΤΑΥΡΟϹ in Greek and *uṣabhe* in Kharoṣṭhī. *Negame* then is a nominative, as is *hirañasame*

[1] *B.M.C.*, *Gk. and Scyth. Kings*, no. 10.
[2] *Ibid.*, no. 15.
[3] *C.I.I.*, i, p. 12, l. 6.
[4] *Ibid.*, p. 51, l. 4; p. 66, l. 9.
[5] *E.I.*, vii, p. 116 f.
[6] Pischel, *Grammatik der Prākrit-Sprachen*, § 363.
[7] *C.I.I.*, i, p. xv.
[8] *J.R.A.S.*, 1905, pp. 786–787.

discussed below (§ 152); the latter is not a locative as suggested by Bühler.[1] *Paṁcanekame* is also a nominative singular, the *dvandva* compound being used as a *bahuvṛhi*. The length of the final vowel in the Brāhmī form of *negama* is another problem. On no. 1 it is short and the word is actually *nigama*, the Sanskrit form, which offers no difficulty. On the *dojaka* series we have *negamā* on nos. 2, 4, and 9, *negama* on 3, 8, and a recent acquisition; on the others it is impossible to say which vowel occurs; one can only suggest that *negamā*—if it is not to be read *negame*—is a nominative plural corresponding to Sanskrit *Naigamāḥ*,[2] 'the traders'; on the other hand, the Pāli *negama* and the Sanskrit *nigama* found on no. 1 suggest the latter, which means town, market, quarter of a town, as already mentioned. Collocations like *nagara-nigama-janapada*[3] and *grāma-nagara-nigama*,[4] however, suggest that *nigama* is an area larger than a town, perhaps a market district. The exact significance of the inscriptions on these coins is not certain, but the fact that the inscriptions are in the nominative suggests a comparison with town-names like Ujeni, Tripurī, &c., and that these are coins of the Rālimasa, Dojaka, Antakatakā, &c., market-quarters or market districts. We also have Hirañasama (Hiraṇyāśrama), Dośanasa, and perhaps also Vāṭaśvaka as names of districts whose local authorities issued coins in the country of Taxila with some system of co-ordination from a central authority.

§ 152. Class 3 of the inscribed coins of Taxila has on the obverse a facing elephant, on the right of which is a palm-tree and on the left  above , two familiar Taxilan symbols. The reverse has a horse to left with  above it and  on l. Above the latter symbol is a Kharoṣṭhī legend: var. *a* and var. *b* are distinguished by their legends. Var. *a* (fig. 1), one of which was found at Sirkap,[5]

[1] *V.O.J.*, viii, p. 207.

[2] On *e* for Sanskrit *ai* cf. the dialect of the Shāhbāzgarhī and Mānsehrā Edicts and compare Odumbara for Audumbara.

[3] Junāgaṛh inscription of Rudradāman, *E.I.*, viii, p. 43, l. 10.

[4] Bāṇa, *Harṣacārita* (Bombay Sanskrit Series), 1909, p. 266.

[5] *A.S.R.*, 1914–15, Pl. XXVIII. 10.

has a legend which is not found complete on any one specimen. Recognizing that it was the same as on certain coins of Agathocles [1] (fig. 2), I used Gardner's transliteration (*Hidujasame*) of it in the text of the Catalogue—more to call attention to the identity of legend

Fig. 1. Fig. 2. Fig. 3.

than because I was satisfied with the reading. The three different types of coin on which the legend occurs are illustrated in figs. 1–3. The legend was discussed by Bühler,[2] who rejected the reading *Hidujasame* as an impossible mixture of Persian and Indian forms. Of several possibilities he decided on *Hitajasame* = Sanskrit *Hitayaśomān*,[3] 'good-fame-possessing', a translation of Agathocles. Plausible as this reading appears, such a translation of a Greek king's name is unparalleled,[4] and in the case of Agathocles we already have his name transliterated into two different Indian dialects on coins closely connected with these. The occurrence of the same inscription on coins which do not bear the name of Agathocles also makes this suggestion less probable. It is thus necessary to examine the inscription again. There is no doubt about the first syllable *Hi-* nor about the last two *-same*. Bühler, who had not seen many specimens of these coins, hesitated between *-me* and *-maṁ* for the last syllable, but there is no doubt it is *-me*; the character is also found on the *Negama* coins. Bühler thought *-me* an unusual masculine nominative, but it seems to be regular at

[1] *B.M.C., Greek and Scythic Coins*, Pl. IV. 10 and *Panjab Museum Catalogue*, vol. i, Pl. II. 52.

[2] *V.O.J.*, viii, pp. 206-207.

[3] One would rather expect *Suyaśomān*.

[4] The only analogy I know of is the Puṣkālavatī piece mentioned in § 151.

Taxila, and it is found in the language of the Shāhbāzgarhī Edicts;[1] in any case it cannot be a genitive, which we should expect if it were the translation of Agathocles. The nominative, therefore, points to a place-name. The third character, always read as *-ja*, is really *-ñ*. The curls at the top of the fork which distinguish this letter from *j* are quite distinct. Bühler suggested this reading as a possibility. The second character *t*, *d*, or *r*?: *d* may be at once rejected as the character is right-angled. If we go to the nearest coins, those of Eucratides, for comparison of the Kharoṣṭhī characters, in order to identify the second character, we find that it is really impossible to distinguish *t* and *r* apart from the context; *r*, however, gives us good sense, and we can safely read *Hirañasame* = Sanskrit *Hiraṇyāśrama*, 'the Golden Hermitage'—a place-name already suggested by Bühler, but rejected in favour of the other reading. It is not, however, in the locative as he suggested.

§ 153. It is probable that we should attribute to Taxila the following coin (*obv.*, fig. 3) as the original copied by Agathocles:

Obv. A conventional representation of a plant; below in Kharoṣṭhī, *Hirañasame.*

Rev. Star over  (*Panjab Mus. Cat.*, i, Pl. II. 51).

Agathocles copied the type, replacing the plant by a tree in railing on one side and retaining the star and mountain on the other, with his name in Kharoṣṭhī below, *Akathukrayasa.*

§ 154. To return to var. *b*, this has types identical with var. *a*, but a different Kharoṣṭhī legend. The reading presents some difficulty. The first character is *Do* or possibly *no*. The vowel is distinct, and it has the short bar at the foot. The second is *-śa* with the little stroke marking the end[2] of the letter. The third is the same as the first, *da* or *na*. Below is *-sa*; as this appears to be attached to the mountain symbol it may not really be a Kharoṣṭhī character

[1] See Hultzsch, *C.I.I.*, i, p. xc; it is more regular in the Prākrit of Magadha.

[2] Bühler, *Indische Paläographie*, § 11.

here. The inscription then is *Dośana*, *Dośadasa*, or *Dośanasa*; the analogy of other inscriptions discussed here (§ 152) suggests that this is not a genitive.

§ 155. The majority of the coins of Taxila are uninscribed and die-struck, that is to say the symbols appear in a fixed order on the coins of the same type. This is also true of the few cast coins. Class 1 consists of a series of square coins stamped on one side only, which are linked together by style, symbols, and provenance. The symbol common to all is  or ; one of these is of a slightly narrower form than the other. This symbol seems to be characteristic of Taxila, and there is probably no distinction intended between the equilateral and isosceles forms. In var. *a* it is accompanied by a monolith; in var. *b* by a tree in railing; in var. *c* by a tree in railing, svastika, and taurine symbol, both common at Taxila. In var. *d* it is accompanied by a river symbol and the plan of the courtyard of a monastery with cells around and a stupa in the centre; in var. *e* by a plan of a monastery with a stupa at its entrance. The fabric of vars. *f*, *g* is their chief claim to be placed here, but the type of *f* is also a link with var. *h*. In var. *h* the type is what Cunningham calls a pile of six balls, apparently with flames at the top, which may represent a mountain or altar, a female figure holding up her right hand with a flower in it, and the usual symbol ; it is doubtful if, as Cunningham[1] first suggested, the figure is that of a male worshipper. I think the figure is female, and would prefer to connect her with the figure on Class 1, var. *f* (see § 147), and take her to be a goddess. These three types are found differently arranged on the coins which bear the legend *Vaṭasvaka* (cf. § 175). The fact that the Vaṭāśvaka coins have been found with these and other Taxila coins has suggested that they also should be attributed to Taxila.[2] Bühler[3] takes *Vaṭasvaka* as a nominative plural, but the name of a people would be in the genitive. A name in the nominative singular like Tripurī, Ujeni,

[1] *A.S.R.*, xiv, p. 22. [2] *C.I.M.*, i, p. 147. [3] *Ind. Stud.*, iii, p. 46.

&c., usually indicates a town, and one naturally expects Vaṭasvaka to be the name of a town or district. Our var. *h*, however, cannot be separated from the coins with which it is here classed to Taxila or moved to Vaṭāśvaka. Insistence upon the attribution of the Vaṭāśvaka coins to Taxila on account of the types would require us to transfer the Tripurī coins with their mountain and hollow cross there also. Var. *i* has a pile of nine balls, which may be another way of representing a mountain, and the symbol , a river, and two bunches of grapes; and var. *j* has a svastika between these two forms of mountain and river below.

A table will show best how these varieties are linked together:

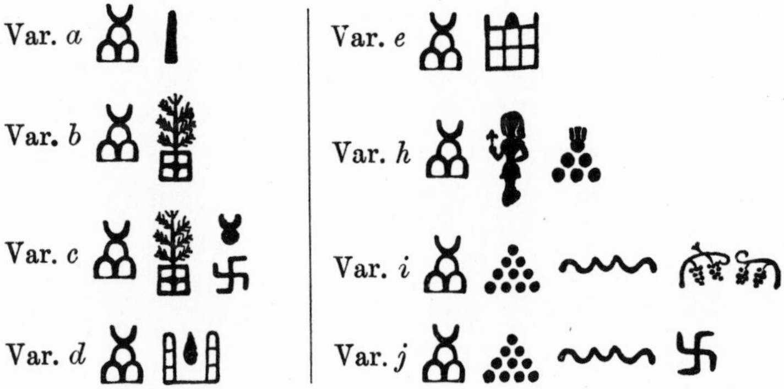

§ 156. Of these coins, vars. *a*, *d*, *h*, *i*,[1] were found by Cunningham in one pot amid ruins of Taxila with Vaṭāśvaka coins and coins of Pantaleon[2] and Agathocles[3] of Taxila fabric. They therefore belong to the first quarter of the second century B.C.; the other varieties, although not recorded as in this find, are so closely connected by types that they must belong to the same mint and date.

§ 157. Class 2 consists of a group of coins of similar fabric. They may be divided into two groups, *a–e* and *f–g*. Var. *a* has as obverse type an elephant with a small  above; the reverse is a lion with two symbols:  on l. and  above, both associated

[1] *A.S.R.*, xiv, 18, Pl. X. 6, 7, 10, 12.
[2] *Ibid.*, Pl. X. 17.
[3] *Ibid.*, Pl. X. 18.

with Taxila. The varieties *a–c* and *e* differ only in the position of the lion or elephant; in case of var. *d* a taurine symbol  replaces  beside the lion.

In vars. *f* and *g* the lion is replaced by a horse with a star above it, and the elephant has  before it, which is a symbol we have elsewhere at Taxila. This takes the place of the Taxila  on the preceding coins. The type of the galloping horse is not an Indian one, nor is the star. The horse is familiar on the coins of Euthydemus and some other Greek kings. On coin no. 107 (Pl. XXIII. 7) we have an Ā below the horse which, it may be suggested, is the initial of Agathocles. The star and the plant link these coins with those bearing the name of Agathocles (§ 150). Vars. *f* and *g* may be attributed to Agathocles or Pantaleon, and as the lion is a favourite type of the latter, it is just possible that vars. *a–d* should also be attributed to Greek kings in Taxila. The idea of a main type with subsidiary symbol is Greek, and not Indian. On purely Indian coins all the symbols are the same size. Vars. *a–d* were represented in the already mentioned find, but apparently not *f* and *g*. The latter may therefore be a little later in date than the former. Cunningham [1] found coins of vars. *a–d* in the Yūsufzai country also; he does not give the exact find-spot.

§ 158. Class 3, var. *a*, should perhaps be placed as a class by itself. It consists of square cast coins of three denominations. The obverse type has a flowering plant in railing  with  on each side. The reverse is  over , both symbols of Taxila. Two of these coins were found at Sirkap.[2] Var. *b*, which is struck, has one of the most remarkable types in the ancient Indian series, a grotesque facing head—called by Cunningham [3] a *Rākṣasa*; above it is , and on the left is a pillar in a railing

[1] *A.S.R.*, v, p. 6. [2] *A.S.R.*, 1914–15, p. 28, Pl. XXVIII. 8–9.
[3] *C.A.I.*, p. 63.

surmounted by a fish-like object . The reverse, a flowering plant in railing between two , recalls the obverse of var. *a*, and is a more conventional representation of the same thing, found again in a still more conventional form on the *Hirañasame* coins discussed above.[1] Vars. *c* and *d* are quite different; they are of the usual early Indian fabric. Var. *c*, which is round, has on the obverse the four symbols 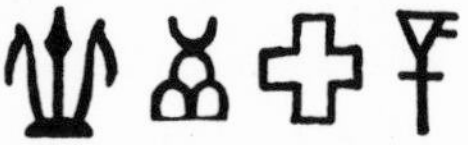 of which the first is found on Class 2, vars. *f* and *g*, and seems to be a crude representation of the elaborate plant of the preceding varieties; the next two are well-known Taxila symbols. The reverse symbols are also four in number , of which the first two are well-known Taxila types; the third, a form of *nandipada*, is that found on the *Paṁcanekame* coins. Var. *d*, which is square, has the first three only of the symbols on var. *c* on each side.

§ 159. Class 4 contains a large number of varieties of coins linked by symbols which we can associate with Taxila, notably  and svastika. Var. *a* consists of coins of early Indian fabric with plain reverse and obverse 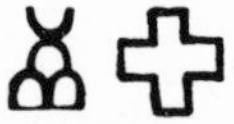. Var. *b* is the remarkable large piece already twice illustrated by Cunningham;[2] on var. *c* a new symbol  appears which resembles the Brāhmī syllable *go*, but there is no reason to suppose it is a character. Obverse and reverse have the same type, but on one coin, no. 146, their order is reversed. Var. *d* has obverse 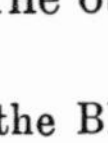 and reverse a simple *nandipada* 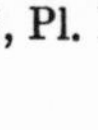 resembling a Brāhmī *m*. These two symbols together occur on both sides of var. *e*. The obverse of var. *f* places

[1] A similar object is found on the seals from the Bhir mound (*A.S.R.*, 1918–20, Pl. XI. 5, 5 a, 6 a).

[2] *A.S.R.*, xii, Pl. X. 2; *C.A.I.*, Pl. II. 15.

it here, but the reverse , tree in railing, and river connect it with Class 1, vars. *b–e*, and serve as a clue to the date of this class; var. *g* has obverse and reverse svastika , two well-known Taxila types; var. *h* with obverse svastika as in *g* and *nandipada* has an elaborate but incomplete reverse. Var. *i* has an uncertain symbol on the obverse and a hill with trees growing from it on the reverse. The attribution to Taxila is not quite certain. Var. *j* has the found associated with the Taxila in var. *d*. Var. *k* has the hollow cross only.

Another variety of this class was found at Sirkap:[1]

> *Obv.* Elephant l. with above;
>
> *Rev.* as in var. *a*;

and another variety[2] with obverse svastika and reverse plain.

§ 160. Class 5 is connected with the preceding class by the hollow cross and , one or both of which form the reverse of the first three varieties, while the elephant connects the obverse of vars. *a–b* with *c–d*. On *d* it is accompanied by on r. and above. Var. *e* has a lion with the symbols a small svastika and rather than the of the text. Vars. *f–j*, all rare, with bull on obverse, may be safely attributed to Taxila from their symbols , as may var. *k* from its reverse. A coin found at Sirkap[3] is one of these varieties, most probably var. *f*. The coin[4] from the Bhir mound seems to be var. *f* also, the taurine being mistaken for a svastika. Another coin from Sirkap[5] should be placed here also, along with the coin[6] from the same site with lion to l. on each side.

[1] *A.S.R.*, 1912–13, p. 45, Pl. XL. 3.
[2] *A.S.R.*, 1914–15, Pl. XXVIII. 3.
[3] *A.S.R.*, 1915–16, p. 31, Pl. XXV. 1.
[4] *A.S.R.*, 1912–13, p. 45, Pl. XL. 2.
[5] *A.S.R.*, 1914–15, p. 28, Pl. XXVIII. 2.
[6] *A.S.R.*, 1914–15, Pl. XXVIII. 11.

§ 161. Class 6 consists of a few rare coins. One is the only known gold coin of ancient India; it was found by Cunningham at Taxila.[1] The bull on the obverse is also a type of the preceding class; and the reverse is the symbol  which is so characteristic of punch-marked silver coins (Class 1, Group II) found at Taxila that Cunningham calls it the 'Taxila' symbol. Var. *b* is a copper coin with the reverse  and obverse a tree in railing of unusual form between a svastika and a taurine symbol. To these we would now add a small bronze coin: obverse , reverse , formerly in the J. P. Rawlins collection.

§ 162. Class 7, a coin with a realistic tree in railing between two Taxila symbols,  and , is attributed here on account of the latter. The provenance (Talbot Collection) also supports the attribution.

§ 163. In conclusion we have put together a number of miscellaneous coins the attribution of which is not quite certain. There is little doubt about no. 1. It has three symbols, a tree in railing and hollow cross, both found at Taxila. The middle symbol  in the Catalogue is, I think, really the fish-headed (?) standard found on Class 3, var. *b*. The obverse of no. 2 is a hunting scene in miniature, and it has an equally remarkable reverse, two figures under a tree. The next coin has a figure on an elephant beside a tree in railing, and the field is crowded with symbols, including a lion r. (?)    .[2] The reverse is the common . No. 4 has as type a steelyard and an elaborate altar with two taurine symbols above. The lion on the next two coins recalls well-known coins of Taxila, but there is an absence of Taxilan symbols.

Nos. 7–11, with lion before  and reverse plain, are more

[1] *A.S.R.*, xii, Pl. X. 19; *C.A.I.*, Pl. XI. 18.

[2] A specimen of this coin was found at Sirkap (*A.S.R.*, 1914–15, p. 28, Pl. XXVIII. 6).

probably from the United Provinces, as two of the B.M. specimens came from the Nelson Wright Collection, and Cunningham,[1] though he illustrates them in Pl. II. 3–5, does not describe them under Taxila. The remaining pieces stamped with taurine symbols may be not coins but weights. Several of these, similar to no. 13, were found at Sirkap.[2]

§ 164. In spite of the great variety in the coins here attributed to Taxila, it is clear that they are so connected by types and symbols with one another and with coins definitely known to have been found on the site that there is no reason to doubt the attribution. They form a homogeneous group, distinct from other groups of copper coins of ancient India, such as those of Ujjain. Their similarity in style and the limited number of symbols and single types suggest that they do not cover a great period in time. The occurrence at Taxila of certain symbols, notably  and , frequent on cast copper coins from other parts of India, suggests that the latter are contemporary with the former issued by order of the same authority, one mint favouring striking and the other casting. The evidence of the finds shows that Classes 1 and 3, so far from being of great antiquity, belong to the first quarter of the second century B.C. The few cast coins may be possibly a little earlier, but the copper coinage of Taxila seems to have been a short-lived one, beginning late in the third century B.C., when Taxila was under Maurya governors, and ending with the Greek conquest before the middle of the second century.

§ 165. TRIGARTA (p. 212, no. 19). The Traigartas, the people of Trigarta, are mentioned in the fourth century B.C. by Pāṇini,[3] and the commentary on the grammarian shows that they are closely connected with the Yaudheyas.[4] They also were 'a republic living by fighting'.[5] They are again mentioned along with the Yaudheyas,

[1] *C.A.I.*, p. 61.
[2] *A.S.R.*, 1915–16, p. 31, Pl. XXV. 2; 1912–13, p. 45, Pl. XL. 4; 1914–15, p. 28, Pl. XXVIII. 4.
[3] v. 3, 116. [4] iv. 1, 178. [5] v. 3, 117.

Śibis, Rājanyas, and other *gaṇas* and *janapadas* of the Panjab in the *Mahābhārata*[1] and the *Bṛhatsaṁhitā*.[2] The Trigarta country is mentioned as a *janapada* as late as the seventh century.[3] The king of Trigarta is mentioned along with the king of Kulūta (see § 110) as a friend and presumably as a neighbour of Sāhilla, founder of the Chamba line, in an inscription of Somavarman and Āsaṭa.[4] To Trigarta we would attribute the coin bearing the legend *Trakatajanapadasa* 'of the tribe of Trigarta' in Brāhmī characters of probably the first half of the second century B.C. There are traces of this same inscription in Kharoṣṭhī on the obverse, but only the end ... *padasa* is legible. The square shape of the coin is further evidence of its early date. The Trigarta country corresponded to the modern Jullundur, the land between the Ravi and Sutlej. Jālandhara and Trigarta seem to have been synonymous.[5]

Closely resembling the preceding in style and fabric is the coin catalogued on p. 213, no. 20, which has a Kharoṣṭhī legend ending .. *tapasa* [or *ra*] *janapadasa*. In the text *Khatapasa* was suggested for the first word. The coin has now been cleaned, and it is certain that there are two letters to be supplied; the second is perhaps *vi* and the first *s* or *g*. When correctly read, this coin will add one more to the coinages of the Panjab of the second century B.C.

§ 166. Tripurī (p. 239). The coins bearing the name *Tipuri* in Brāhmī characters of the late third or early second century B.C. are exceedingly rare. They are not cast, but struck with that seal-like effect, as if the die had been impressed on hot metal, which is characteristic of the earliest Indian copper coins. The types are  above  with the legend *Tipuri* written perpendicularly

[1] *Śabhaparvan*, xxxii. 7, where they are conquered by Nakula along with the Śibis and Mālavas; for other reference, see Sörensen's Index.

[2] xiv. 25; xvi. 20.

[3] *Daśakumāracaritam*, Bk. vi, p. 216 of the Bombay edition (Nirnaya Sagara) 1906.

[4] J. P. Vogel, *Antiquities of Chamba State*, 1911 = *A.S.R.*, vol. xxxvi, pp. 193, 195.

[5] See Stein's note in his translation of the *Rājataraṅgiṇī*, iii, 100. Cunningham, *A.S.R.*, v, 148.

from the bottom. It is doubtful if the curved line (? river symbol) mentioned by Bhagvanlal Indraji [1] really occurs in the type. The reverse is plain.

The coins are to be attributed to the ancient Tripurī [2] (modern Tewar) on the Narbadā, in medieval times the capital of the Kalachuri dynasty. The fact that two of the three specimens in the Museum come from the Bhagvanlal collection indicates a Western Indian provenance, and is against an attribution to Tripura, the modern Tipperah.

§ 167. UDDEHIKA (p. 240). The coins bearing the inscription *Udehaki* [3] in Brāhmī characters of the second century B.C. are very rare. They are to be attributed to the Uddehikas, Audehikas, or Auddehikas, mentioned by Varāhamihira (xiv. 3) and located in the middle country. Al-Bīrūnī, writing in the eleventh century, says that Uddehika is near 'Bazana', 112 miles south-west of Kanauj.

No information is recorded regarding the provenance of the coins.

The types Ujjain symbol, tree in railing, two fishes in tank, and the square shape suggest a connexion with the coins of Eran and Ujjain. One of the two known coins bears the name of the tribe *Udehaki* in Brāhmī characters of the early second century B.C. The other has as an additional legend the name of King Sūryamitra, *Suyamita(sa)* = *Sūryamitrasya*. The absence of the title king is evidence of the early date. The reverse of the former is a bull with a tree in railing above it on its side, and the reverse types of the latter include an elephant. The latter coin is countermarked either with  as in the text or  as suggested by Rapson.

§ 168. UJJAYINĪ (pp. 241–261). We have retained Cunningham's [4] attribution of the extensive series of copper coins, which Vincent Smith [5] proposed to ascribe, along with the coins from Eran (cf. §§ 101–102), to the country of Avanti. In spite of a certain com-

[1] *J.R.A.S.*, 1894, p. 553 (Pl., no. 15). [2] *Bṛhatsaṁhitā*, xiv. 9.
[3] On the form see Rapson in *J.R.A.S.*, 1900, pp. 98–102.
[4] *C.A.I.*, pp. 94–99. [5] *C.I.M.*, i, p. 145.

munity of symbols, notably several varieties of the Ujjain symbol, and the tree in railing, neither of which, however, is by any means confined to these two mints, the coins of these two cities are of very distinct fabric, and are not readily mistaken for one another. The Eran style is well illustrated in the coins from Besnagar on Pls. LXIV–LXV of *A.S.R.*, 1913–1914. Besides, coins are known of both these places bearing the name of the town. There is no reason to dispute the allocation of coins to the city of Ujjayinī rather than to the country of Avanti, which, unless these coins are much earlier than we believe, had no longer an independent existence when they were issued.

We have arranged the coins of Ujjayinī into six classes of uninscribed coins and one of inscribed. They are struck on the same principle as the punch-marked coins; that is to say, on the obverse we have several symbols—often, as on the silver punch-marked coins, five—some of which change more frequently than others. Unlike the great majority of punch-marked silver coins these have regularly a single symbol or type on the reverse.

§ 169. There is not much to add to the descriptions of the coins in the text of the Catalogue, but a few notes will show how they are linked together. Eleven varieties of Class 1 are distinguished. Throughout these we have a tree in railing  , and on most of them the well-known symbol  or , the latter of which is a characteristic of this series. Four or two fishes in a tank are found on several varieties, and a river with fishes. The reverses show three forms of the Ujjain symbol: vars. *a*, *j*, and *k* ; var. *b* ; vars. *c–i* .

The characteristic symbol of Class 2 is a deity    whom we have identified as Kārttikeya since he holds a spear; on

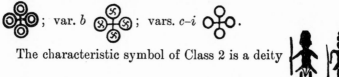

var. *l* he is shown with three heads ; the other three are behind and naturally not represented because they cannot be seen, so that he is six-headed—which identifies him as Kārttikeya. The possibility that he is Śiva, whose plurality of heads would be indicated in the same way, must not be overlooked; the absence of the trident or other symbol of Śiva, and the fact that he has only two arms—although this need not be stressed—is against this. The importance of the cult of Śiva Mahākāla at Ujjayinī is well known; it is of course not impossible that, as on the coins of the Yaudheyas, both deities are represented. Other symbols which link this class with Class 1 are the tree in railing, river with fishes, and  or . Vars. *f* and *g* show the deity in a form found on certain punch-marked silver coins  (see § 37. 3). The reverses show the following forms of the Ujjain symbol: vars. *a–c*, *g*, *l*, *m*, and *q* ; vars. *d* and *i* ; vars. *e*, *f*, *h*, *k*, *n*, and *o* ; var. *j* ; var. *p* 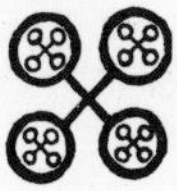. Vars. *p* and *q* replace Kārttikeya by Lakṣmī, but are connected with the preceding varieties by their other symbols.

§ 170. Class 3 forms a group from which the Ujjain symbol is completely absent, and only the evidence of provenance and certain links with other classes justify their attribution to this series. The obverse symbols are   or     and , which is presumably a very crude representation of Kārttikeya. The rev. of var. *a* is a frog, and the other reverse symbols are elaborate svastikas sometimes occurring twice  .

The occurrence of this symbol on coins from Besnagar with many Eran coins makes the attribution to Ujjain somewhat doubtful.[1]

Var. *g* has a peculiar reverse  not found elsewhere.

We have grouped together as Class 4 four varieties with deities on the obverse. Var. *a* has the *abhiṣeka* of Lakṣmī. Var. *b*, two standing female figures with a river with fishes below. Var. *c* is a broken coin, but seems to have had three figures on it; the type was probably the same as the three figures found on certain punch-marked silver coins  (p. 37 (1)). Var. *d* has a standing figure and three other symbols. Three varieties of Ujjain symbols    all found in the preceding classes justify the attribution.

§ 171. Class 5 is characterized by a bull before a tree in a railing, a symbol found on several other series of coins. It is connected with Class 1 by the symbols   . Vars. *e* and *g* have a rare symbol  which connects them with Class 3, and supports the attribution of the latter class. Var. *a* is countermarked with the well-known figure of Kārttikeya  found on Class 2. The reverses are usual forms of Ujjain symbols   with the exception of var. *d*, which has the symbol  very rarely found on a reverse;[2] the obverse, however, bears the bull before tree found on the rest of this class. Var. *f* has the war-god on the reverse in addition to the Ujjain symbol, and one specimen of it is countermarked with a tree in a railing.

[1] *A.S.R.*, 1913–1914, Pl. LXIV. 27, 28–37.

[2] Cf. Eran, p. 144, var. *n*.

Class 6, var. *a*, has a lion on the obverse and the Ujjain symbol on the reverse. Var. *b* resembles Class 5, but has an elephant in place of the bull. The reverse is the very elaborate Ujjain symbol with small symbols in each of the circles . Var. *c* has an elephant on obverse and Ujjain symbol  on reverse.

§ 172. Class 7 is linked with the preceding by the elephant on obverse; the reverse type is a symbol  frequent in the preceding classes, and a hand. The inscription[1] is transliterated *Ujaniyi* in the text, but the true reading seems to be *Ujeni*, a form supported by the Pāli *Ujjenī*. The second vowel is certainly *e*, and the *yi*, although apparently distinct, seems really to be a fragment of the border. The characters are of the first half of the second century B.C.

The date of the uninscribed coins is probably the third and second centuries B.C., when this region was a Maurya province. We know that Aśoka was governor in Ujjayinī when he was summoned to the throne. These coins are probably the local issues of the time of the Maurya governors.

The types of the inscribed coin attributed by Vincent Smith[2] to Ujjayinī, and read by him *Runamāsa*, suggest that it is a coin of Kauśāmbī. It has no link with any coin of Ujjayinī; the legend is incomplete, and probably ends in *-mitasa*.

§ 173. Upagoda (p. 263). The unique cast piece bearing the legend *Upagodasa* in characters of the late third century B.C. with a circle with pellet in centre above and a taurine symbol below is still unique. The reverse is blank. It was known to Thomas,[3] and described by Rapson.[4] It is still uncertain whether Upagoda

[1] Read *Ujeniya* by Cunningham, *A.S.R.*, xiv, p. 148.
[2] *C.I.M.*, i, Pl. XX. 3, p. 154, no. 27.
P.E., i. 216.
[4] *J.R.A.S.*, 1900, pp. 102–103.

(Upagauda) is the name of a person or a place, and the piece may even be a seal and not a coin.

§ 174. UPĀTIKYĀ (p. 263). The piece of about the same date as the preceding, bearing the legend *Upātikyā*, may also be a seal and not a coin. It was found at Ambarikha, north of Mathurā, by Cunningham.[1] On the *ky* = *k* see Franke, *Pāli und Sanskrit*, p. 111.

§ 175. VAṬĀŚVAKA (p. 264). The coins bearing the legend *Vaṭasvaka* in characters of the early second century B.C. are of the same characteristic Indian fabric as those of Tripurī, which they also resemble in the position of the legend with respect to the type, i.e. it is written perpendicularly from the bottom upwards. The type is an unusual one, a figure to l. with raised hand in front of a mountain; below the mountain is a pile of balls also found on certain coins from Taxila; below the figure is a taurine symbol. There is a close resemblance of type between certain coins here catalogued under Taxila (see p. 221, Uninscribed, Class 1, var. *h*) and this type (cf. § 155). There is something Mithraic about the attitude of the figure apparently worshipping the mountain, but it should be remembered that the two elements are, as usual on coins of this date, quite separate and not intended to form one type. When we remember that the same three elements are found in a different order on the coins from Taxila just mentioned, it seems certain that the symbols are to be taken separately, and that the figure is not a worshipper, but a female whom we have suggested may be a city goddess. These two types of coin were actually found together with coins of Taxila at Taxila (cf. § 156).[2] The real difficulty is whether some of the coins, here catalogued under Taxila (Class 1, var. *h*), should not be removed to Vaṭāśvaka.

Bühler[3] took the inscription *Vaṭasvaka* to be for a Sanskrit *Vaṭāśvakāḥ*, a nominative plural, the Vaṭāśvakas or 'Aśvakas of the Vaṭa (fig-tree) division'. As the language of the Shāhbāzgaṛhī Edicts[4] shows, *Vaṭasvaka* could be a nominative plural in the

[1] *A.S.R.*, iii, p. 14.
[2] *A.S.R.*, xiv, p. 18.
[3] *Ind. Stud.*, iii, p. 46.
[4] *C.I.I.*, i, p. 90.

Prākrit of the north-west, but the objection to Bühler's interpretation is that we should expect a genitive plural in a coin-legend. It is therefore better to take Vaṭāśvaka as a singular and as a place-name, which preserves the memory of the Aśvakas, the Assakenoi, of the Greeks.[1] If not in the territory of Taxila, it was near enough to be in close commercial relations with it (cf. § 151).

§ 176. Yaudheya (pp. 265–278, 288). The first group, Class 1, of the coins of the Yaudheyas consists of a series of small coins of potin without the name of the tribe. The slightly scyphate fabric, metal, and provenance connect them with coins of Class 2 bearing the name of the tribe. These coins are all round and bear a stamp from a round die much smaller than the flan of the coin. The first variety has on the obverse a tree in railing , the second the same tree with a small Ujjain symbol  on the left. On var. *c* a third symbol  is added on the right. Var. *d* has the same tree in railing beside a star or sun . Var. *e* has it again between  (not  as in the text) and the same star or sun. Below it is the legend *Mahārājasa* in Brāhmī characters of the first century B.C. This variety also has a reverse type 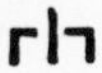. The legend is an unusual one. One would expect *Mahārāja* here to be a king's name, but there seems to be no authority for this as a name, so that it is 'of the Mahārāja', and shows that the Yaudheyas had a monarchical constitution until a fairly late date. These coins of Class 1 were found at Behat[2] with coins bearing the name of the Yaudheyas.

§ 177. The four varieties of Class 2, the metal of which varies from potin to copper, have the same reverse type, an elephant to r. with a *nandipada* above it and a flowing pennon behind it. The obverse type is a bull before , a sacrificial post? (*yūpa*) in

[1] Arrian, *Anab.*, iv. 27.

[2] *J.A.S.B.*, 1834 (vol. iii), pp. 227–229, Pl. IX. 3, 4; 1835 (vol. iv), p. 626, Pl. XXXIV. 13, 19; *P.E.*, i, 83, Pl. IV. 3, 4; *C.A.I.*, p. 77.

a railing. Var. *a* with bull to r. is only distinguished by its smaller module from *c*, which it otherwise resembles. On var. *b* the bull is to left and on var. *d* (p. 288) the bull is alone. The object in front of bull in *b* is not  as in the text, simply  reversed. The type is probably the same as that of the coins of the Ārjunāyanas, who are regularly associated with the Yaudheyas in literature. The legend on these coins, which is apparently distinct, has not been explained. *Yaudheyānā[ṁ]* above the bull presents no difficulty. This is preceded by five characters, of which various readings have been given: *Kṛpudhanaba*,[1] *Bhūpadhanusha*,[2] *Bhūmidhanusha*,[3] *Bahudhañake*.[4] The differences in these readings are due in part to the fact that some are read as an exergual legend, others as immediately preceding *Yaudheyānā[ṁ]*. An examination of a large number of specimens suggested that these five characters precede *Yaudheyānāṁ*,[5] and that Rodgers's reading, at least of the consonants, is correct. *-dhanaba* is certainly right; the first syllable may be *Ku* or *Kra* and the second *pra* or *pu*. The most likely reading would be 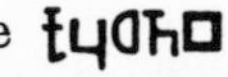 *Kupradhañaba*—and the inscription would mean 'of the Yaudheyas of Kupradhañaba', the latter being a geographical term.

The serious objection to this reading, which is that suggested on pp. 267–270, is that it requires two different forms of *dh* in the same inscription,  in Yaudheya and  in the other word. This suggests that the mysterious word should be read the other way, although it is usually joined with *Yaudheyānāṁ*. It is, however, to be noted that on no. 21 in which the legend is completely reversed it begins *Yaudh-*, and on var. *d* there is a distinctive break in the inscription. If then we read from left to right 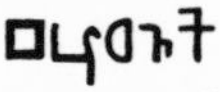 we have Rapson's reading *Bahudhañake*, which gives a good Sanskrit geographical term *Bahudhānyaka*, 'rich in corn', and the termination *-e* would again be explained as the N. W. Prākrit

[1] Rodgers, *Lahore Museum Catalogue*, i, Part III, p. 136, note 2.
[2] Vincent Smith, *C.I.M.*, i, p. 181, note 1.
[3] Cunningham, *A.S.R.*, xiv, p. 141.
[4] Rapson, *J.R.A.S.*, 1900, p. 107, note 1.

nominative already discussed in § 151. Bahudhānyaka is mentioned in the *Mahābhārata* [1] as one of Nakula's conquests in the west. If Marubhūmi, with which it is contrasted, be a real place —the modern Mārwār (Jodhpur State)—Bahudhānyaka may also be a real place-name in the *Mahābhārata*. The inscription on the coin may therefore be the name of an unusually fertile part of the Panjab in the possession of the Yaudheyas. Other Panjab tribes are mentioned in the same context in the epic.

Two fabrics may be distinguished in these coins, a larger size with square characters in the inscription and a smaller neater size with the inscription in rather cursive Brāhmī characters. There seem to have been at least two mints for this type of coin. Var. *d*, on which the legend is in two distinct words, is found with cursive characters only. These coins may be dated in the late second–first century B.C.

§ 178. The third class is later in date, and is closely connected in style and type with the coinage of the Kuṇindas. Corresponding to the silver coinage of the latter we have a unique silver Yaudheya coin [1] (no. 47, Pl. XXXIX. 21), the obverse of which is the six-headed Kārttikeya and reverse Lakṣmī standing facing on lotus between  and  with a river below, all symbols found on the reverse of the Kuṇinda coins, while the goddess appears in the same attitude on the obverse of the latter. The legend in Brāhmī beginning on the left is

Bhāgavata-svamino-Brahmaṇya[-]-*Yaudheya.*

The name of the tribe on this coin enables us to attribute the extensive series of copper coins with similar types and inscription to the Yaudheyas. A space between *ṇya* and *Yau* suggests we should supply *sa* from the copper coins. The legend should then be read

Yaudheya-bhāgavata-svamino Brahmaṇya(*sa* or *sya*)

'Of Brahmaṇya (a name of Kārttikeya), the divine lord of the Yaudheyas.'

[1] Sabhaparvan II, 35. 5 (Bombay 1906 edition, Calcutta ed. II, 1187).
[2] *C.A.I.*, Pl. VI. 9.

§ 179. The copper coins of this series are much more numerous; they are of very rough workmanship and have very fragmentary legends. As on the coins of the Kuṇindas the inscriptions vary between Sanskrit and Prākrit. The full form is

Bhāgavata-svamino Brahmaṇya-devasya (or *sa*) *Kumarāsya* (or *sa*)
'Of Kumāra the divine lord Brahmaṇyadeva',

again alluding to the war-god of the type.

The types are similar to those of the silver. Var. *a* is the same as the silver; var. *b* differs only in that the symbols on each side of the goddess exchange places. On var. *c* Lakṣmī and Kārttikeya exchange positions. On vars. *d–h* the goddess on the reverse is replaced by the deer with whom she appears on the obverse of the coins of the Kuṇindas, and the deer is accompanied by certain small symbols 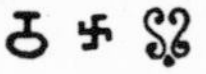 which we have already met on the coins of the Kuṇindas. The differences in these varieties are slight. On var. *h* the word *darma* appears above the deer, presumably for *dharma*, and the tree in railing is replaced by a temple. On var. *i* Kārttikeya is replaced by Śiva holding his trident. The date of these copper coins is the second century A.D.

§ 180. Class 4, which is of the same module as Class 3, has the incomplete legend—*bhanuva*—between a mountain and svastika above and a snake below. The reverse has a trident and a standard, each in a railing. The full inscription is perhaps *Bhanuvarmasa*. This coin was found with upwards of 300 of the preceding class.[1]

Class 5 consists of a single small square copper coin with the legend [*Yau*]*dheyān*[*āṁ*] above a bull to r., in characters of the first century B.C.

§ 181. Class 6 consists of a series of well-made copper coins showing Kushān influence in style and types but of quite late date, third–fourth century A.D., for the Brāhmī of the inscriptions might almost be called Gupta. The obverse bears the war-god standing facing accompanied by his peacock. The reverse is a goddess to l. with r. hand raised. On var. *a* she is alone. On the analogy of

[1] *A.S.R.*, xiv, p. 145.

Class 3 a goddess is to be expected. The type recalls, it is true, figures of Helios, Mithra or Mao on Kushān coins, as Cunningham has pointed out, but I am inclined to think Lakṣmī is intended. On var. *b* there is a *kalaśa* on the left and an inverted trisul on the right; the latter may be a copy of the well-known Kushān symbol which was also taken over by the Guptas; on var. *c* the symbols are a conch-shell on l. and two snakes on r. . The legend on all is *Yaudheyagaṇasya jaya*, 'Victory of the Yaudheya tribe'. On var. *b* we have *dvi* at the end of the legend, and on var. *c* *tṛ* interpreted as contractions of *Dvitīya* and *Tṛtīya*, second and third sections of the tribe. Var. *d* is a mule with *obv.* of var. *a* and *rev.* of *c*. One of this class (var. *c*) was found at Behat.[1]

§ 182. There is not a great deal accurately recorded about the provenance of the coins of the Yaudheyas. Captain Cautley found specimens of Class 1, vars. *b*, *c*, and *e*, Class 2 and Class 6 at Behat,[2] an ancient site near Sahāranpur, which also yielded Kuṇinda coins. According to Cunningham [3] these coins are found all over the country (i.e. the Panjab) as far as Delhi and Ludhiāna; in another place [4] he says they are found in the eastern Panjab and all over the country between the Sutlej and the Jumna. Two large finds were made at Sonpat between Delhi and Karnāl.[5] Cunningham obtained four specimens of Class 3 in the Kāngra district.[6] The coins are found plentifully in the country to the westward of the Jumna.[7] Again he tells us that the coins are found 'to the west of the Satlej, in Depalpur, Satgarha, Ajudhan, Kahror, and Multan, and to the eastward in Bhatner, Abhor, Sirsa, Hânsi, Pânipat, and Sonpat'.[8] Rodgers [9] obtained specimens of Class 6 at Hānsī and Kharkaudah near Sonpat. The evidence of coin-finds shows that the Yaudheyas occupied an area which may be roughly described as the Eastern Panjab.

[1] *J.A.S.B.*, iv (1835), Pl. XXXIV. 22, p. 626.
[2] *J.A.S.B.*, iii (1834), Pl. XVIII; iv (1835), Pl. XXXIV; *P.E.*, Pls. IV and XIX.
[3] *A.S.R.*, xiv, p. 140. [4] *C.A.I.*, p. 76. [5] *Ibid.*
[6] *Ibid.*, p. 79. [7] *A.S.R.*, ii, p. 14. [8] *A.G.I.*, p. 245.
[9] MSS. notes in Dept. of Coins.

§ 183. The literary and epigraphical evidence shows that the Yaudheyas were one of the most powerful of the tribes of the Panjab. They are mentioned by Pāṇini and the commentary along with the Trigarta people (cf. § 166) and others as 'living by fighting'. In the *Mahābhārata* they appear in the usual passages with other Panjab tribes. They do not seem to be mentioned in connexion with Alexander. In the Junāgaṛh inscription of Rudradāman of the year 72 = A.D. 150, the Mahākṣatrapa claims to have destroyed the Yaudheyas, 'who would not submit because they were proud of their title of heroes among the Kṣatriyas'.[1] This reference suggests that their lands in the second century extended into Western Rājputāna. The Bijayagaḍh inscription confirms this. Two centuries later Samudragupta[2] in his Allahabad inscription mentions them along with the Mālavas and Ārjunāyanas among the frontier tribes who paid tribute and homage to him. Varāhamihira[3] puts the Yaudheyas with the Rājañyas, Mālavas, and other tribes in the northern division. After this date they seem to disappear from history, but Cunningham[4] thinks their name has survived in that of the modern Johiyas who occupy both banks of the Sutlej along the Bahāwalpur frontier.

Hoernle[5] has given an account of a number of clay seals from Sonait in Ludhiāna, some of which bore impressions from Yaudheya coins of Class 6. One very large one had as type a bull as on the coins of the Yaudheyas and the legend '*Yodheyānaṁ jayamaṁtra-dharāṇāṁ*' (seal) 'of the Yaudheya councillors of victory'. A fragmentary inscription in characters of the second-third century A.D. from Biyayagaḍh[6] in the Byānā tahsil of Bharatpur State contains a reference to a Mahārāja-Mahāsenapati appointed leader of the *Yaudheya gaṇa.*

§ 184. The coins of the Yaudheyas fall into three periods, Classes 1, 2, and 5 of the late second and first centuries B.C. indicating a period of independence, from the fall of the Mauryas to the

[1] *E.I.*, viii, pp. 44 and 47.
[2] Fleet, *C.I.I.*, iii, pp. 8, 14.
[3] *Bṛhatsaṁhitā*, xiv. 28.
[4] *A.S.R.*, xiv, p. 140; *A.G.I.*, p. 245.
[5] *Proc. A.S.B.*, 1884, pp. 137–141.
[6] Fleet, *C.I.I.*, iii, p. 252.

coming of the Kushāns. Classes 3–4 belong to the later second century A.D., and the poor state of the currency probably reflects the disastrous effects of Rudradāman's victory and the war with the Śakas. The fine coins of Class 6, which like the seals above mentioned reveal strong Kushān influence, show the tribe well established again in the third and early fourth centuries A.D. Their currency came to an end with the Gupta conquest.

§ 185. Uncertain Coins (pp. 279–281). There is little to add to the descriptions in the text of the coins classed as uncertain. Those that bear names are given first and arranged in alphabetical order:

No. 1 has a reverse type not found on any of the tribal coins, which recalls a type familiar from punch-marked silver coins. The same symbol  has been used in the text, but a closer examination shows that the animal is not a dog but a lion. The inscription is in Brāhmī characters of the second century B.C. *Agodaka* [-]*napadasa*; one missing *akṣara* is obviously *ja*, and the coin would give the name of a hitherto unknown *janapada*, that of the Agodakas or Aṅgodrakas. I think, however, that the inscription is continued below the tree, and that the full legend is as on nos. 22–29, most of which have the same types: lion on hill and tree in railing (see below, § 194).

§ 186. The complete legend on no. 2 which is fully preserved on a specimen in the Indian Museum[1] is *Jyeṣṭhadattasya*.[2] The male deity on the obverse is off the flan of the I.M. specimen and the B.M. specimen shows the reverse type to be Lakṣmī, and not an elephant. Carlleyle found a specimen at Bairāṅt, 22½ miles S.W. of Ghazipur.[3] Another of these coins is that obtained at Indor Khera by Cunningham;[4] he read the legend *Ajyeṣṭhaḍattama*, taking the remains of the figure as an initial *A*: the reverse he rightly says has an erect human figure. Carlleyle and Cunningham both talk of the Aśokan character of the inscription, but the coin probably belongs to the end of the second century B.C.

[1] *I.M.C.*, i, Pl. XXIII. 7, p. 209.

[2] Not *Jyeṣṭhadattadevasya* as read by Vincent Smith.

[3] *A.S.R.*, xxii, p. 115.

[4] *A.S.R.*, xii, p. 41.

§ 187. The next two coins, nos. 3–4, have the legend—certain on no. 3, not so clear on no. 4—*Mahāsenasa* in characters of the early second century B.C. The types are a standing male deity, a svastika, and the symbol . The general style recalls the inscribed coins of Ujjayinī; nos. 5–7 have the legend *Puṁgasenasa* with the symbol  above and a river below. The reverse type is a tree in railing. Nothing is known of the issuer Puṅgasena, who belongs to the second century B.C.

§ 188. No. 8 was published by Rapson [1] with the suggestion that it may belong to the region of Mathurā. As to the reading of the inscription given in the text, *Rājā-Śaśacaṁdrātasa*, I now think that traces of *ñ* can be seen below *ja*, so that the first word is *Rājño*, a genitive, which is what we should expect. The form *Rajño* is also found before sibilants (cf. § 124). There is no trace of a vowel on the first *Ś*, but as that of the second may be *u*, Rapson's reading *Śiśucaṁdāta* is equally possible. *Caṁd*[or -*dr*]*āta* is, as he points out, for a Sanskrit *Candradatta*. No ruler of this name is otherwise known. The coin may be dated in the first century B.C.

§ 189. The next coin, no. 9, which at first sight looks like a late Greek [2] or Scythic coin, e.g. of Azes, has types bull and elephant, which we find on the silver coins of the Audumbaras, Mahādeva, and Rudravarman. The Brāhmī legend is very uncertain. It seems possible to read *Rāja* (this may, however, be a *nandipada*) *V*-*mak*[-] [-]*napapasa*: *Vemaka*, if this is the reading, would suggest a further link with Rudravarman and the Audumbaras. The coin came from the Panjab, probably from the Hoshiārpur district, and belongs to the first century B.C.

No. 10, the reverse of which is obliterated, has the obverse fully occupied by a legend in Brāhmī characters of the third or fourth century A.D.—*Vasu* [--]: apparently not *Vasudeva*. The coin was in the Rawlins collection, and therefore presumably came from the Hoshiārpur district of the Panjab.

[1] *J.R.A.S.*, 1900, pp. 114–115, Pl. no. 14.

[2] Indeed, Rodgers in his MS. notes describes it as an unpublished coin of Hermaeus.

§ 190. Nos. 11–16 are of a type already published by Cunningham,[1] Vincent Smith,[2] and Rapson.[3] They have the legend *Vīrasenasa*, in Brāhmī characters of the third century A.D., above a palm-tree between two *nandipadas*, and Lakṣmī on the reverse. Cunningham attributed them to Mathurā, where he obtained over 100. While they are found there, they are distributed over a wider area. Carlleyle found a dozen at Indore Khera,[4] and Sir Richard Burn[5] has specimens from Sankīsā in the Farrukhābād district and Sarai Aghat in the Etah district and from Kanauj. They are, therefore, found also over an area to the south and east of Mathurā, where the coins of the Mathurā dynasties are not found. These coins are almost all square and have no links with the round Mathurā coins in style. The issuer of these coins is to be identified with the Swāmi Vīrasena mentioned in an incomplete inscription[6] found by Sir Richard Burn at Jānkhat in the Farrukhābād district.

§ 191. No. 17, which Cunningham[7] published without comment along with the coins of the Audumbaras as a coin of Rāja Vṛṣṇi, is unique in every way. One of the very few silver coins of the period, it has remarkable types. The obverse is a pillar surmounted by an animal, half-lion and half-elephant, above which is a *nandipada*. It is not possible to be absolutely certain that the *nandipada* is not on the top of the standard, with the animal in front, but such monuments as the Mathurā Lion Capital suggest the first interpretation of the type. The reverse is an elaborate wheel, probably to be interpreted as a *dharmacakra*. The legend, in Brāhmī on the obverse and Kharoṣṭhī on the reverse, is the same on both sides, with slight dialectic differences as usual in such cases (cf. § 150). Cunningham's transliteration of the legend is

Vṛishṇi Raja jnāgaṇasya bhubarasya

on which the reading given on p. 281 of the Catalogue is based. It is, however, impossible to make sense of this.

[1] *C.A.I.*, p. 89, Pl. VIII. 19.
[2] *C.I.M.*, i, pp. 191, 197.
[3] *J.R.A.S.*, 1900, p. 115.
[4] *A.S.R.*, xii, p. 41.
[5] *J.R.A.S.*, 1900, p. 553.
[6] *J.R.A.S.*, 1900, pp. 552–553; Pargiter, *E.I.*, xi, pp. 85–87.
[7] *C.A.I.*, p. 70, Pl. IV. 15.

The legend was fully discussed by Monsieur A. Bergny,[1] and he concluded that the inscriptions were:

Br. *Vṛṣṇ*[-]*r*[*ā*]*jajñāgaṇasya tratarasya*

Khar. *Vṛṣṇirajāṇṇa* [*ga*] - *tra* - - -

The last word may be dealt with first; *bhubarasya* or *tratarasya*? I was reluctant to accept the latter reading as I believed the legend was good Sanskrit, in which case *tratarasya* is impossible. But the legend is better explained not as Sanskrit but as Prākrit which has been given a Sanskrit appearance—gen. in *-sya* instead of *sa*; in inscriptions of this time when we have a rounded *g* ∩, the *bh* is square, so that ∧ must be *t*, and Bergny's *tratarasya* = *tratarasa* in the Kharoṣṭhī—is the correct reading.

Tratarasa is the familiar form of the genitive in the Prākrit of the north-west corresponding to the genitive of Sanskrit *trātṛ*. *Tratarasya* is an illiterate attempt to give the Sanskrit by some one who thought that if *gaṇasya* corresponded to Prākrit *gaṇasa*, *tratarasya* must be the Sanskrit for *tratarasa*. On the other hand, it may be a dialect similar to that of the Mathurā Kushān inscriptions, which shows forms like *swamisya*.

§ 192. There is no doubt about the first two syllables *Vṛṣṇi*— the Kharoṣṭhī supplies the *i* — ; *r*[*a*]*ja* is clear on both sides. The next *akṣara*, transliterated *jñā* by Bergny, is more probably *jño*; we are very familiar with it in the Prākrit genitive *rajño*, on the coins of Pañcāla, for example. The Kharoṣṭhī equivalent is probably *ṇṇa*. The next three letters are *gaṇasya* (*gaṇasa* in Kharoṣṭhī).

The Brāhmī inscription then is:

Vṛṣṇi-r[*ā*]*jajño-gaṇasya tratarasya*

Vṛṣṇi is well known as the name of a people, and *gaṇa* presents no difficulty. We are left with *rājajño*—or *rājajñā*, which is no easier to explain. I think, and the Kharoṣṭhī form *ṇṇ* supports this, that the compound represents a Sanskrit *-ny-* and the word is *Rājanya*. *Rājajño* may be an engraver's mistake for a genitive on the analogy of Rājño, Prākrit *raṇṇo*—in which case the legend means 'of the

[1] *J.R.A.S.*, 1900, pp. 416–421.

protector of the tribe Vṛṣnirājanya', but a compound is more in the spirit of the language. It is possible that the engraver copied the vowel-mark also from the very familiar compound consonant  although it was not needed here, and we should pay no heed to it, but translate 'of the protector of the Rājanya [or warrior] tribe of Vṛṣṇis'. We should naturally prefer an explanation which would not assume an engraver's error; but there does seem to be evidence that he was more familiar with the Kharoṣṭhī dialect and was doing his best to put the inscription into Sanskrit on the obverse. The coin belongs to the first century B.C., presumably to the northern Panjab.

§ 193. No. 18 has the monogram Yajñabhu in Brāhmī characters of the third or fourth century A.D.; the reverse type cannot be distinguished.

No. 19, with reverse type a tree in railing between two svastikas, has on the obverse an inscription of the second century A.D. above a mountain (?). The first *akṣara* is illegible, but the remainder are [-] *śajanasa*.

Nos. 20 and 21 seem to belong to the Almorā series, with which they are connected by the elaborate symbol occupying the reverse, and the obverse symbols of a bull before a tree in railing with  behind it; all found at Almorā, although differently arranged. The legend on no. 20 ends - - *śaśasa*; on no. 21 begins *Rāja*.

§ 194. Nos. 22–29 form a puzzling group. They come from the Panjab, where a number were procured by Rodgers at Barwalla. They all have as obverse type a tree in railing; nos. 22–23 have reverse a bull and the others a lion, sometimes on a hill. Taking nos. 26, 28, 29 first of all, we find the inscriptions are:

agodakā agācajanapad -

agodakā agācuja - - - -

agodakā a - - - - - - -

The full inscription—and this is probably the full legend on no. 1 (see above, p. 1), which has the same types—then is

agodakā agāca-janapadasa

which I am unable to explain. It contains the name or names of a *janapada*, but I have been unable to identify it with any known Sanskrit form of the name of a Panjab tribe. Agodaka or Aṅgodraka may represent another claimant for identification with the Oxudrakai of the Greeks. *Agāca* suggests a Sanskrit *agastya*, but this does not help us.

Nos. 22–24 have the inscriptions

agācamitra - - - - -

- - - - *trapadabhisa*

agacamitrapa - - - -

which I am unable to explain.

No. 27 has only a fragment of a legend

- - *dabhicaya* - -

No. 25 has a shorter legend of which one can only read

- *napada* -

I.M.C., Pl. XXIII. 12, is another of these coins, which do not seem to be rare. The British Museum has a number of poorer specimens chiefly collected by Rodgers, but they throw no further light on the inscription.

§ 195. I am unable to make any suggestion about the attribution of the little group of coins, nos. 31–36, the inscriptions of which are faithfully reproduced in the text. They are from the Panjab (Rodgers and Clive-Bayley). Nos. 37–38 are in very poor condition, but the types suggest Kauśambī as their place of origin. The name seems to end in - - *samita*[*sa*].

There is little to say about the remaining coins: no. 41 may be of the Ārjunāyanas. No. 43 has a name ending in *-mitasa*, possibly Gomitra, in early Brāhmī characters above the bull. No. 44 may be connected with nos. 30–36. Nos. 45 and 46 are the same as *I.M.C.*, Pl. XXIII. 2. There are traces of an inscription above the bull on no. 45, *-nade-*, Dhanadevasa (?). Better specimens of nos.

47–48, both with unusual types, from the Panjab, may enable the legends to be read.

§ 196. ADDITIONS. The coins in the 'Additions' have been dealt with in the text,[1] with the exception of p. 288, no. 108 (Pl. XXXIX. 9), which presents similarities to the earlier Yaudheya coins (Class I, var. *c*), and probably came from Behat (cf. *J.A.S.B.*, iii (1834), Pl. IX. 4). I am now more inclined to connect it with the Kanauj coins (§ 104), but in view of the poor condition of the coin certainty is unattainable.

METROLOGY

§ 197. Very little is known concerning the denominations and standards of ancient India. The information given in the law-books and similar literary sources is of little practical value when applied to the coins that have survived, and for the period covered by this volume we get no help from inscriptions. We need not here go again into the problem, fully discussed by Rapson,[2] of reconciling the simplicity of the theoretical system given in the law-books with the great diversity in weights found in the coins themselves. Nor shall we go over the ground already covered by Cunningham[3] in his discussion of the weights of the earliest Indian coins. We shall be content to point out that the ratio 16 annas = 1 rupee goes back at least 2,000 years to the 16 *māṣakas* = 1 *kārṣāpaṇa*[4] of the law-books.

§ 198. If we look for references to coins in literature we find a number of allusions to mercantile transactions in the *Jātaka*, but many of these, notably to gold coins,[5] cannot be taken as accurately reflecting the currency conditions of the period of composition of the work, still less of the period in which the story is placed.

[1] See especially § 78 for a correction.

[2] *Cat. A.W.K.*, pp. clxxvii ff.

[3] *C.A.I.*, pp. 44 ff.

[4] Mr. A. S. Hemmy found the ratio 16 to be the most frequent in his analysis of the weights from Mohenjo-Daro (Sir John Marshall, *Mohenjo Daro*, ii, 596).

[5] Some of the allusions to gold pieces in the translation have no foundation in the original text.

Mrs. Rhys Davids[1] has investigated the material for the economic history of India to be found in the *Jātaka,* and the subject has also been dealt with by Professor D. K. Bhandarkar.[2] I have read through the translation[3] and compared the references to coins in it with the original.[4] The material is much less than one would expect. The coin most frequently mentioned is the *kahāpaṇa* (*kārsāpaṇa*), which is to be identified with the silver punch-marked coin. It is clearly the currency familiar to the narrators of certain stories in the *Jātaka,* and we also know from finds that the punch-marked coin was the sole silver currency of a certain period (see §§ 80–82). This is, of course, evidence for the date of compilation of parts of the *Jātaka,* and does not mean that punch-marked coins were in circulation 'when Brahmadatta was reigning in Benares'.

The *kahāpaṇa* is so well known as the standard coin that it is often not mentioned by name. Just as we say a 'millionaire' without explaining that pounds are meant, so the Pāli has *asītikoṭi-vibhava,* 'one who has a fortune of 80 crores', i.e. of silver *kārsāpaṇas.* Many of the allusions to money—when they allude to coins at all—are to coins which probably never existed, such as the *suvannanikkha* (*suvarṇaniṣka*), and need not concern us here. It is worth noting that the name *purāṇa* is not found in the *Jātaka*; as its meaning the 'old-fashioned' coin shows, the name only came to be applied to the silver *kārṣāpaṇa* after it was no longer struck but still retained an important place in circulation along with coins of more modern type. We find *purāṇa,* for example, in the *Divyāvadāna* playing the part of *kahāpaṇa* in the *Jātaka.* The chief copper coin is the *māsaka* (*māṣaka*), although there are occasional references to *kārsāpaṇas* of copper. Mention of individual coins is rare in the *Jātaka,* but there is the passage in the *Gaṅgamāla-jātaka*[5] where the king goes through various sums in descending order in order to ascertain the amount of the poor water-carrier's hidden treasure. From this it is clear that

[1] *J.R.A.S.*, 1901, pp. 859 ff.
[2] *Carmichael Lectures*, 1921, ch. I–II.
[3] Ed. Cowell, Cambridge, 1895 ff.
[4] Ed. Fausböll, London, 1877 ff.
[5] Ed. Fausböll, iii, p. 448.

the following coins at least existed: 1, ½, ¼ *kārsāpaṇa* in silver and 1 and ½ *māṣaka* in copper; one wonders why the king mentioned both ¼ *kahāpaṇa* and 4 *māsakas*, as they are presumably equivalent. It suggests a *pādika* or ¼ *kārsāpaṇa* in silver and a 4 *māṣaka* piece in copper, but the latter would be a large coin. There are references in other stories to the *māṣaka* and ½ *māṣaka*[1] as coins of small value, in addition to vaguer references, much as we talk of a few pence. The smallest coin mentioned is the *kākaṇika*.[2]

§ 199. With regard to the coins themselves we do not propose to do much more than present the materials.[3] Taking first of all the earliest coins, Part I, Class 1 belonging to extreme N.W. India, it is to be noted that they are struck on a Persian standard, and are double sigloi or 'Persic staters', ½ and ¼ sigloi. The weights, 172–177 grains, of the larger pieces are just those of the 'Persic staters' of the Achaemenid governors in Lycia, Cyprus, &c., and this is further evidence for dating these coins not earlier than the fourth century. If the coins are actually the issues of Achaemenid governors they would belong to the first half of the century. If struck after the extreme N.W. had passed from Persia they must be of the second half and probably later than, say, 330 B.C., when Darius III still had Indians in his army.[4]

§ 200. Class 2 are ½ *kārṣāpaṇas* of an Indian standard. The usual weight is between 25 and 26 grains, which gives a *kārṣāpaṇa* —not known of this type—of the weight of the majority of the punch-marked silver coins. Class 3 are also ½ *kārṣāpaṇas*, presumably from a different part of India. The most frequent weight is between 26 and 27 grains, which gives a *kārṣāpaṇa* 2–3 grains heavier than the preceding. Only the half is known of this type also. Class 4, from the Sultanpur find, consists of single and

[1] e.g. *Macchudānajātaka*, ii, p. 424; *Visayhajātaka*, iii. 130.

[2] *Cullakaseṭṭhijātaka*, i, p. 120.

[3] Mr. A. S. Hemmy has investigated by graphical methods the weights given for various series in this Catalogue, and will shortly publish his results in the *J.R.A.S.*

[4] *C.H.I.*, i, p. 341.

double *kārṣāpaṇas*, but we have not sufficient specimens to enable us to generalize about the weights. The two *kārṣāpaṇas* are of rather light weight, as is one of the doubles, but the weight of the other double, 108·7, brings them into connexion with the preceding. Class 5, which weighs between 14·4 and 14·9 grains, are $\frac{1}{4}$ *kārṣāpaṇas* or *pādikas* of a heavier standard. This weight is slightly above Cunningham's[1] theoretical *pādika* of 14·4 grains and gives a *kārṣāpaṇa* of 58–59 grains, or $\frac{1}{3}$ Persic stater or $\frac{2}{3}$ siglos; the same standard is found in the first class of punch-marked coins (see § 201).

These miscellaneous groups, 2–5, show two different standards, a heavier and perhaps earlier one, and a lighter one of 51–53 grains. As the former is $\frac{2}{3}$ of a siglos or $\frac{1}{3}$ of the Persic stater or double siglos, it probably belongs to areas once under Achaemenid influence, while the lighter is the Indian—perhaps later—standard.

§ 201. Passing to Part II of the Catalogue, the punch-marked silver pieces, a frequency table shows two standards again. The weights of most of Class 1, which we have already seen is a separate find from the N.W. (§ 43) and which is characterized by the two forms of mountain symbol  associated with Taxila, lie between 55 and 56 grains, and some are higher. They are heavy *kārṣāpaṇas* or $\frac{2}{3}$ sigloi, and are not too light for Cunningham's theoretical weight of 57·6 grains for the *kārṣāpaṇa*. All the rest of the punch-marked coins were struck on a slightly lighter standard. The majority of the weights lie between 51·5 and 52·5 grains, although good specimens are found as high as 54 and as low as 50. The interesting point about those of lighter weight is that they come from all parts of India (cf. § 58), and show that a single standard was in use over a vast area, enforced by a central authority. This again points to the Maurya period and the third century as their date of issue.

It is to be noted that the great majority of the silver coins of ancient India are full *kārṣāpaṇas*; halves and quarters are much rarer, and belong to different series, probably outside of the Maurya

[1] *C.A.I.*, p. 47.

empire. Very small silver coins are known (Class 9) weighing from 2 to 3 grains. These are $\frac{1}{16}$ *kārṣāpaṇas* or *kṛṣṇālas*.

§ 202. The few silver coins in the latter part of the Catalogue issued by the Audumbaras, Kulūtas, Kuṇindas, and Yaudheyas, are all based on the hemidrachms of the later Greek and Śaka kings, and are hemidrachms of the later or Persian standard.

§ 203. The weights of the early Indian coins may throw some light on the origin of coinage in India. It would appear that the earliest coins were struck in Achaemenid territory in the N.W., and that the Mauryas adopted the idea of a coinage, like many other things, from Persia, and developed a coinage on Indian lines using a standard which was either a native Indian standard, slightly lighter than the Persian, or the latter slightly reduced.

§ 204. It is difficult to generalize about the weights of the copper coins. In the first place they are not struck or cast so carefully as the silver coins, and secondly they have suffered much more in course of time. In most series we have not sufficient specimens available, and in the few cases where we have long runs, as in the case of the punch-marked copper coins, the gradation of weights offers a well-nigh hopeless puzzle.

I cannot conclude without a tribute to the memory of General Sir Alexander Cunningham, whose magnificent bequest to the nation of his collection of Indian coins forms the basis of this Catalogue. I trust that my debt to his published work is sufficiently apparent in the Introduction.

J. ALLAN.

CORRIGENDA

PAGE xxv, last two lines: delete 'with the exception .. no. 1'; and for 'no. 10' read 'no. 11'.

PAGE xxviii, § 27, l. 1: for 'rabbit' read 'hare'.

PAGE xxxii, l. 4: on no. 7 see also L. D. Barnett in *Bulletin of the School of Oriental Studies*, 1928, p. 714 note.

PAGE xxxvi: delete last sentence on the page 'Hanumān . . . coin', and see now p. lxix, ll. 10–16.

PAGE l, l. 14: for 'Elah' read 'Etah'.

PAGE l, l. 3 from foot: read '(see p. 84)'.

PAGE lxxxii, l. 7 from foot: var. *c* is really a coin of the Śibis, cf. § 142.

PAGE xci, l. 15: delete 'and might even be earlier'.

PAGE xcii, l. 20: read 'suggested by Bühler (*Ind. Stud.*, iii[2], p. 49, note 1)'.

PAGE xcvi, l. 5: delete 'and might . . . century'.

PAGE xcvii, l. 1: for 'deity' read 'Lakṣmī'.

PAGE 39, no. 64: for '**Pl. VI. 4**' read '**VI. 5**'.

PAGE 44, no. 15: for '(wt.) 83' read '53'.

PAGE 59, no. 7: for  substitute ; transfer to Class 7 and see § 70.

PAGE 70, no. 37: for '**Pl. VI. 2**' read '**Pl. VII. 2**'.

PAGE 71, no. 38: delete **Pl. VIII. 24.**

PAGE 71, no. 39: from Eran cf. *A.S.R.* Pl. XXIV. 3.

PAGE 80, no. 10: add **Pl. VIII. 24.**

PAGE 84, no. 1: add **Pl. VI. 17.**

PAGE 121, var. *c*: transfer to Śibis and see Introd., § 142.

PAGE 125, no. 23: the last letter in the Kharoṣṭhī legend is *-ya* not *-ta*; see Introd., § 95.

PAGE 133, nos. 24, 25: read '**Pl. XVII**' for '**Pl. XVIII**'.

PAGE 133, no. 29: read '**Pl. XVII**' for '**Pl. XVI**'.

PAGE 134, no. 31: the weight is 19·5 not 9·5.

PAGE 154: for 'JEṬṬHAMITRA' read 'JYEṢṬHAMITRA'.

PAGE 174, no. 31 a: for 'GOṢADATTA' read 'ŚEṢADATTA' and see Introd., § 124.

PAGE 182, nos. 80–84: on these coins see Introd., § 124.

PAGE 184: for 'HAGĀMAŚA' read 'HAGĀMAṢA'.

PAGE 212, no. 19: on this coin see Introd., § 165.

PAGE 213, no. 20: delete '*Kha*' and read '[- -]', and see Introd., § 165 at end.

PAGE 213, nos. 21–22: on these coins see Introd., §§ 142–3.

PAGE 214, no. 1: on the reverse legend see Introd., § 146.

PAGE 215, var. *f*: on the reverse type see Introd., § 147.

PAGE 218, Class 3: on the legends of these coins see Introd., §§ 152 and 154.

PAGE 220, var. *d*: add  to the description of obverse.

PAGE 221, var. *h*: for  substitute 

PAGE 226, no. 98: add  to description of reverse.

PAGE 232, var. *f*: add  to reverse.

PAGE 234, var. *e*: substitute  for 

PAGE 237: the second symbol is probably not  but the fish-headed [?] standard found on Class 3, var. *b*.

PAGE 260: for  substitute 

PAGE 262, nos. 134–137: delete  and read '*Ujeni*' (see Introd., § 172).

PAGES 267–270: for 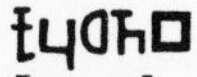 read 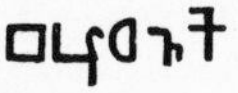 and see the discussion of the legend in Introd., § 177.

PAGE 278, var. *c*: for '*cakra* on r. 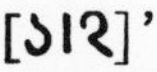' read '*nāga* symbol on r. 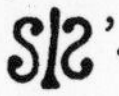'.

PAGE 279, no. 2: the full reading is '*Jyeṣṭhadattasya*', see Introd., § 186.

PAGES 279–285: for fuller readings of a number of Uncertain Coins see Introd., §§ 185–195.

PAGE 286, Class 8: this is not a new type; see § 78.

LIST OF ABBREVIATIONS

A.G.I.	Cunningham, Alexander. The Ancient Geography of India, London, 1871.
A.S.R.	Archaeological Survey of India: Annual Reports. Old Series (Cunningham) quoted by volume. New Series (Marshall) by years.
B.M.C.	British Museum Catalogue.
C.	Cunningham, General Sir Alexander.
C.A.I.	Cunningham, Coins of Ancient India, London, 1891.
Cat. A.W.K.	E. J. Rapson, Catalogue of Coins of the Andhras, Western Kṣatrapas, &c., in the British Museum, London, 1908.
C.H.I.	Cambridge History of India, Cambridge, vol. i, 1922.
C.I.I.	Corpus Inscriptionum Indicarum, vol. I (new ed.). Inscriptions of Asoka by E. Hultzsch, Calcutta, 1925, Vol. II, i. Kharoṣṭhi Inscriptions, by Sten Konow, Calcutta, 1929.
	Vol. III, Inscriptions of the Early Gupta Kings, by John Faithfull Fleet, Calcutta, 1888.
C.I.M., i.	Vincent A. Smith, Catalogue of Coins in the Indian Museum, Calcutta, vol. i, Oxford, 1906.
C.M.I.	Cunningham, Coins of Mediaeval India, London, 1894.
E.I.	Epigraphia Indica.
I.A.	Indian Antiquary.
Ind. Stud. III	J. G. Bühler: On the Origin of the Indian Alphabet (second revised edition of Indian Studies, no. III), Strassburg, 1898. Originally published in *Sitz.-ber. K.Ak.* Wien, cxxxii, 1895.
J.A.S.B.	Journal of the Asiatic Society of Bengal.
J.B.B.R.A.S.	Journal of the Bombay Branch of the Royal Asiatic Society.
J.B.O.R.S.	Journal of the Bihar and Orissa Research Society.
J.R.A.S.	Journal of the Royal Asiatic Society.
Num. Chron.	Numismatic Chronicle.

Num. Suppl.	Numismatic Supplement to the Journal of the Asiatic Society of Bengal.
Num. Glean.	(Sir) Walter Elliot: Numismatic Gleanings by. Descriptions and Figures of the Coins of India reprinted from The Madras Journal of Literature and Science, vol. xix, p. 220 f.
Ostas. Zeitsch.	Ostasiatische Zeitschrift.
P.E.	James Prinsep, Essays on Indian Antiquities, London, 1858.
Proc. A.S.B.	Proceedings of the Asiatic Society of Bengal.
Proc. B.B.R.A.S.	Proceedings of the Bombay Branch of the Royal Asiatic Society.
Prog. Rep. N.W.P. and O., 1891–2.	Progress Reports of the Epigraphical & Architectural Branches of the North-Western Provinces and Oudh for 1891–2: Roorkee [1892].
Rev. Num.	Revue Numismatique.
S.B.E.	Sacred Books of the East.
Sitz.-ber. K.Ak. Wien.	Sitzungsberichte der kaiserlichen Akademie der Wissenschaften (Wien).
S.B.A.W.	Sitzungsberichte der Akademie der Wissenschaften (Berlin).

PART I

VARIOUS EARLY SINGLE TYPE SILVER

No.	Wt.	Metal. Size.	Obverse.	Reverse.
			CLASS 1. NORTH-WEST INDIA.	
			Persian Standard.	
			Doubles.	
1	173·6	Æ *oblong* ·95 × ·6	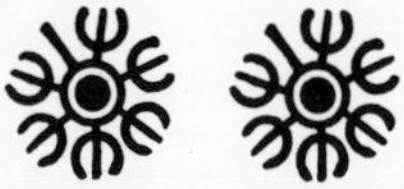	Plain. [Whitehead, 1922.] **Pl. I. 1.**
2	177·3	1·0 × ·6	As 1, but no pellet in centre.	,, [Whitehead, 1922.]
3	176·5	1·2 × ·5	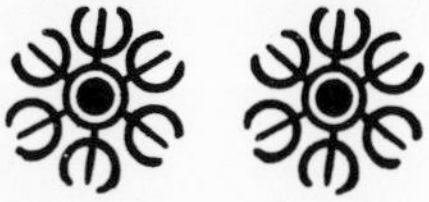	,, ,, **Pl. I. 2.**
4	155·7 *much worn*	1·15 × ·5	,,	,, [India Office, 1882.]
5	175·0	1·0		,, [Stubbs, 1865.]
6	173·5	1·0 × ·5	,,	,, ,,

No.	Wt.	Metal. Size.	Obverse.	Reverse.
7	175·0	Æ *oblong* 1·0 × ·45	As preceding.	Plain. [Stubbs, 1865. **Pl. I. 3.**
8	174·2	1·0 × ·46	,,	,, [Stubbs, 1865.
9	174·0	1·0 × ·45	,,	,,
			Halves.	
10	43·5	Æ *round* ·6		Plain. [Gen. M. Clerk, 1920. **Pl. I. 4.**
11	38·5	·6	,,	,, [Cunningham, 1894.
			Quarters.	
12	19·9	·55	 The design in third quadrant is a countermark.	Plain. [Cunningham, 1894.

No.	Wt.	Metal. Size.	Obverse.	Reverse.
		AR *round*		
3	19·6	·45		Plain. [Cunningham, 1894.] **Pl. I. 5.**
4	19·2	·6	,,	,, [Cunningham, 1894.]
5	19·0	·5	,,	,, ,,
6	19·7	·45		,, [Grant, 1885.]

CLASS 2. NORTH INDIA.

Small oblong ingots.

Var. *a*.

No.	Wt.	Metal. Size.	Obverse.	Reverse.
1	25·5	AR *oblong* ·35		Plain. [Grant, 1885 **Pl. I. 8.**
2	25·5	·45 × ·2	,,	,, [Cunningham, 1894.
3	24·3	·5 × ·2	,,	,, ,,
4	25·2	·4 × ·2	,,	,, ,,
5	25·6	·45 × ·2	,,	,, ,,
6	22·5	·45 × ·2	,,	,, ,,
7	24·8	·4 × ·2	,,	,, ,,
8	24·6	·45 × ·25	,,	,, [Thomas, 1850
9	24·0	·45 × ·25	,,	,, ,,
10	26·0	·4 × ·2	,,	,,
11	22·0	·4 × ·2	,,	,, [Thomas, 1850
12	25·4	·5 × ·2	,,	,, [Grant, 1881

No.	Wt.	Metal. Size.	Obverse.	Reverse.
		AR *oblong*	Var. *b.*	
3	25·5	·5 × ·2		Plain. [Cunningham, 1894.] **Pl. I. 9.**
			C., *C.A.I.*, Pl. I. 17.	
4	24·6	·5 × ·2	”	Plain. [Cunningham, 1894.] **Pl. I. 10.**

CLASS 3. NORTH INDIA.

Var. *a*.

No.	Wt.	Metal. Size.	Obverse.	Reverse.
1	25·6	Æ *square* ·5		Plain. [Whitehead, 1922. **Pl. I. 15.**
2	27·0	·55	,,	,, [Whitehead, 1922.
3	25·0	·5	,,	,, ,,
4	25·9	·4	,,	,, [Cunningham, 1894.
5	25·5	·5	  in place of four pellets.	,, [Whitehead, 1922.
6	27·0	·4	,,	,, ,,
7	26·8	·4	,,	,, ,,
8	24·0	·4		,, [Cunningham, 1894.
9	26·7	·45	,,	,, ,,
10	25·0	·45	,,	,, ,,
11	25·4	·55	,,	,, ,,
12	27·3	·35	,,	,, ,,
13	27·5	·35	,,	,, ,,

No.	Wt.	Metal. Size.	Obverse.	Reverse.
14	25·0	AR square ·5		Plain. [Whitehead, 1922.]
15	27·0	·35	”	” [Cunningham, 1894.]
16	26·6	·35	”	” ”
17	27·2	·4	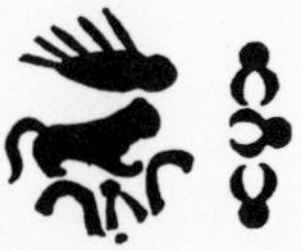	” ”
18	26·7	·35	”	” ” **Pl. I. 7.**
19	28·3	·35	 in front. From Mathura.	” [Cunningham, 1894.] **Pl. I. 13.**
20	26·7	·35		” [Cunningham, 1894.] **Pl. I. 11.**
21	23·9	·45		” [Cunningham, 1894.]
			Var. *b*.	
22	21·5	·45	 over 	Plain. [Cunningham, 1894.] **Pl. I. 12.**
			C., *C.A.I.*, Pl. I. 18.	

CLASS 4. SOUTH-WEST INDIA.

Sultanpur[1] Find Type.

No.	Wt.	Metal. Size.	Obverse.	Reverse.
		Æ *round*		
1	98·3	·85		Plain. [Codrington, 1922.] **Pl. I. 16.**
2	108·7	·9	,,	,, [Sir Walter Elliot, Pres., 1886.] **Pl. I. 17.**
			E., *C.S.I.*, Pl. IX. 62.	
3	50·0	·7	,,	Plain. [J. H. Daniels, Esq., Pres. 1921.] **Pl. I. 18.**
4	49·5	·7	,,	,, [Codrington, 1922. **Pl. I. 19.**

[1] Found in a field near Sultanpur two miles north of Wai in Satāra district; O. Codrington on some silver coins found near Wai; *J.B.B.R.A.S.*, 1876, pp. 400–403.

No.	Wt.	Metal. Size.	Obverse.	Reverse.
			CLASS 5. SOUTH-WEST INDIA.	
		Æ *square*	**Konkan Find[1] Type.**	
1	14·4	·5	 surrounded by border of 	Uncertain object in circle. [Codrington, 1922.]
2	14·5	·5	Similar	Illegible. „ **Pl. I. 20.**
3	14·5	·5 × ·3	„	„ [Codrington, 1922.]
4	12·9	·4	„	Branch (?). „ **Pl. I. 21.**
5	14·9	·6	„	 surrounded by  [Sir Walter Elliot, Pres., 1886.] **Pl. I. 22.**
			E., *C.S.I.*, Pl. II. 61.	
6	14·8	·6	Similar.	Similar. [Codrington, 1922.] **Pl. I. 23.**
7	14·4	·6	„	„ [Codrington, 1922.] **Pl. I. 24.**
8	14·5	·5	„	„ [Cunningham, 1894.]
9	14·7	·5	„	? as obverse. „

[1] Elliot, *C.S.I*, pp. 50 and 152 c.

No.	Wt.	Metal. Size.	Obverse.	Reverse.
			CLASS 6. UNKNOWN (probably northern) PROVENANCE.	
1	17·3	Æ square ·4	 C., *C.A.I.*, Pl. I. 19.	Plain. [Cunningham, 1894.] **Pl. I. 25.**
2	20·2	·5	Similar.	Plain. [Cunningham, 1894.]
3	17·5	·4	”	” **Pl. I. 26.**
			CLASS 7. UNKNOWN PROVENANCE.	
1	17·8	·5	  and two other punches, possibly elephants. C., *C.A.I.*, Pl. I. 16.	Plain. [Cunningham, 1894.] **Pl. I. 27.**

PART II

PUNCHMARKED SILVER COINS

No.	Wt.	Metal. Size.	Obverse.	Reverse.
			CLASS 1. GROUP I. Var. *a.*	
1	55·6	Æ *square* ·6 × ·55		 [Swiney, 1869.] Pl. II. 1.
2	54·0	·55 × ·45	” ”	” [Swiney, 1869.]
3	55·8	·6 × ·4	” ”	” ”
4	55·0	·6 × ·5	” ”	” ”
5	50·6	·55	” ”	” ”
6	54·4	·5	” ”	” ”
7	51·7	·55	” ”	” ”
8	51·6	·5	” ”	” ”
9	53·7	·55	” ”	” ”
0	56·8	·6 × ·45	” ”	” ” Pl. II. 2.

No.	Wt.	Metal. Size.	Obverse.	Reverse.
11	54·7	Æ *square* ·5 × ·4	As preceding.	As preceding. [Swiney, 1869.
12	53·7	·55 × ·35	,,	,, ,,
13	51·7	·5 × ·35	,,	,, ,,
14	53·5	·55 × ·4	,,	,, ,,
15	53·0	·55	,,	,, ,,
16	52·5	·7 × ·4	,,	,, ,,
17	53·4	·55	,,	,, ,,
18	54·0	·55	,,	,, ,, **Pl. II. 3.**
19	46·0	·65 × ·45	,,	,, [Swiney, 1869
20	53·2	·6 × ·5	,,	,, ,,
21	53·3	·6	,,	,, ,,
22	55·2	·6 × ·4	,,	,, ,,
23	49·0	·6 × ·4	,,	,, ,, **Pl. II. 4.**
24	51·0	·75 × ·4	,,	,, [Swiney, 1869
25	56·4	·65	,,	,, ,, **Pl. II. 5.**

No.	Wt.	Metal. Size.	Obverse.	Reverse.
26	55·8	AR *square* ·6	As preceding.	As preceding. [Swiney, 1869.]
27	50·0	·7 × ·55	,,	,, ,,
28	52·0	·55	,,	,, ,,
29	47·0	·4 × ·65	,,	,, ,,
30	51·7	·6 × ·4	,,	,, ,,
31	53·7	·6 × ·35	,,	,, ,,
32	53·0	·6 × ·45	,,	,, ,,
33	55·0	·55	,,	,, ,,
34	49·0	·55	,,	,, ,,
35	56·7	·6 × ·51	,,	,, ,,
36	54·0	·6	,,	,, ,, **Pl. II. 7.**
37	57·0	·5	,,	,, [Swiney, 1869.]
38	53·8	·55	,,	,, ,,
39	57·4	·55	,,	,, ,,
40	49·5	·55	,,	,, ,,

No.	Wt.	Metal. Size.	Obverse.	Reverse.
41	53·8	Æ *square* ·55	As preceding.	As preceding. [Swiney, 1869.]
42	54·0	·6	,,	,, ,,
43	55·4	·5	,,	,, ,,
44	55·5	·5	,,	,, ,, **Pl. II. 8.**
45	55·3	·5 × ·4	,,	,, [Swiney, 1869.]
46	57·0	·5	,,	,, ,,
47	50·8	·5	,,	,, ,,
48	58·0	·5	,,	,, ,,
49	56·0	·6 × ·45	,,	,, ,,
50	54·3	·6	,,	,, ,,
51	55·0	·6 × ·5	,,	,, ,,
52	44·3	·4	,,	,, ,,
53	49·5	·5	,,	,, ,,
54	53·0	·5	,,	,, ,,
55	54·4	·55	,,	,, ,,

No.	Wt.	Metal. Size.	Obverse.	Reverse.
56	55·0	AR square ·8 × ·4	As preceding.	As preceding. [Theobald, 1906.]
57	55·2	·5	,,	,, [Prinsep, 1850.]
58	51·5	·5	,,	,, [Cunningham, 1894.]
			Var. *b*.	
59	53·2	·7 × ·6	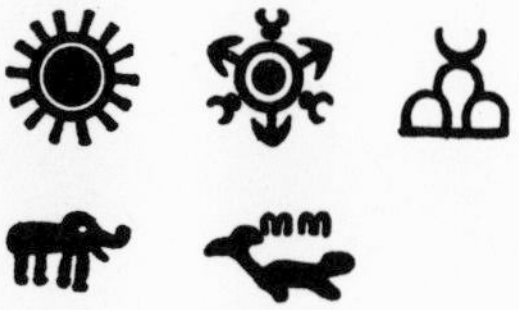	 [Thomas, 1850.] **Pl. II. 6.**
60	53·5	·55	,, ,,	,, [Gen. M. Clerk, 1920.] **Pl. II. 9.** From Kopiyadeh, two miles north of Balursasan Bust.
61	51·5	·55	,, ,,	Similar. [Gen. M. Clerk, 1920.] From Ayodhya.
62	54·4	·8	,, ,,	,, [Swiney, 1869.]
63	49·2	·5	,, ,,	,, [Theobald, 1906.]
64	51·0	·55	,, ,,	,, [Cunningham, 1894.]
65	53·4	·55	,, ,,	,, [Prinsep, 1850.]
66	53·0	·5	,, ,,	,, —

No.	Wt.	Metal. Size.	Obverse.	Reverse.
67	53·3	Æ *round* ·5	As preceding.	As preceding.
68	53·3	·5	,,	,, [Eden, 1853.]
			Var. *c.*	
69	48·5	*square* ·6		Similar. [Swiney, 1869.] **Pl. XLI. 1.**
			Var. *d.*	
70	54·5	·6		Similar. [Whitehead, 1922.] **Pl. II. 10.**
71	54·5	·55	,, ,,	,, [Eden, 1853.]

o.	Wt.	Metal. Size.	Obverse.	Reverse.
			CLASS 2. GROUP I. Var. *a*.	
1	49·5	Æ *square* ·65		 [Whitehead, 1922] **Pl. III. 1.**
2	49·9	·7	,, ,,	,, [Cunningham, 1924.]
3	49·0	·7 × ·5	,, ,,	,, [Whitehead, 1922.]
4	52·1	·6	,, ,,	,, [Thomas, 1850.]
5	41·3	·6	,, ,,	,, [Cunningham, 1894.]
6	51·8	·6	,, ,,	,, [Swiney, 1869.]
7	51·6	·65	,, ,,	,, [Cunningham, 1894.] **Pl. III. 3.**
8	50·7	·7 × ·55	,, ,,	,, [Cunningham, 1894.]
9	51·0	·65	,, ,,	,, ,,
0	52·0	·7 × ·55	,, ,,	,, [Whitehead, 1894.] **Pl. III. 4.**
1	49·0	·7	,, ,,	,, [Cunningham, 1894.]
2	44·8	·7	,, ,,	,, ,,

No.	Wt.	Metal. Size.	Obverse.	Reverse.
13	48·8	Æ ·7	As preceding.	As preceding. [Cunningham, 1894
14	49·6	·9 × ·35	,,	,, ,,
15	48·3	·7	,,	,, [Thomas, 1850
16	42·4	*square* ·7	,, ,,	,, [Cunningham, 1894
17	54·2	·7	,, ,,	,, ,, (from Shahpur)
18	49·0	·7	,, ,,	,, [Whitehead, 1894
19	49·5	·7	,, ,,	,, ,,
19*a*	47·8	·7	,, ,,	,, ,,
20	53·6	·65	,, ,,	,, [Cunningham, 1894
21	50·2	·65	,, ,,	,, [Whitehead, 1894
22	50·2	·55	,, ,,	,, ,,
23	50·2	·8 × ·6	,, ,,	,, [Hay, 1860
24	52·7	·75	,, ,,	,, [Theobald, 1906 **Pl. III. 7.**
25	52·0	·55	,, ,,	,, [Cunningham, 1894 **Pl. III. 9.**
			C., *C.A.I.*, Pl. II. 1.	

o.	Wt.	Metal. Size.	Obverse.	Reverse.
6	52·5	Æ *square* ·75	As preceding.	As preceding. [Whitehead, 1922.] **Pl. III. 11.**
7	38·0	·7	”	” [Theobald, 1906.] **Pl. III. 12.**
8	54·5	·6 × ·5	”	” [Theobald, 1906.]
9	49·5	·65	”	” [Cunningham, 1894.]
0	58·7	(Æ *pl.*) ·65	”	” [Gen. M. Clerk, 1920.]
1	48·7	·65	”	” [I. O. C., 1882.]
2	43·2	·8 × ·3	”	” ”
3	43·4	·6	”	” [Whitehead, 1906.]
4	50·7	Æ *round* ·5	”	” [Cunningham, 1894.]
			Var. *b*.	
5	51·6	*square* ·65		 countermarked  [Cunningham, 1894.] **Pl. III. 10.**
			C., *C.A.I.*, Pl. II. 2.	

No.	Wt.	Metal. Size.	Obverse.	Reverse.
			Var. *c.*	
36	45·5	Æ *square* ·6		 countermarked  [Whitehead, 192 **Pl. VI. 23.**
			Var. *d.*	
37	45·3	·65		 [Eden, 185
38	54·0	·75 × ·6	,, ,,	,, [A. S. B., 189 **Pl. III. 5.** (from Shahpur)
39	45·7	·6 × ·4	,, ,,	,, [Theobald, 190
40	49·5	·65	,, ,,	,, [Whitehead, 192
41	48·3	·7	,, ,,	,, [Major Hay, 186
42	30·5	(Æ *pl.*) ·6	,, ,,	,, [Cunningham, 189 **Pl. III. 2.**
			Var. *e.*	
43	52·7	Æ *square* ·55		 [Theobald, 190 **Pl. III. 6.**
44	55·0	·7 × ·45	,, ,,	,, [Whitehead, 192

No.	Wt.	Metal. Size.	Obverse.	Reverse.
45	50·0	Æ round ·55	As preceding.	As preceding. [Theobald, 1906.] **Pl. III. 15.**
46	52·6	·7	,,	,, [Whitehead, 1922.]
47	54·0	·7	,,	,, ,, **Pl. III. 14.**
48	53·7	·65	,,	,, [Cunningham, 1894.] **Pl. III. 13.**
49	35·0	(Æ. *pl*) ·5	,,	,, [I. O. C., 1882.]
			Var. *f*.	
50	54·3	Æ square ·55		 [Cunningham, 1894.] **Pl. III. 8.**
51	56·5	·6 × ·4	,, ,,	,, [Cunningham, 1894.] **Pl. VI. 3.**
			Var. *g*.	
52	53·4	·6 × ·3		 [Theobald, 1906.]
53	54·8	·55	,, ,,	,, [Cunningham, 1894.]
54	52·6	·5	,, ,,	,, ,,
55	53·3	·6 × ·4	,, ,,	,, ,,

No.	Wt.	Metal. Size.	Obverse.	Reverse.
56	53·8	Æ *square* ·6	As preceding.	As preceding. [Cunningham, 1894. **Pl. IV. 4.**
57	55·0	·6	,,	,, [Cunningham, 1894.
58	52·8	·6	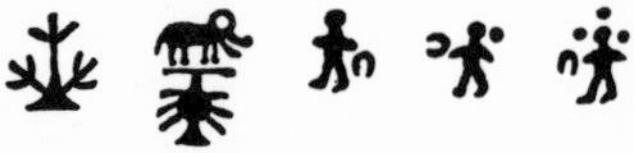	,, ,, **Pl. III. 16.**
59	54·2	·6		,, [Cunningham, 1894. **Pl. III. 17.**
60	53·8	·55	,, ,,	,, [Cunningham, 1894.
61	54·1	·6 × ·4	,, ,,	,, ,,
62	53·0	·75		,, ,, **Pl. III. 18.**
63	53·8	·6	,, ,,	,, [Cunningham, 1894
64	52·7	·55		,, ,,
65	52·7	·65	,, ,,	,, ,, **Pl. III. 20.**
66	53·4	·6		,, [Cunningham, 1894
67	53·0	·55	,, ,,	,, ,,

No.	Wt.	Metal. Size.	Obverse.	Reverse.
8	53·5	Æ *square* ·6		As preceding. [Cunningham, 1894.] **Pl. III. 19.**
9	52·8	·55		,, [Cunningham, 1894]
0	54·7	·6	,, ,,	,, ,,
1	54·4	·6	,, ,,	,, ,,
2	51·4	*round* ·75		,, [Whitehead, 1922.] **Pl. III. 21.**
3	52·3	·6		,, [Cunningham, 1894.]
4	53·2	·6	,, ,,	,, ,, **Pl. IV. 1.**
5	56·2	·6	,, ,,	,, [Cunningham, 1894.]
6	54·1	·6		,, ,, **Pl. IV. 2.**
			Var. *h*.	
7	53·5	*square* ·5		 [Cunningham, 1894.] **Pl. IV. 5.**
8	55·7	·55		,, [Cunningham, 1894.]

No.	Wt.	Metal. Size.	Obverse.	Reverse.
79	53·9	Æ *round* ·6		As preceding. [Cunningham, 1894 **Pl. IV. 3.**
80	47·4	·6		” [Thomas, 1850

No.	Wt.	Metal. Size.	Obverse.	Reverse.
			GROUP II.	
			Var. *a*.	
1	49·9	Æ *square* ·6		 [Cunningham, 1894.]
2	47·0	·6	,, ,,	,, ,,
3	47·3	·5	,, ,,	,, [Whitehead, 1922.]
4	49·5	·55	,, ,,	,, [Cunningham, 1894.]
5	51·2	·65	,, ,,	,, [Theobald, 1906.] **Pl. IV. 12.**
6	49·8	·6 × ·3	,, ,,	,, [Theobald, 1906.]
7	50·6	·6	,, ,,	,, [I. O. C., 1882.] **Pl. IV. 13.**
8	48·2	·65	,, ,,	,, [Capt. Barrow, 1877.]
9	50·2	·65	,, ,,	,, [Thomas, 1850.]
0	53·5	·65	,, ,,	,, [Major Reynolds, 1865.]
1	43·5 *worn*	·65	,, ,,	,, [Eden, 1853.]
2	51·4	*round* ·55	,, ,,	,, ,, **Pl. IV. 14.**

No.	Wt.	Metal. Size.	Obverse.	Reverse.
			Var. *b*.	
13	46·5	Æ *round* ·75		 and an un certain stamp. [Major Hay, 1860. **Pl. X. 18.**
			Var. *c*.	
14	45·7	*square* ·55		 [Grant, 1885. **Pl. IV. 10.**
15	46·8	·55	,, ,,	,, [Cunningham, 1894.
16	44·0	·55	,, ,,	,, [Thomas, 1850.
			Var. *d*.	
17	48·6	·6	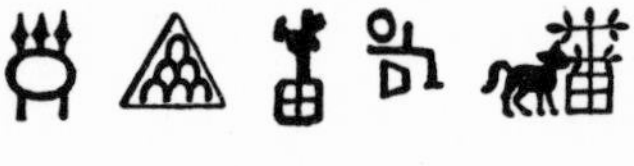	 [Cunningham, 1894 **Pl. XLI. 2.**
			Var. *e*.	
18	45·0	·45		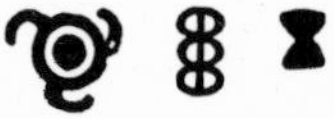 [Theobald, 1906 **Pl. V. 16.**
19	51·9	·55	,, ,,	,, [Cunningham, 1894
20	52·2	·55	,, ,,	,, ,,
21	46·4	·6	,, ,,	,, ,, **Pl. V. 14.**

o.	Wt.	Metal. Size.	Obverse.	Reverse.
2	48·0	Æ *square* ·6	As preceding.	As preceding. [Thomas, 1850.]
3	46·9	·55	”	” [I. O. C., 1882.] **Pl. V. 13.**
4	41·9 *worn*	*round* ·65	”	” [Cunningham, 1894.] (from Bodh Gaya)
5	33·5	·55	”	” [Grant, 1885.] **Pl. V. 10.**
			Var. *f.*	
6	45·8	·6		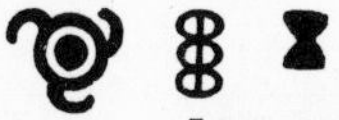 [Cunningham, 1894.] **Pl. V. 15.**
			C., *C.A.I.*, Pl. I. 11.	
			Var. *g.*	
7	45·8	*square* ·6	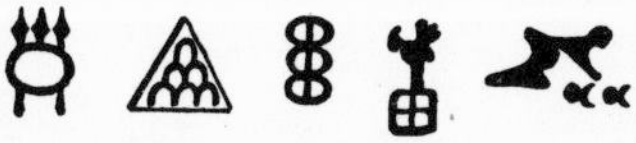	 [Cunningham, 1894.]
8	52·4	·5	” ”	 [Cunningham, 1894.] **Pl. V. 12.**
			Var. *h.*	
9	51·0	·7 × ·5		 [F. Fawcett, Esq., 1909.] **Pl. XLI. 3.**

No.	Wt.	Metal. Size.	Obverse.	Reverse.
			GROUP III.	
			Var. *a.*	
1	49·0	Æ *square* ·55		 [Theobald, 1906.
2	51·8	·6	„ „	„ [Cunningham, 1894.
3	50·8	·55	„ „	„ [Whitehead, 1922.
4	52·0	·6	„ „	 [Theobald, 1906.
5	52·4	*round* ·6	„ „	 [Cunningham, 1894. **Pl. V. 7.**
			C., *C.A.I.*, Pl. I. 14.	
6	51·2	·6	„ „	„ [Whitehead, 1922.
			Var. *b.*	
7	52·0	*square* ·6 × ·5		 [Theobald, 1906. **Pl. V. 5.**
8	52·5	·6 × ·4	„ „	„ [Theobald, 1906. **Pl. V. 11.**
9	48·5	·55	„ „	„ [Whitehead, 1922. **Pl. V. 17.**

No.	Wt.	Metal. Size.	Obverse.	Reverse.
			Var. *c*.	
10	47·0	Æ *square* ·6		 [Cunningham, 1894.] **Pl. V. 6.**
			Var. *d*.	
11	52·3	·6		 [Gen. Sandys, 1860.] **Pl. XLI. 4.**
12	52·2	·55	" "	" [Eden, 1853.] **Pl. XLI. 5.**
			Var. *e*.	
13	52·5	·45		 [Theobald, 1906.] **Pl. XLI. 6.**
14	52·5	·45	" "	" " **Pl. VI. 10.**
15	52·4	·45	" "	" "
16	53·0	·45	" "	" "
			Var. *f*.	
17	59·2	·6		 [Cunningham, 1894.] (from Benares)
18	49·9	·6	" "	" [Cunningham, 1894.] **Pl. XLI. 7.**

No.	Wt.	Metal. Size.	Obverse.	Reverse.
19	51·5	Æ *square* ·55	As preceding.	As preceding. [Cunningham, 1894.] **Pl. V. 1.**
20	47·8	·6	"	" [Thomas, 1850.] **Pl. XLI. 8.**
21	47·2	·6	"	" "
22	37·0 *worn*	·55 × ·3	"	" [Theobald, 1906.] **Pl. XLI. 9.**
23	53·2	·5	"	" " **Pl. XLI. 10.**
			Var. *g.*	
24	48·0	·55		 countermarked  [Prinsep.] **Pl. IV. 24.**
25	47·0	·55	" "	" [Thomas, 1850.] **Pl. XLI. 11.**
26	45·0	·55	" "	" [Thomas, 1850.]
			Var. *h.*	
27	51·6	·75 × ·3		 [Major Hay, 1860.] **Pl. V. 9.**

No.	Wt.	Metal. Size.	Obverse.	Reverse.
			Var. *i.*	
28	50·8	Æ *round* ·5		 [Theobald.] **Pl. V. 18.**
29	37·1	*square* ·55 × ·3 *worn*	,, ,,	,, [Cunningham, 1894.]
			Var. *j.*	
30	45·0	·65 × ·4		 [Theobald, 1906.] **Pl. V. 8.**
			GROUP II or IV.	
1	52·1	·55		 [Cunningham, 1894.] **Pl. IV. 9.**

No.	Wt.	Metal. Size.	Obverse.	Reverse.	
			GROUP IV.		
			Var. *a*.		
1	53·4	Æ *square* ·5			[Prinsep, 1847. **Pl. VI. 6.**
2	51·6	·45	” ”	”	[Prinsep, 1847.
3	53·3	·5	” ”	”	[Eden, 1853.
4	53·7	·5	” ”	”	**Pl. IV. 11.**
5	41·5 *worn*	·5	” ”	”	[Theobald, 1906.
6	52·9	*round* —	” ”	”	[Cunningham, 1894.
7	51·5	—	” ”	”	**Pl. IV. 7.**
			Var. *b*.		
8	52·0	·3			
			Var. *c*.		
9	52·3	*square* ·55			[Eden, 1853

No.	Wt.	Metal. Size.	Obverse.	Reverse.
10	45·0	Æ *square* ·65 × ·5	As preceding.	As preceding. **Pl. XLI. 12.** [Theobald, 1906.]
11	53·4	·55	,,	,, **Pl. XLI. 13.** [Prinsep, 1847.]
12	52·2	·5	,,	,, ,,
13	54·0	·5	,,	,, ,,
14	55·0	·5	,,	,, ,,
15	52·7	*round* ·5	,,	,, ,, **Pl. IV. 6.**
16	54·4	·55	,,	,, [Elliot, 1885.]
			Elliot, *C.S.I.*, Pl. I. 5; *Gleanings*, Pl. VII. 11.	
17	51·5	·5	,,	,, **Pl. IV. 8.**
18	52·8	·5	,,	,,
19	52·9	·5	,,	,,
20	50·5	·5	,,	,,
21	52·4	·5	,,	,,
22	44·5	·55	,,	,, [Cunningham, 1894.]

No.	Wt.	Metal. Size.	Obverse.	Reverse.
			Var. *d.*	
23	52·5	Æ *square* ·5		 traces of another stamp. [Cunningham, 1894.] **Pl. XLI. 14.**
24	51·5	·55	,, ,,	,, ,,
25	53·4	·6 × ·4	,, ,,	,, [Eden, 1853.]
26	52·6	·5	,, ,,	,, [Prinsep, 1847.] **Pl. XLI. 15.**
			Var. *e.*	
27	53·4	·5		 **Pl. V. 4.**
28	52·5	·5	,, ,,	,, [Prinsep, 1847.]
29	48·0	·55	,, ,,	,, [Bombay B.R.A.S., 1915.] **Pl. XLI. 16.**
30	49·0	·55	,, ,,	,, [I. O. C., 1882.]
31	52·5	*round* ·5	,, ,,	,, (from Azimgarh) **Pl. VI. 9.**

o.	Wt.	Metal. Size.	Obverse.	Reverse.
2	50·0	Æ round ·5	As preceding.	As preceding. [Madras Govt., 1896.] (from Bimlipatam)
3	51·5	·55	”	” **Pl. XLI. 17.**
			Var. *f.*	
4	52·5	·5		 [Eden, 1853.] **Pl. XLI. 20.**
			Var. *g.*	
5	53·6	square ·55		 [Prinsep, 1847.] **Pl. XLI. 21.**
6	51·0	·5	” ”	” [Prinsep, 1847.] **Pl. XLI. 22.**
7	51·5	·5	” ”	” ”
8	52·0	·5	” ”	” ”
9	51·7	round ·45	” ”	”
			Var. *h.*	
0	53·0	square ·5	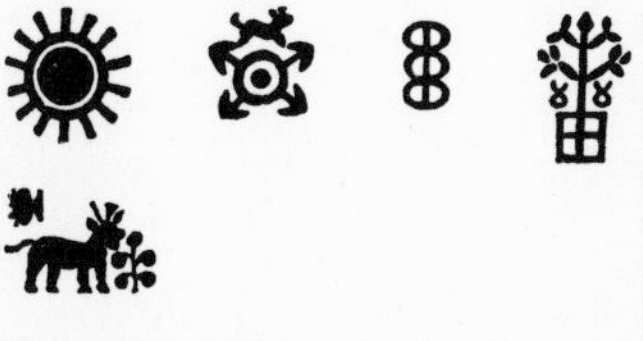	 [Prinsep, 1847.] **Pl. XLI. 23.**

No.	Wt.	Metal. Size.	Obverse.	Reverse.
40*a*	52·0	Æ *square* ·55	As preceding.	As preceding.
			Var. *i.*	
41	51·7	·5 × ·3		 [Major Reynolds, 1865. **Pl. XLI. 18.**
			Var. *j.*	
42	52·2	*round* ·55		 [Major Reynolds, 1865. **Pl. XLI. 19.**
43	52·3	·5	,, ,,	,, [Prinsep, 1847.
			Var. *k.*	
44	49·6	*square* ·45		 [Theobald, 1906. **Pl. VI. 4.**
			Var. *l.*	
45	52·8	·5		 [Thomas, 1850
46	52·3	·5	,, ,,	,, [Eden, 1853.

No.	Wt.	Metal. Size.	Obverse.	Reverse.
47	52·6	Æ square ·5	As preceding.	As preceding. [Prinsep, 1847.]
48	49·4	round ·5	,,	,, [Whitehead, 1922.] **Pl. VI. 12.**
49	51·5	·5	,,	 [Theobald, 1906.] **Pl. V. 22.**
49a	51·6	·5	,,	,, ? [Theobald, 1906.]
			Var. *m.*	
50	52·8	square ·5		 [Eden, 1853.]
51	52·2	·5	,, ,,	,, ,,
52	51·5	·5	,, ,,	,, [Prinsep, 1847.] **Pl. IV. 20.**
53	50·8	·5	,, ,,	,, [Madras Govt., 1896.] (from Bimlipatam)
54	53·5	·5	,, ,,	,, [Major Reynolds, 1865.] **Pl. IV. 17.**
55	46·4	·45	,, ,,	,, [Thomas, 1850.]

No.	Wt.	Metal. Size.	Obverse.	Reverse.	
		Æ	Var. *n.*		
56	49·2	*square* ·5			[Theobald, 1906.] Pl. **XLI. 24.**
57	51·5	·5	,, ,,		[Theobald, 1906.] Pl. **XLI. 25.**
			Var. *o.*		
58	54·2	·55			[Prinsep, 1847.] Pl. **XLII. 1.**
59	52·2	·55	,, ,,	,,	[Prinsep, 1847.] Pl. **XLII. 2.**
			Var. *p.*		
60	52·4	·45	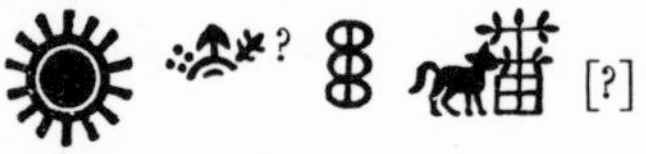		[Prinsep, 1847.] Pl. **VI. 11.**
			Var. *q.*		
61	51·0	·5			Pl. **VI. 7.**
62	52·0	*round* ·55	,, ,,		[Cunningham, 1894.] Pl. **VI. 8.**
63	52·4	·5	,, ,,		[Eden, 1853.] Pl. **VI. 14.**

o.	Wt.	Metal. Size.	Obverse.	Reverse.
			Var. *r.*	
4	45·4	Æ *square* ·5		 [Theobald, 1906.] **Pl. VI. 4.**
			Var. *s.*	
5	51·5	·55		 [Prinsep, 1847.] **Pl. XLII. 3.**
6	51·0	·5	,, ,,	,, [Whitehead, 1922.] **Pl. XLII. 4.**
7	52·4	·5	,, ,,	,, [Eden, 1853.]
8	52·2	·5	,, ,,	,, ,,
			Var. *t.*	
9	53·2	·45		 [Eden, 1853.] **Pl. XLII. 5.**
0	45·0	·4	,, ,,	,, ,,
1	44·5	·45	,, ,,	,, [Prinsep, 1847.]
2	52·0	*round* ·5	,, ,,	,, [Thomas, 1850.]

No.	Wt.	Metal. Size.	Obverse.	Reverse.
			Var. *u.*	
73	43·7	Æ *square* ·85		 [Major Hay, 1860. **Pl. IV. 15.**
74	50·5	·85 × ·35	,, ,,	,, [Major Hay, 1860. **Pl. IV. 19.**
75	46·3	·75 × ·55	,, ,,	,, [Eden, 1853. **Pl. IV. 16.**
76	50·0	·55	,, ,,	,, [Thomas, 1850.
77	37·0 *much worn*	·55 × ·4	,, ,,	,, ,,
78	51·7	·5	,, ,,	,, [Cunningham, 1894.
			C., *C.A.I.*, Pl. I. 12.	
79	51·0	·6 × ·3	,, ,,	,, [Whitehead, 1922.
80	53·3	*round* ·5	,, ,,	,, [Eden, 1853.
81	51·8	·5	,, ,,	,, ,,
82	50·5	·5	,, ,,	,, ,,
			Var. *v.*	
83	53·5	*square* ·45		 [Eden, 1853. **Pl. XLII. 6.**

No.	Wt.	Metal. Size.	Obverse.	Reverse.
			GROUP V.	
			Var. a.	
	52·5	AR *square* ·5 × ·35	  [variant ]	 [Eden, 1853.] **Pl. XLII. 7.**
	52·6	·45	,, ,,	 [Eden, 1853.]
	52·0	·45	,, ,,	? ? ,, **Pl. XLII. 8.**
			Var. b.	
	55·0	·45		 [Eden, 1853.] **Pl. II. 11.**
	53·7	·45	,, ,,	 [Theobald, 1906.] **Pl. II. 17.**
	53·7	·5 × ·4	,, ,,	? [Parkes Weber, 1906.]
			Var. c.	
	53·5	·55 × ·4	  [or a variant ]	 **Pl. II. 13.**
	52·0	·45	,, ,,	,, [Prinsep, 1847.]

No.	Wt.	Metal. Size.	Obverse.	Reverse.
9	51·6	Æ *round* ·5	As preceding.	As preceding. **Pl. II. 16.**
10	53·0	—	"	" **Pl. II. 18.**
11	51·4	·5	"	? **Pl. XLII. 9.**
12	53·4	·5	"	 [Eden, 185 **Pl. VI. 15.**
13	49·8	·55	"	 [Cunningham, 189 **Pl. XLII. 10.**
14	51·4	·7	"	? [Major Reynolds, 186 **Pl. IV. 19.**
15	50·4	·6	"	? [Theobald, 190 **Pl. IV. 18.**
16	52·5	·6	"	? **Pl. IV. 13.**
			Var. *d.*	
17	52·8	·55		 [Parkes Weber, 190 **Pl. VI. 20.**
18	51·0	·65	" "	 [I. O. C., 188
19	55·0	·6	" "	? [Theobald, 190 **Pl. VI. 21.**
20	45·3 *much worn*	·55	" "	 [Cunningham, 189

Wt.	Metal. Size.	Obverse.	Reverse.
		GROUP VI.	
		Var. *a.*	
52·8	Æ *round* ·6	 ? ?	
		Var. *b.*	
51·4	*square* ·5		 [Whitehead, 1922.] **Pl. V. 19.**
50·5	·65	,, ,,	,, [Whitehead, 1922.]
52·5	·65	,, ,,	 [Prinsep, 1847.]
51·5	·5 × ·3	,, ,,	 ,, **Pl. V. 23.**
52·7	·55	,, ,,	 [Cunningham, 1894.]
		C., *C.A.I.*, Pl. I. 9.	
44·0	·65 × ·3	,, ,,	Illegible. [Gen. M. Clerk, 1920.]
		Var. *c.*	
51·5	·5		 [Prinsep, 1847.]
50·0	·5	,, ,,	 [Eden, 1853.]

No.	Wt.	Metal. Size.	Obverse.	Reverse.	
10	52·0	Æ *square* ·6	As preceding.	 ?	[Eden, 1853
11	52·3	·5	,,	 ?	[Theobald, 1906 **Pl. V. 21.**
			Var. *d.*		
12	48·9	·45			[Cunningham, 1894
			Var. *e.*		
13	50·5	*round* ·5			[Whitehead, 192
			Var. *f.*		
14	50·7	·5			,,
			Var. *g.*		
15	83·0	*square* ·45		?	[Prinsep, 184
16	51·4	·45	,, ,,		,,
			Var. *h.*		
17	50·3	·5	 [?]		[Whitehead, 192 **Pl. VI. 25.**

No.	Wt.	Metal. Size.	Obverse.	Reverse.
			GROUP VII.	
		Æ *square*	Var. *a*.	
1	52·4	·5		 [Theobald, 1906.] **Pl. XLII. 11.**
2	55·0	·5	„ „	„ [Eden, 1853.]
3	53·0	·5	„ „	„ „ **Pl. XLII. 14.**
4	51·5	·45	„ „	„ [Thomas, 1850.]
5	52·5	·55	„ „	„ [Prinsep, 1847.]
6	52·4	·4	„ „	„ **Pl. XLII. 12.**
7	53·6	·4	„ „	„
8	52·0	·45	„ „	„
9	51·2	*round* ·45	„ „	„ [Thomas, 1850.]
10	52·2	·45	„ „	„ [A. S. B., 1895.] (from Shahpur)
11	52·7	·5	„ „	„ [Prinsep, 1847.]

No.	Wt.	Metal. Size.	Obverse.	Reverse.
			Var. *b.*	
12	49·0	Æ *square* ·5 × ·4		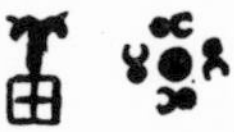 [Whitehead, 1922. **Pl. XLII. 13.**
			Var. *c.*	
13	52·8	·65		 [Cunningham, 1894. **Pl. XLII. 12.**
14	52·6	*round* ·6	,, ,,	,, [Whitehead, 1922. **Pl. IV. 23.**
			Var. *d.*	
15	52·3	*square* ·55		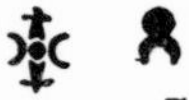 and an uncertai stamp [? ] [Ouseley. **Pl. XLII. 15.**
			Var. *e.*	
16	52·4	·45		 [Prinsep, 1847. **Pl. VI. 1.**
17	53·5	·5	,, ,,	,, [Prinsep, 1847.
18	53·3	·5	,, ,,	,, ,,

No	Wt.	Metal. Size.	Obverse.	Reverse.
19	53·3	*AR* *square* ·45	As preceding.	As preceding. [Eden, 1853.]
20	52·3	·5	,,	,, ,,
21	46·8	·5	,,	,, [Cunningham, 1894.] (from Karra)
2	52·5	·45	,,	,,
3	51·2	·5	,,	,, **Pl. VI. 2.**
4	49·7	*round* ·55	,,	,, [Cunningham, 1894.]
5	52·0	·55	,,	,, [Thomas, 1850.]
			Var. *f.*	
6	54·8	·6 × ·45		 [Theobald, 1906.] **Pl. XLII. 16.**
			Var. *g.*	
7	50·7	·6 × ·45		 and another stamp. [Eden, 1853.] **Pl. XLII. 17.**
3	51·0	·5	,, ,,	 [Eden, 1853.]

No.	Wt.	Metal. Size.	Obverse.	Reverse.
29	52·3	Æ *round* ·5 × ·3	As preceding.	 [Prinsep, 1847 **Pl. IV. 18.**
30	50·4	·45	,,	Four small stamps. [Prinsep, 1847 **Pl. XLII. 18.**
31	51·7	·45	,,	Four small stamps. [Prinsep, 1847
32	52·2	·55	,,	,, ,, **Pl. XLII. 19.**
33	52·5	·55	,,	 and other stamps. [Prinsep, 1847
34	50·7	·65	,,	Illegible. [Whitehead, 1922
35	51·4	·5	,,	Uncertain stamps. (from Palanpur state) [Bombay Govt., 1918
36	51·5	·7 × ·4	,,	 and other uncertai stamps. [Bombay Govt., 1918
37	52·5	·7 × ·5	,,	 and other stamps. **Pl. X. 11.**
38	52·0	·45	,,	 and other stamps.

No.	Wt.	Metal. Size.	Obverse.	Reverse.
39	48·5	Æ ·55	As preceding.	Uncertain stamps. [Theobald, 1906.]
40	43·5	·5	,,	 and a number of uncertain stamps. [Gen. Clerk, 1920.] (from Ayodhya) **Pl. X. 2.**
41	51·4	*round* ·6	,,	Uncertain stamps.
			Var. *h*.	
42	51·0	·6		Various stamps. [Thomas, 1847.]
43	52·0	·6	,, ,,	Various stamps. [Eden, 1853.]
44	51·2	·7	,, ,,	Various stamps. [Prinsep, 1847.] **Pl. X. 9.**
45	50·0	·7	,, ,,	Various stamps. **Pl. X. 12.**
46	53·0	·75	,, ,,	Various stamps.
47	52·0	·7	,, ,,	 **Pl. X. 14.**

No.	Wt.	Metal. Size.	Obverse.	Reverse.
			Var. *i*.	
48	50·0	Æ *round* ·7		 [Prinsep, 1847.] **Pl. XLII. 20.**
			Var. *j*.	
49	51·2	*square* ·55		 and other stamps. [Cunningham, 1894.]
50	52·7	·6	,, ,,	 and other stamps. [Thomas, 1850.] **Pl. II. 21.**
51	50·5	·65	,, ,,	Similar. [Madras Govt., 1896.]
52	50·4	·65	,, ,,	,, **Pl. XLII. 21.**
53	51·5	·6	,, ,,	,, [Dir. of Agric. C. P., 1925.] (from Thathari)
			Var. *k*.	
54	50·3	·6		Illegible. [Whitehead, 1922.]
55	52·7	·7	,, ,,	 [Eden, 1853.] **Pl. X. 3.**

No.	Wt.	Metal. Size.	Obverse.	Reverse.
56	52·0	AR *square* ·7	As preceding.	 and other stamps. [Eden, 1853.] **Pl. X. 1.**
			Var. *l*.	
57	45·0	·65		Plain. [Theobald, 1906.]
58	52·5	·65	” ”	” [Eden, 1853.] **Pl. X. 5.**

No.	Wt.	Metal. Size.	Obverse.	Reverse.
			GROUP VIII.	
			Var. *a.*	
1	51·3	Æ *round* ·65		 Pl. X. 13.
			Var. *b.*	
2	51·0	*square* ·7 × ·5		 [Prinsep, 1847. Pl. II. 14.
			Var. *c.*	
3	51·6	·6		Various stamps. [Prinsep, 1847. Pl. XLII. 22.
			Var. *d.*	
4	52·7	·7 × ·5		 and an uncertain stamp. [Sir W. Elliot, 1858. Pl. II. 20.
			Elliot, *C.S.I.*, Pl. I, no. 3.	
5	50·0	·7	,, ,,	 [I. O. C., 1882.
6	51·5	*round* ·7	,, ,,	Uncertain stamp. [Eden, 1853.

No.	Wt.	Metal. Size.	Obverse.	Reverse.
		Æ *square*	Var. *e.*	
7	51·8	·7 × ·4		 and illegible stamps. [Eden, 1853.] **Pl. II. 12.**
8	42·0	·7 × ·4	,, ,,	Uncertain stamps, including three figures, perhaps  [Theobald, 1906.] **Pl. XLII. 23.**
9	52·0	·7	,, ,,	Uncertain stamps. [Prinsep, 1847.] **Pl. XLII. 24.**
10	39·0 *much worn*	·7	,, ,,	Uncertain stamp. [Theobald, 1906.]

No.	Wt.	Metal. Size.	Obverse.	Reverse.
			GROUP IX.	
			Var. *a*.	
1	46·0	Æ *square* ·7	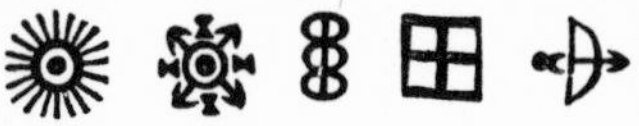	 [Theobald, 1906.] **Pl. IX. 11.**
2	53·5	·6	,, ,,	,, [Eden, 1853.]
3	52·0	·7	,, ,,	,, **Pl. IX. 15.**
			Var. *b*.	
4	42·5	·35		 [Theobald, 1906.] **Pl. IX. 13.**
5	45·7	·6	,, ,,	,, [Cunningham, 1894.]
6	52·5	*round* ·65	,, ,,	,, [Prinsep, 1847.] **Pl. IX. 16.**
			Var. *c*.	
7	52·5	*square* ·6		 and other stamps. [Prinsep, 1847. **Pl. IX. 14.**
			Var. *d*.	
8	51·5	·7	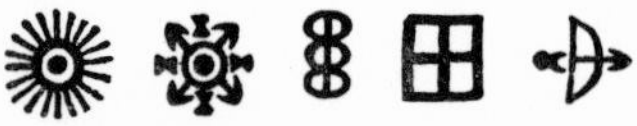	 [Prinsep, 1847. **Pl. IX. 12.**
			Var. *e*.	
9	47·4	·6	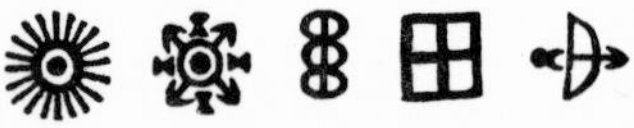	 ? [I. O. C., 1882.

No.	Wt.	Metal. Size.	Obverse.	Reverse.
			GROUP X.	
			Var. *a.*	
1	47·0	Æ *square* ·7 × ·5		 and another stamp. [Theobald, 1906.] **Pl. II. 15.**
			Var. *b.*	
2	51·0	·8 × ·4		 [Theobald, 1906.] **Pl. XLII. 25.**
3	50·0	—	,, ,,	 [Prinsep, 1847.] **Pl. IX. 22.**
4	50·8	·7	,, ,,	 [Eden, 1853.] **Pl. V. 24.**
5	51·2	·75	,, ,,	 &c. [Eden, 1853.] **Pl. X. 4.**
6	50·5	·7	,, ,,	 [Prinsep, 1847.]
7	50·5	·75	,, ,,	,, ,,
8	51·0	·7 × ·5	,, ,,	Uncertain stamps. [Whitehead, 1921.]

No.	Wt.	Metal. Size.	Obverse.	Reverse.
			Group XI.	
			Var. *a.*	
1	53·0	Æ *square* ·55	 uncertain.	 and another stamp. [Prinsep, 1847.
			Var. *b.*	
2	52·2	·55	 uncertain.	 over  **Pl. V. 20.**
3	45·7	·6	,, ,,	
4	46·0	*round* ·6	,, ,,	,, **Pl. IV. 22.**
			Var. *c.*	
5	44·4	·65	  [?]	 and another. [Dir. of Agric. C. P., 1924. (from Hinganghat)
6	41·5	·65	,, ,,	,, ,, **Pl. VI. 22.**

No.	Wt.	Metal. Size.	Obverse.	Reverse.
			CLASS 3.	
			Var. *a*.	
1	52·8	Æ *round* ·8		Plain. [Cunningham, 1894.] (from Dharawat) **Pl. VI. 26.**
			C., *C.A.I.*, Pl. I. 1.	
			Var. *b*.	
2	39·8	*square* ·8 × ·5		 [Theobald, 1906.] **Pl. VI. 27.**

No.	Wt.	Metal. Size.	Obverse.	Reverse.
			CLASS 4.	
			Var. *a*.	
1	52·3	Æ *square* 1·05 × ·8		Plain. [Cunningham, 1894. (from Chiriyakot) **Pl. IX. 6.**
			C., *C.A.I.*, Pl. I. 2.	
2	52·5	1·0 × ·8	,, ,,	,, ,, **Pl. IX. 7.**
			C., *C.A.I.*, Pl. I. 3.	
			Var. *b*.	
3	50·0	·8	 in centre  and narrow spray on side.	Plain. [Cunningham, 1894. (from Mirzapur) **Pl. IX. 5.**
			C., *C.A.I.*, Pl. I. 4.	
4	51·7	·8	,, ,, additional 	 and  [Cunningham, 1894. **Pl. IX. 8.**
			C., *C.A.I.*, Pl. I. 5.	
			Var. *c*.	
5	48·4	·85	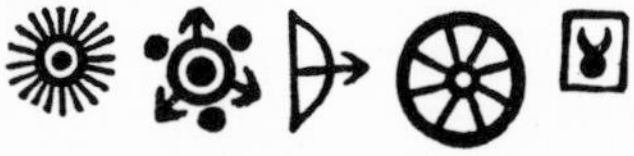	Plain. [Theobald, 1906. **Pl. IX. 4.**

No.	Wt.	Metal Size.	Obverse.	Reverse.
			Var. *d*.	
6	49·6	Æ *square* 1·1	 traces of other stamps below.	Plain. [Cunningham, 1894.] (from Chiriyakot) **Pl. VIII. 1.**
			Var. *e*.	
7	40·5	·75 × ·5		 [Cunningham, 1894.] **Pl. IX. 9.**
			C., *C.A.I.*, Pl. I. 10.	
			CLASS 5.	
			Var. *a*.	
	52·2	*round* ·7		Plain. [Cunningham, 1894.] (from Mirzapur) **Pl. X. 17.**
			Var. *b*.	
	45·5	*square* ·7		Illegible stamp. [Theobald, 1906.]

No.	Wt.	Metal. Size.	Obverse.	Reverse.
			CLASS 6.	
			GROUP I.	
			Var. *a*.	
1	52·3	Æ *square* ·75		Four stamps. [Cunningham, 1894. (from Mirzapur)
2	52·9	·8	,, ,,	One punch. [Cunningham, 1894. (from Chiriyakot) **Pl. VIII. 8.**
3	49·4	·65	,, ,,	Plain. [Cunningham, 1894. **Pl. VIII. 11.**
4	50·0	·75	,, ,,	 [Cunningham, 1894. **Pl. VIII. 10.**
5	52·0	·85	,, ,, Elephant double struck.	Illegible. [Cunningham, 1894. (from Chiriyakot) **Pl. VIII. 9.**
6	50·2	·7 × ·5	,, ,,	Three stamps. [Eden, 1853
7	50·0	·8	,, ,,	,, [Prinsep, 1847

No.	Wt.	Metal. Size.	Obverse.	Reverse
8	37·5	Æ *square* ·7	As preceding.	Many punches including  [Theobald, 1906.]
9	51·0	·9	,, additional 	Many punches including 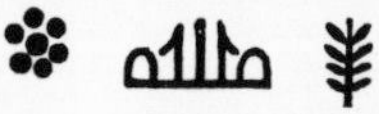 [Cunningham, 1894.] **Pl. VIII. 5.**
10	50·7	·7	,, additional 	Many punches including  [Cunningham, 1894.] (from Mirzapur) **Pl. VIII. 6.**
11	47·5	·8	,, additional 	Many punches including  [Prinsep, 1847.]
12	53·2	·8	,, ,,	Many punches including  [Prinsep, 1847.]
13	48·6	1 × ·55	,, ,,	Many punches including  [Theobald, 1906.] **Pl. VIII. 12.**
14	49·0	·75	,, ,,	Many punches including  [Major Hay, 1860.]

No.	Wt.	Metal. Size.	Obverse.	Reverse.
15	50·8	Æ *round* ·8	As preceding.	Uncertain punch. [Cunningham, 1894. (from Mirzapur) **Pl. VIII. 13.**
			Var. *b.*	
16	51·7	*square* ·8		Plain. [Parkes Weber, 1906. **Pl. VIII. 7.**
			Var. *c.*	
17	49·7	*round* ·9		Three punches. [Theobald, 1906. **Pl. VIII. 15.**
			Var. *d.*	
18	38·2	·8		Many punches including  [Cunningham, 1894. **Pl. VIII. 14.**
			Var. *e.*	
19	51·8	*square* ·8 × ·1	 [?]	Three punches. [Eden, 1853.

Io.	Wt.	Metal. Size.	Obverse.	Reverse.
		Æ	Var. *f.*	
0	49·0	*round* ·75		Uncertain punches. [I. O. C., 1882.] **Pl. VIII. 4.**
			Var. *g.*	
1	42·8	·75		Uncertain punches. [Theobald, 1906.]
			Var. *h.*	
2	49·5	·75		Various punches. [Eden, 1853.]
3	42·8	*square* ·7 × ·4	” ”	Illegible. [Theobald, 1906.] **Pl. VIII. 21.**

No.	Wt.	Metal. Size.	Obverse.	Reverse.
			GROUP II.	
			Var. *a*.	
1	48·7	Æ *square* ·85		Four small punches. [Prinsep, 1847 **Pl. X. 19.**
			Var. *b*.	
2	50·5	*round* ·75		Three small punches. [I. O. C., 1882.
			Var. *c*.	
3	47·4	·75		Two uncertain stamps. [Whitehead, 1922.
4	50·0	·7	,, ,,	 [Prinsep, 1847
			Var. *d*.	
5	53·0	*round* ·7		Plain. [I. O. C., 1882
6	34·4	·75	,, ,,	,, [Cunningham, 1894 (from Bhita)

No.	Wt.	Metal. Size.	Obverse.	Reverse.
			Var. *e.*	
7	54·0	Æ *round* ·8		Much punched. [Madras Govt., 1910.] (from Trichinopoli)
8	51·5	·85	,, ,,	 [Theobald, 1906.] **Pl. VIII. 22.**
9	50·8	·75	,, ,,	Various punches. [Theobald, 1906.]
10	45·5	*square* ·9 × ·6	,, ,,	Illegible punch. [Whitehead, 1922.]
11	50·0	·8	,, ,,	 and another punch. [Prinsep, 1847.] **Pl. VIII. 23.**
12	51·5	*round* —	,, ,, countermarked 	Various punches.

No.	Wt.	Metal. Size.	Obverse.	Reverse.
			GROUP III.	
			Var. *a*.	
1	49·2	Æ *round* ·8		Various small punches. [Bombay Govt., 1918. (from Palanpur State) **Pl. VII. 9.**
2	49·4	*square* ·75	,, ,,	,, ,,
			Var. *b*.	
3	52·6	·75		Plain. [Thomas, 1850. **Pl. VIII. 3.**
4	50·3	·75	,, ,,	Various punches. [Prinsep, 1847.
			Var. *c*.	
5	45·0	·75		Several punches, including  [Eden, 1853.
6	51·0	·7	,, ,,	Several punches, including  [Eden, 1853.
7	49·8	·8	,, ,,	Several punches. [Bombay Govt. Pres. (from Palanpur State)
8	46·7	·75	,, ,,	Several punches. [Cunningham, 1894.

No.	Wt.	Metal. Size.	Obverse.	Reverse.
9	40·1	Æ *square* ·8	As preceding.	Several punches. [Cunningham, 1894.]
10	50·8	·7	,,	Several punches, including  [Cunningham, 1894.] (from Rajghat, Benares) **Pl. VII. 16.**
11	47·0	·75 × ·55	,,	Several punches, including  [Gen. Clerk, 1920.] (from Kopiya Dih)
12	48·5	·75	,,	Several punches, including  [I. O. C., 1882.]
13	48·5	·78 × ·6	,,	Several punches, including  [Prinsep, 1847.]
14	51·5	·75 × ·6	,,	Several punches. ,,
15	50·7	·7	,,	Several punches, including  [Prinsep, 1847.]
16	30·0	·75	,,	Several punches, including  [Prinsep, 1847.]

No.	Wt.	Metal. Size.	Obverse.	Reverse.
17	52·0	Æ *square* ·7 × ·6	As preceding.	Several punches. [Elliot, 1886.
			Elliot, *Gleanings,* Pl. VII. 8.	
18	52·0	*round* ·75	,,	Several punches, including  [Theobald, 1906. **Pl. VII. 17.**
19	49·5	·75	,,	Several punches, including  [Whitehead, 1922.
20	49·4	·8	,,	Several punches, including  [Elliot, 1886. **Pl. VII. 3.**
			Elliot, *Gleanings,* Pl. VIII. 21.	
21	50·0	·7	,,	Several punches, including  [Prinsep, 1847.
22	52·8	·7	,,	Several punches, including  [Theobald, 1906. **Pl. VII. 6.**
23	46·3	·85	,,	Several punches, including  [Theobald, 1906.

No.	Wt.	Metal. Size.	Obverse.	Reverse.
		Æ *round*		
4	47·8	·8	As preceding.	Several punches, including  [Bombay Govt., 1918.] (from Palanpur State)
5	51·2	·8	,,	Two punches. [Bombay Govt., 1918.] (from Palanpur State)
6	48·5	·7	,,	Traces of punches. [Madras Govt., 1896.]
7	52·8	·8	,,	Plain. [Cunningham, 1894.] (from Koron Dih) **Pl. VII. 1.**
8	47·8	·8	,,	Many small countermarks. [Theobald, 1906.] **Pl. VIII. 20.**
9	51·1	·8	,,	Many small countermarks. [Elliot, 1886.] **Pl. IX. 1.**
			Elliot, *Gleanings*, Pl. VII. 15.	
0	48·5	·8	,, countermarked on side 	Various small punches, including  [Bombay Govt., 1918.] (from Palanpur State) **Pl. VII. 10.**

No.	Wt.	Metal. Size.	Obverse.	Reverse.
		Æ	Var. *d*.	
31	49.2	*square* ·8 × ·6		Various small punches. [Theobald, 1906.
32	49·9	·8	,, ,,	Various small punches, including  [Prinsep, 1847. **Pl. X. 15.**
33	52·4	*round* ·85	,, ,,	Various small punches, including  [Elliot, 1886. **Pl. VIII. 19.**
			Elliot, *Gleanings*, VIII. 19.	
			Var. *e*.	
34	46·0	*square* ·7		Several punches, including  [Gen. M. Clerk, 1920.
35	46·0	*round* ·75	,, ,,	 [Theobald, 1906
36	49·0	·75	,, ,,	 [A. S. B., 1895. (from Shahpur)
37	50·4	·8	,, ,,	Plain. [Cunningham, 1824. (from Mirzapur) **Pl. VI. 2.**

o.	Wt.	Metal. Size.	Obverse.	Reverse.
		Æ square	Var. *f.*	
8	40·0	·75		Various stamps, including  [Cunningham, 1894.] **Pl. VIII. 24.**
9	48·6	·9	,, ,,	Various stamps, including  [Cunningham, 1894.] **Pl. VII. 13.**
			C., *C.A.I.*, Pl. I. 7.	
			Var. *g.*	
0	48·5	·75		Various small punches. [Whitehead, 1922.] **Pl. VII. 12.**
1	51·0	·75	,, ,,	Various small punches. [Eden, 1853.]
2	50·0	·75	,, ,,	,, [Prinsep, 1847.] **Pl. VIII. 18.**
			Var. *h.*	
3	51·0	·75 × ·6		Various small punches. [Prinsep, 1847.] **Pl. VII. 11.**
4	49·0	·8 × 55	,, ,,	,, ,,

No.	Wt.	Metal. Size.	Obverse.	Reverse.
			Var. *i.*	
45	52·6	Æ *square* ·6	 [?]	Various small punches. [Theobald, 1906 **Pl. IX. 24.**
			Var. *j.*	
46	52·2	·6		 [Prinsep, 1847
47	53·7	*round* ·7	,, ,,	Plain. [Cunningham, 1894
			Var. *k.*	
48	50·5	*square* ·6		Small punches, including  [Prinsep, 1847
49	51·8	·8 × ·6	,, ,,	Plain. [Theobald, 1906

No.	Wt.	Metal. Size.	Obverse.	Reverse.
			GROUP IV.	
			Var. *a*.	
1	50·4	Æ *square* ·7		Two punches. [Prinsep, 1847.] **Pl. X. 8.**
2	48·0	·65	” ”	Several small punches. [Cunningham, 1894.]
3	49·5	·78	” ”	Several small punches, including  [Theobald, 1906.] **Pl. X. 6.**
4	44·5	·7	” ”	Illegible. [I. O. C., 1882.]
5	50·0	·8 × ·5	” ”	One illegible punch. [Prinsep, 1847.] **Pl. VII. 15.**
6	50·3	·7	” ”	Numerous small punches, including  [Prinsep, 1847.] **Pl. X. 7.**
7	45·1	·7	” ”	Illegible. [Cunningham, 1894.]
8	45·5	·75	” ”	” [Major Hay, 1860.]

No.	Wt.	Metal. Size.	Obverse.	Reverse.
9	52·7	Æ *round* ·7	As preceding.	Plain. [Cunningham, 1894. (from Koron Dih)
			Var. *b.*	
10	50·3	·85		Several small punches. [Cunningham, 1894
11	50·2	·65	,, ,,	Several small punches. [Cunningham, 1894.
			Var. *c.*	
12	50·0	·65		Several small punches, in-cluding  [Cunningham, 1894.
			Var. *d.*	
13	47·5	·75		Various small punches. [Theobald, 1906
			Var. *e.*	
14	42·5	*square* ·7	 	Illegible. [Theobald, 1906
15	48·3	·6	,, ,,	,, [Whitehead, 1922

o.	Wt.	Metal. Size.	Obverse.	Reverse.
		Æ	Var. *f.*	
6	44·4	*square* ·7		Various small punches, including 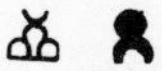 [Theobald, 1906.]
7	53·0	*round* ·75	,, ,,	Plain. [Cunningham, 1894.]

No.	Wt.	Metal. Size.	Obverse.	Reverse.
			Group V.	
		Æ	Var. *a*.	
1	47·8	*round* ·8		Various small punches, in-cluding  and other forms of spray. [Prinsep, 1847. **Pl. VII. 5.**
2	43·3	·9	" "	Various punches. [Madras Govt., 1896. **Pl. VII. 7.**
3	45·0	·85	" "	Various punches, including  [Elliot, 1886.
			Elliot, *Gleanings*, Pl. VII. 13.	
4	54·6	·8	" "	Various punches, including  [Bombay Govt., 1918. (from Palanpur State)
5	48·7	*square* ·1 × ·4	" "	" "
6	48·2	·7	" "	Various punches. [Madras Govt., 1896.
7	47·2	·8	" "	" "

o.	Wt.	Metal. Size.	Obverse.	Reverse.
8	49·0	Æ *square* ·8	As preceding.	Numerous punches, including  **Pl. IX. 10.** [Cunningham, 1894.] (from Mirzapur)
			C., *C.A.I.*, Pl. I. 6.	
9	50·0	·8	,, additional 	Various punches, including  [Prinsep, 1847.]
0	46·0	·8 × ·4	,,	Various punches. [Edwards, 1850.]
			Var. *b.*	
1	51·2	*round* ·75		 surrounded by several circular punches. [Madras Govt., 1896.]
			Var. *c.*	
2	40·7	·9		Various punches, including  [Theobald, 1906.] **Pl. VII. 8.**
			Var. *d.*	
6	48·0	*square* ·85 × ·45		Various punches. [Madras Govt., 1896.]

No.	Wt.	Metal. Size.	Obverse.	Reverse.
			Var. *e.*	
14	49·7	Æ *round* ·7		 [Bombay Govt., 1918. (from Palanpur State)
15	48·5	*square* ·8 × ·5	,, ,,	Various punches, including  [Director of Industries, C. P. 1925.] (from Thathari)
16	49·0	*round* ·9	,, ,,	Various punches, including  [Cunningham, 1894 (from Mirzapur)
			Var. *f.*	
17	47·0	*square* ·8		Various punches, including  [Capt. Barrow, 1877
			Var. *g.*	
18	48·8	*round* ·85	 countermarked 	Various punches. [Cunningham, 1894 **Pl. VIII. 17.**
			Var. *h.*	
19	48·5	·85	 [?]	Star. [Director of Industries, C. P. 1925.] (from Thathari)

No.	Wt.	Metal. Size.	Obverse.	Reverse.
			GROUP VI.	
		Æ	Var. *a*.	
1	51·5	*square* ·75	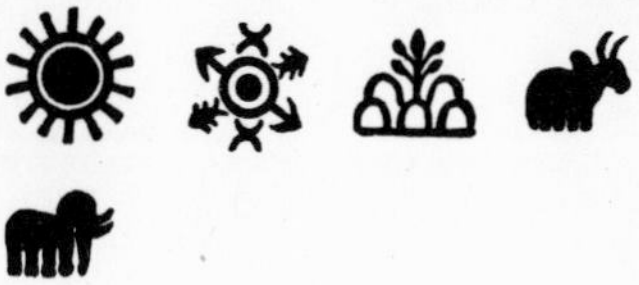	Plain. [Whitehead, 1922.] **Pl. VII. 19.**
2	43·0	·7 × ·5	” ”	Illegible punch. [Theobald, 1906.]
3	50·0	·8	” ”	Various punches. [Theobald, 1906.] **Pl. IX. 3.**
4	45·6	*round* ·8	” ”	Various punches, including  [Theobald, 1906.]
5	51·7	·8	” ”	Plain. ” **Pl. VIII. 2.**
6	51·0	·6	” ”	Illegible punch. [Whitehead, 1906.] **Pl. VII. 18.**
			Var. *b*.	
	49·5	*square* ·8		Numerous punches. [Prinsep, 1847.] **Pl. IX. 23.**
	49·0	*round* ·8	” ”	Illegible punch.

No.	Wt.	Metal. Size.	Obverse.	Reverse.
			Var. *c.*	
9	48·3	Æ *square* ·8		Various punches. [Cunningham, 1894.] **Pl. VIII. 16.**
			Var. *d.*	
10	49·5	*round* ·7		Illegible punches. [Bombay Govt., 1918.] (from Palanpur State)
			Var. *e.*	
11	51·3	*square* ·7		Plain. [Cunningham, 1894.
			Var. *f.*	
12	46·7	·9 × ·5		Various punches. [Whitehead, 1922 **Pl. IX. 21.**
			Var. *g.*	
13	34·2	·6		Numerous punches. [I. O. C., 1882

No.	Wt.	Metal. Size.	Obverse.	Reverse.
			Var. *h*.	
14	43·4	AR *square* ·7		 [Cunningham, 1894.] **Pl. X. 10.**
			Var. *i*.	
15	27·5	·6 × ·35		Plain. [Theobald, 1906.]
			Var. *j*.	
16	50·0	·8 × ·4	 [?]	Various punches. [Prinsep, 1847.] **Pl. IX. 20.**

No.	Wt.	Metal. Size.	Obverse.	Reverse.
			GROUP VII.	
			Var. a.	
1	41·0	Æ *round* ·95		Numerous punches, including  [Whitehead, 1922.] **Pl. X. 16.**
			Var. b.	
2	50·6	·8	 [?]	Various punches, including  [Cunningham, 1894.] **Pl. IX. 19.**
			C., *C.A.I.*, Pl. I. 13.	
			Var. c.	
3	50·7	·8		Various punches. [Cunningham, 1894.] **Pl. X. 21.**
			Var. d.	
4	49·3	·9	 [?]	Various punches. [Parkes Weber Gift, 1906.] **Pl. IX. 18.**

No.	Wt.	Metal. Size.	Obverse.	Reverse.
		Æ	Var. *e.*	
5	54·8	*square* ·8		Various punches. [Cunningham, 1894.] **Pl. X. 20.**
6	38·4	*round* ·8	,, ,,	,, ,,
			C., *C.A.I.*, Pl. I. 8.	
			Var. *f.*	
7	46·8	*square* ·9		Various punches. [Cunningham, 1894.] **Pl. IX. 17.**

No.	Wt.	Metal. Size.	Obverse.	Reverse.
			GROUP VIII.	
			Var. a.	
			 FIG. 1.	
1	51·2	Æ *round* ·6	 [?]	Various punches. See fig. 1.
			CLASS 7.	
			 FIG. 2.	 FIG. 3.
2	39·5	·6	Includes rudely drawn elephant and smaller animal.	Miscellaneous punches. See fig. 2. [Theobald, 1906.
3	40·8	·7 × ·4	” ”	” ” See fig. 3.

PART III

UNINSCRIBED CAST COINS

No.	Wt.	Metal. Size.	Obverse.	Reverse.
		Æ *square*	Var. *a.*	
1	37·5	·6	Three standing figures, the central one facing and the two on side turned towards him.	On l. tree in railing. On r. elephant to l. Below  [Cunningham, 1894.] **Pl. XI. 1.**
			Var. *b.*	
2	62·5	·6	Building (?) on l.; tree in centre. On r. female figure to l.	Tree in railing on l.; lingam on square pedestal on r. [Cunningham, 1894.] **Pl. XI. 2.**
			Var. *c.*	
3	21·0	·45	Lion l.  above on r.  below.	Tree in railing on l. On r.  above 
4	25·0	·6	,,	,, ,, [Cunningham, 1894.]
5	13·5	·5	,,	,, ,, **Pl. XI. 3.**

No.	Wt.	Metal. Size.	Obverse.	Reverse.
			Var. *d.*	
6	22·0	Æ *square* ·5	Elephant r.  on r.  below.	Tree in railing on l. On r. wheel above  [Cunningham, 1894. **Pl. XI. 4.**
			Var. *e.*	
7	17·5	·5	Elephant l.  on r.  below.	Tree in railing on r. On l.  above and belo wheel. [Cunningham, 1894.
			Var. *f.*	
8	11·0	·45	Elephant l.  on l.  below.	  on l. Uncertain object on r. [Cunningham, 1894
9	13·0	·4	,,	,, ,,
			Var. *g.*	
10	68·6	·6	 on l. Elephant to l. on r.   below.	 [Bhagvanlal, 1889

No.	Wt.	Metal. Size.	Obverse.	Reverse.
1	65·0	Æ *square* ·55	As preceding.	As preceding. [Bhagvanlal, 1889.] **Pl. XI. 5.**
2	76·5	·65	,,	,, [Cunningham, 1894.]
			Var. *h.*	
3	80·3	·6	Elephant to r. on l.  on r.  below.	 [Clive Bailey, 1889.] **Pl. XI. 6.**
4	51·0	·5	,, ,,	,, ,, [Bhagvanlal, 1889.]
			Var. *i.*	
5	60·0	·6	 on l. Elephant to l.  above on r.	 [Eden, 1853.]
6	70·5	·6	,,	,, [Bhagvanlal, 1889.]
7	61·5	·6	,,	,, [I. O. C., 1882.] **Pl. XI. 7.**

Var. *j*.

No.	Wt.	Metal. Size.	Obverse.	Reverse.
18	55·0	Æ *square* ·6	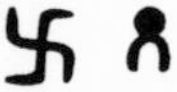 above elephant l.  on l.  below.	 [Bhagvanlal, 1889.
19	41·8	·6	,,	,, [E. G. Coutts, Esq., Pres., 1907. **Pl. XI. 8.**
20	47·2	·6	,,	,, [Gen. Stubbs, 1865. **Pl. XI. 9.**
21	49·5	·6	,,	,, [Eden, 1853
22	46·0	·6	,,	,, —
23	47·8	·6	,,	,, [Thomas, 1850
24	41·0	·5	,,	,, [Knutt, 1850.
25	37·2	·55	,,	,, [Cunningham, 1894
26	27·5	·5	,,	,, ,,

o.	Wt.	Metal. Size.	Obverse.	Reverse.
7	30·0	Æ *square* ·45	As preceding.	As preceding. [Cunningham, 1894.] **Pl. XI. 10.**
8	25·0	·45	”	” ”
9	25·0	·5	”	” ”
0	19·8	·5	”	” ”
1	28·0	·5	”	” ”
2	25·7	·58	”	” ”
3	10·0	·4 *broken*	”	” ”
			Var. *k*.	
4	51·0	·6	 Elephant l. 	 [Cunningham, 1894.] **Pl. XI. 11.**
5	52·0	·6	”	” ” [Major Hay, 1860.] **Pl. XI. 13.**
6	58·7	·6	”	” ” [Eden, 1853.]
7	60·0	·6	”	” ” **Pl. XI. 14.**

No.	Wt.	Metal. Size.	Obverse.	Reverse.
38	61·0	Æ *square* ·6	As preceding.	As preceding. [Cunningham, 1894 **Pl. XI. 15.**
			C., *C.A.I.*, Pl. I. 28.	
39	60·0	·6	,,	,, [Cunningham, 1894
40	101·0	·6	,,	,, ,,
41	56·5	·55	,,	,, ,,
42	55·0	·6	,,	,, ,,
43	45·5	·6	,,	,, ,,
44	55·0	·55	,,	,, [Bhagvanlal, 1889
45	58·7	·65	,,	,, —
46	52·0	·58	,,	,, [I. O. C., 1882
47	56·0	·6	,,	,, [Bhagvanlal, 1889
48	51·5	·6	,,	,, [Thomas, 1850
49	51·0	·6	,,	,, ,,

o.	Wt.	Metal. Size.	Obverse.	Reverse.
		Æ *square*		
)	49·0	·6	As preceding.	As preceding. [Bhagvanlal, 1889.]
l	48·5	·6	"	" "
2	46·0	·6	"	" "
3	39·0	·6	"	" "
4	42·0	·55	"	" "
5	40·0	·6	"	" "
6	40·0	·6	"	" [Prinsep, 1847.]
7	45·0	·6	"	" [Bhagvanlal, 1889.]
3	42·0	·65	"	" "
)	35·0	·5	"	" [Eden, 1853.] **Pl. XI. 12.**
)	31·5	·5	 Elephant l.	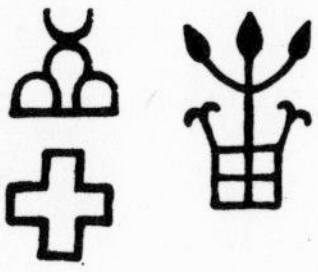 [Eden, 1853.]
l	44·0	·53	"	" [Thomas, 1850.]

No.	Wt.	Metal. Size.	Obverse.	Reverse.
			Var. *l.*	
62	93·5	Æ *square* ·7 × ·5	Elephant l.	 on r. and l. [Prinsep, 1847
63	48·5	·5 × ·45	Elephant r.	,, [Thomas, 1850 **Pl. XI. 22.**
64	43·0	·7 × ·5	,,	,,
			Var. *m.*	
65	144·5	*round* ·85		 [Bhagvanlal, 1889 **Pl. XI. 16.**
			Var. *n.*	
66	54·0	·55		 [H. Nelson Wright, Esq., Pre 1915 **Pl. XI. 17.**
67	50·0	·55	,,	,, [Bhagvanlal, 188
68	52·5	·5	,,	,, ,,
69	51·0	·45	,,	,, ,,
70	53·5	·6	,,	,, [J. Burgess, 189 **Pl. XI. 18.**
71	35·0	·5	,,	,,

No.	Wt.	Metal. Size.	Obverse.	Reverse.
		Æ square	Var. *o.*	
2	51·0	·55	 Pellet on r.	 [Eden, 1853.] **Pl. XI. 20.**
3	50·0	·55	,, ,,	,, ,,
4	41·5	·5	,, ,,	,, ,,
5	68·0	·45	,, Pellet on l.	,, [Cunningham, 1894.] **Pl. XI. 19.**
			C., *C.A.I.*, Pl. I. 29.	
6	41·3	·5	,, ,,	,, ,,
7	45·0	·55	,, Pellet on r.	,, [Prinsep, 1847.]
8	42·1	·5	,, Pellet on l.	,, [Thomas, 1850.] **Pl. XI. 21.**
9	59·0	·5	Pellet on l. and in each compartment of 	,, ,,
			Var. *p.*	
0	46·5	·65	Elephant l. with rider.	 [Eden, 1853.] **Pl. XI. 23.**
1	37·0	·65	,, ,,	,, [Cunningham, 1894.]

No.	Wt.	Metal. Size	Obverse.	Reverse.
82	25·5	Æ *round* ·55	As preceding.	As preceding. [Bhagvanlal, 1889.]
83	32·5	·5	,,	,, —
84	34·0	·5	,,	,, —
			Var. *q.*	
85	58·5	·68	Elephant l.	 [Thomas, 1850.]
86	58·5	·65	,,	,, ,,
87	51·0	·55	,,	,, ,,
88	45·0	·55	,,	,, [Stacey.
89	41·5	·6	,,	,, —
90	41·0	·6	,,	,, [Gen. Stubbs, 1865. **Pl. XI. 25.**
91	47·5	·55	,,	,, [Cunningham, 1894
92	40·0	·45	,,	,, ,,
93	32·8	·45	,,	,, [Prinsep, 1847

o.	Wt.	Metal. Size.	Obverse.	Reverse.
4	36·0	Æ *round* ·5	As preceding.	As preceding. [Cunningham, 1894.]
5	33·5	·55	,,	,, ,,
6	31·0	·5	,,	,, ,, **Pl. XI. 26.**
7	37·5	·55	,,	,, ,,
8	31·5	·5	,,	,, [Thomas, 1850.] **Pl. XII. 4.**
9	32·0	·5	,,	,, [Cunningham, 1894.]
00	41·5	·5	,,	,, [Thomas, 1850.] **Pl. XII. 3.**
01	71·0	1 × ·5 *double coin*	,,	,, [Cunningham, 1894.] **Pl. XII. 1.**
			C., *C.A.I.*, Pl. I. 25.	
02	32·0	·45	,,	,, ,,
03	34·0	·5	,,	,, ,,
04	35·0	·45	,,	,, ,,

No.	Wt.	Metal. Size.	Obverse.	Reverse.
105	26·5	Æ *round* ·5	As preceding.	As preceding. [Cunningham, 1894.] **Pl. XI. 24.**
106	30·0	·5	,,	,, [Eden, 1853.]
107	29·0	·5	,,	,, ,,
108	26·5	·5	,,	,, ,,
109	27·0	·5	,,	,, [Thomas, 1850.]
110	29·0	·5	,,	,, ,,
111	26·0	·45	,,	,, [Steuart, 1853.]
112	24·0	·5	,,	,, [Cunningham, 1894.]
113	29·5	·5	,,	,, ,,
114	25·0	·5	,,	,, [Thomas, 1850.
115	28·0	·5	,,	,, [Eden, 1853.
115 *a*	26·5	·5	,,	,, ,,
116	28·0	·5	,,	,, [Bhagvanlal, 1894.
117	25·0	·5	,,	,, ,,

No.	Wt.	Metal. Size.	Obverse.	Reverse.
118	27·2	Æ *round* ·45	As preceding.	As preceding. [Stuart, 1853.]
119	29·0	·45	”	” [Eden, 1853.]
120	29·0	·45	”	” [Thomas, 1850.]
121	35·0 *double coin*	·4	”	” [Cunningham, 1894.] **Pl. XII. 2.**
122	20·0	·4	”	” [Eden, 1853.]
123	21·0	·4	”	” —
124	21·0	·5	”	” [Cunningham, 1894.]
125	26·0	·55	”	” ”
126	21·5	·5	”	” ”
127	18·0	·4	”	” ”
128	14·0	·4	”	” [Thomas, 1850.]
129	10·5	·35	”	” ”

No.	Wt.	Metal. Size.	Obverse.	Reverse.
			Var. *r.*	
130	45·5	Æ *round* ·6	Bull r.  above.	 [Cunningham, 1894.]
131	41·5	·65	,, ,,	,, [H. Nelson Wright, Esq., Pres. 1915.]
132	50·0	·6	,, ,,	,, [Thomas, 1850.] **Pl. XII. 6.**
133	56·5	·6	,, ,,	,, ,,
134	65·0	·6	,, ,,	,, [Eden, 1853.]
135	45·0	·6	,, ,,	,, [Cunningham, 1894.] **Pl. XII. 7.**
			C., *C.A.I.*, Pl. I. 26.	
136	60·0	·6	,, ,,	,, [Thomas, 1850.] **Pl. XII. 5.**
			Var. *s.*	
137	75·0	·6	 Lion l.	 [Bhagvanlal, 1889.]
138	70·0	·65	,,	,, [H. Nelson Wright, Esq., Pres. 1915.]

No.	Wt.	Metal. Size.	Obverse.	Reverse.
		Æ *round*		
39	58·5	·6	As preceding.	As preceding. [Cunningham, 1894.]
40	50·0	·6	,,	,, ,, C., *C.A.I.*, Pl. I. 27.
41	46·5	·55	,,	,, [Thomas, 1850.]
42	68·0	·6	,,	,, ,, **Pl. XII. 8.**
43	91·0	·65	,,	,, ,,
44	73·5	·65	,,	,, ,,
45	66·0	·6	,,	,, ,,
46	67·0	·65	,,	,, ,,
47	76·0	·65	,,	,, ,,
48	70·5	·6	,,	,, ,,
49	60·5	·6	,,	,, ,,
50	64·0	·6	,,	,, ,,
51	65·0	·6	,,	,, ,,
52	66·5	·6	,,	,, [Prinsep, 1847.]

No.	Wt.	Metal. Size.	Obverse.	Reverse.
		Æ *round*		
153	69·0	·6	As preceding.	As preceding. [Prinsep, 1847.
154	75·5	·6	,,	,, [Gen. Stubbs, 1865. **Pl. XII. 9.**
155	64·2	·6	,,	,, [Stuart, 1853.
156	72·5	·6	,,	,, ,, **Pl. XII. 10.**
157	62·5	·6	,,	,, [Eden, 1853.
158	48·0	·6	,,	,, ,,
159	46·0	·6	,,	,, [Thomas, 1850.
160	45·0	·6	,,	,, ,,

PART IV

PUNCHMARKED COPPER COINS

No.	Wt.	Metal. Size.	Obverse.	Reverse.
1	35 9	Æ *square* 1·0 × ·9		 [Purchased, 1921.]
2	347	1·1 × ·8	” ”	” ”
3	341	·9	” ”	” ”
4	339	1·05 × ·9	” ”	” ” **Pl. XII. 12.**
5	337	1·0 × ·9	” ”	” ”
6	337	1·0 × ·75	” ”	” ”
7	327	1·0 × ·85	” ”	” ”
8	328	·95	” ”	” ”
9	325	1·1 × ·95	” ”	” ”
0	321	1·0 × ·8	” ”	” ”

No.	Wt.	Metal. Size.	Obverse.	Reverse.
11	317	Æ *square* ·55 × ·8	As preceding.	As preceding. [Purchased, 1921. **Pl. XII. 10.**
12	315	·5	,,	,, ,,
13	275	·8 × ·9	,,	,, ,, **Pl. XIII. 6.**
14	273	·75 × ·85	,,	,, ,,
15	269	·7 × ·8	,,	,, ,,
16	267	·8 × ·9	,,	,, ,,
17	267	1·0 × ·75	,,	,, ,,
18	266	·6 × ·9	,,	,, ,,
19	265	·85	,,	,, ,,
20	263	·9 × ·7	,,	,, ,,
21	262	·85	,,	,, ,,
22	262	·85	,,	,, ,,
23	262	·8	,,	,, ,,
24	262	·9 × ·7	,,	,, ,,
25	260	1·0 × ·6	,,	,, ,,

No.	Wt.	Metal. Size.	Obverse.	Reverse.
26	260	Æ *square* ·75 × ·7	As preceding.	As preceding. [Purchased, 1921.]
27	260	·85	"	" "
28	258	1·1 × ·75	"	" "
29	258	·85 × ·7	"	" "
30	257	·95	"	" "
31	257	·8 × ·95	"	" "
32	257	1·25 × ·7	"	" " **Pl. XII. 11.**
3	256	1·2 × ·7	"	" "
4	255	1·1 × ·65	"	" "
5	255	1·4 × ·7	"	" "
6	255	·9 × ·8	"	" "
7	255	·95	"	" "
8	255	·75 × ·85	"	" "
9	255	1·0 × ·85	"	" "
0	254	·85	"	" "

No.	Wt.	Metal. Size.	Obverse.	Reverse.
41	253	Æ *square* ·85	As preceding.	As preceding. [Purchased, 1921
42	252	·85 × ·75	,,	,, ,,
43	252	·85 × ·8	,,	,, ,,
44	252	1·25 × ·6	,,	,, ,,
45	252	1·05 × ·7	,,	,, ,,
46	252	·9 × ·7	,,	,, ,,
47	251	1·2 × ·7	,,	,, ,,
48	251	1·0 × ·7	,,	,, ,,
49	251	1·0 × ·8	,,	,, ,,
50	251	·95 × ·7	,,	,, ,,
51	250	·9 × ·75	,,	,, ,,
52	250	·9	,,	,, ,,
53	250	1·1 × ·5	,,	,, ,,
54	250	·8 × ·7	,,	,, ,,
55	250	·9 × ·6	,,	,, ,,

No.	Wt.	Metal. Size.	Obverse.	Reverse.
6	250	Æ *square* ·95 × ·75	As preceding.	As preceding. [Purchased, 1921.]
7	250	·8 × ·6	"	" "
8	249	·7 × ·55	"	" [Cunningham, 1894.]
			C., *C.A.I.*, Pl. I. 21.	
9	249	1·0 × ·8	"	" [Purchased, 1921.]
0	248	·85	"	" "
1	248	1·0 × ·8	"	" "
2	247	1·3 × ·7	"	" "
3	247	·85	"	" "
4	247	·9 × ·65	"	" "
5	247	1·0 × ·8	"	" "
6	247	1·0 × ·65	"	" "
7	247	·9 × ·75	"	" "
8	247	1·1 × ·6	"	" "
9	247	·8 × ·65	"	" "

No.	Wt.	Metal. Size.	Obverse.	Reverse.
70	247	Æ *square* 1·0 × ·75	As preceding.	As preceding. [Purchased, 1921.
71	247	·85 × ·65	"	" "
72	246	·85	"	" "
73	246	1·4 × ·5	"	" "
74	246	·7 × ·9	"	" "
75	245	·8 × ·7	"	" "
76	245	·9 × ·75	"	" "
77	245	·9 × ·65	"	" "
78	245	·85	"	" "
79	243	·8 × ·9	"	" "
80	243	1·1 × ·7	"	" "
81	243	·75	"	" "
82	243	·8 × ·75	"	" "
83	243	·7	"	" "
84	243	1·0 × ·7	·	" "

o.	Wt.	Metal. Size.	Obverse.	Reverse.
5	242	Æ *square* ·9 × ·7	As preceding.	As preceding. [Purchased, 1921.]
6	242	·8 × ·7	,,	,, ,,
7	242	·8 × ·5	,,	,, ,,
8	241	1·2 × ·6	,,	,, ,,
9	240	1·3 × ·7	,,	,, ,,
0	240	·9 × ·65	,,	,, ,,
1	240	1·0 × ·8	,,	,, ,,
2	239	1·0 × ·7	,,	,, ,, **Pl. XIII. 12.**
3	239	·95 × ·65	,,	,, ,, **Pl. XIII. 7.**
4	239	·9 × ·85	,,	,, ,, **Pl. XIII. 9.**
5	239	·7 × ·7	,,	,, ,,
6	238	1·1 × ·6	,,	,, ,,
7	238	1·05 × ·7	,,	,, ,,
8	238	·8 × ·9	,,	,, ,,

No.	Wt.	Metal. Size.	Obverse.	Reverse.
99	238	Æ *square* 1·1 × ·8	As preceding.	As preceding. [Purchased, 1921 **Pl. XIII. 4.**
100	238	·8 × ·6	,,	,, ,,
101	238	·85 × ·9	,,	,, ,, **Pl. XIII. 5.**
102	238	1·4 × ·6	,,	,, ,,
103	237	1·1 × ·8	,,	,, ,,
104	237	·9	,,	,, ,,
105	237	1·2 × ·6	,,	,, ,,
106	237	1·0 × ·7	,,	,, ,,
107	236	·8 × ·75	,,	,, ,,
108	236	·85 × ·8	,,	,, ,,
109	235	·7 × ·8	,,	,, ,,
110	235	1·3 × ·5	,,	,, ,,
111	235	1·1 × ·6	,,	,, ,,
112	235	·8	,,	,, ,,

No.	Wt.	Metal. Size.	Obverse.	Reverse.
13	235	Æ *square* ·85 × ·65	As preceding.	As preceding. [Purchased, 1921.]
14	235	·85	”	” ”
15	235	·9 × ·6	”	” ”
16	235	1·0 × ·6	”	” ” **Pl. XIII. 1.**
17	234	1·0 × ·7	”	” ”
18	233	·9 × ·7	”	” ”
19	233	·85	”	” ”
20	233	·8 × ·75	”	” ”
21	232	1·0 × ·75	”	” ”
22	232	1·3 × ·8	”	” ”
23	232	1·2 × ·75	”	” ”
24	232	·85	”	” ” **Pl. XIII. 8.**
25	232	1·2 × ·65	”	” ”
26	232	·85	”	” ”

No.	Wt.	Metal. Size.	Obverse.	Reverse.
127	231	Æ *square* ·9 × ·7	As preceding.	As preceding. [Purchased, 1921.
128	231	1·2 × ·55	„	„ „
129	231	·95 × ·7	„	„ „
130	231	·95 × ·8	„	„ „
131	230	·85	„	„ „
132	230	·95	„	„ „
133	230	·85	„	„ „ [Cunningham, 1894
			C., *C.A.I.*, Pl. I. 22.	
134	230	·9 × ·6	„	„ [Purchased, 1921
135	230	·95 × ·7	„	„ „
136	229	1·7 × ·6	„	„ „ **Pl. XII. 15.**
137	227	·85	„	„ „
138	227	1·0 × ·65	„	„ „
139	227	·85	„	„ „

No.	Wt.	Metal. Size.	Obverse.	Reverse.
40	227	Æ *square* ·85 × ·75	As preceding.	As preceding. [Purchased, 1921.]
41	226	·9 × ·6	,,	,, ,,
42	226	·85 × ·65	,,	,, ,,
43	226	1·0 × ·8	,,	,, ,,
44	225	1·0 × ·8	,,	,, ,, **Pl. XIII. 3.**
45	225	1·0 × ·6	,,	,, ,,
46	225	·9 × ·75	,,	,, ,,
47	225	1·0 × ·75	,,	,, ,,
48	225	·9 × ·75	,,	,, ,,
49	225	1·0 × ·6	,,	,, ,,
50	224	·95 × ·75	,,	,, ,,
51	224	·95 × ·75	,,	,, ,,
52	223	·8	,,	,, ,,
53	222	·9 × ·75	,,	,, ,,

No.	Wt.	Metal. Size.	Obverse.	Reverse.
154	222	Æ *square* ·8 × ·85	As preceding.	As preceding. [Purchased, 1921
155	221	·9 × ·7	,,	,, ,,
156	221	·85	,,	,, ,,
157	220	·9 × ·7	,,	,, ,,
158	220	·9	,,	,, ,,
159	219	·9	,,	,, ,,
160	218	1·0 × ·75	,,	,, ,,
161	218	1·2 × ·6	,,	,, ,,
162	217	1·1 × ·6	,,	,, ,,
163	217	1·0 × ·8	,,	,, ,,
164	217	1·1 × ·85	,,	,, ,, **Pl. XII. 13.**
165	216	·8	,,	,, ,,
166	216	·8	,,	,, ,,
167	216	·95 × ·7	,,	,, ,,

No.	Wt.	Metal. Size.	Obverse.	Reverse.
68	216	Æ *square* ·8	As preceding.	As preceding. [Purchased, 1921.]
69	215	·75	”	” ”
70	215	·75	”	” ”
71	215	·8 × ·95	”	” ”
72	214	·8 × ·9	”	” ”
73	213	1·0 × ·75	”	” ”
74	213	1·0 × ·75	”	” ”
75	212	1·0 × ·75	”	” ”
76	212	·9 × ·8	”	” ”
77	212	·8 × ·65	”	” ”
78	211	1·0 × ·7	”	” ”
79	211	·9 × ·85	”	” ”
80	211	1·1 × ·7	”	” ”
81	211	1·35 × ·6	”	” ”
82	210	·85	”	” ”

No.	Wt.	Metal. Size.	Obverse.	Reverse.
183	210	Æ *square* ·85	As preceding.	As preceding. [Purchased, 1921.]
184	208	·85	”	” ”
185	208	1·2 × ·65	”	” ”
186	208	·8 × ·9	”	” ” **Pl. XII. 14.**
187	207	·9	”	” ” **Pl. XIII. 2.**
188	207	·8 × ·7	”	” ”
189	206	·8 × ·7	”	” ”
190	205	·7 × ·75	”	” ”
191	205	·9 × ·7	”	” ”
192	205	·8	”	” ”
193	205	·8	”	” ”
194	205	1·3 × ·5	”	” ”
195	205	·85	”	” ”
196	205	·8 × ·65	”	” ”

[N]o.	Wt.	Metal. Size.	Obverse.	Reverse.
[.]97	205	Æ *square* ·8 × ·7	As preceding.	As preceding. [Purchased, 1921.]
[.]98	203	1·0 × ·7	„	„ „
[.]99	203	1·05 × ·6	„	„ „ **Pl. XIII. 11.**
[.]00	203	·9 × ·75	„	„ „
[.]01	202	·75	„	„ „
[.]02	200	1·1 × ·7	„	„ „
[.]03	199	1·0 × ·75	„	„ „
[.]04	198	·9 × ·65	„	„ „
[.]05	198	·85	„	„ „
[.]06	197	·6 × ·9	„	„ „
[.]07	197	·75	„	„ „ **Pl. XIII. 13.**
[.]08	194	·6 × ·85	„	„ „
[.]09	193	·8 × ·65	„	„ „
[.]10	189	·9 × ·7	„	„

No.	Wt.	Metal. Size.	Obverse.	Reverse.
211	187	Æ *square* 1·2 × ·55	As preceding.	As preceding. [Purchased, 1921.
212	185	·75	,,	,, ,,
213	178	·7 × ·9	,,	,, ,,
214	176	·75	,,	,, ,,
215	175	·8	,,	,, ,,
216	172	1·5 × ·6	,,	,, ,, **Pl. XII. 16.**
217	162	·8	,,	,, [Cunningham, 1894.

C., *C.A.I.*, Pl. I. 20.

PART V

TRIBAL COINS

No.	Wt.	Metal. Size.	Obverse.	Reverse.
			ACYUTA	
		Æ	Early Fourth Century A. D.	
1	25·0	*round* ·5	𑀅𑀘𑁆𑀬𑀼 (*Acy-*) in border of dots.	 [Cunningham, 1894.] **Pl. XIV. 1.**
2	26·5	·5	,, ,,	,, ,,
3	28·5	·5	,, ,,	,, ,,
4	25·0	·55	,, ,,	,, ,,
5	23·5	·5	,, ,,	,, ,, **Pl. XIV. 2.**
6	23·0	·5	,, ,,	,, ,,
7	23·5	·5	,, ,,	,, ,,
8	21·0	·5	,, ,,	,, ,, **Pl. XIV. 3.**

No.	Wt.	Metal. Size.	Obverse.	Reverse.
		Æ *round*		
9	23·7	·5	As preceding.	As preceding. [Cunningham, 1894.
10	26·0	·5	„	„ „ Pl. XIV. 4.
11	21·0	·5	„	„ „
12	21·0	·5	„	„ „
13	20·3	·5	„	„ „
14	20·0	·5	„	„ „
15	18·5	·5	„	„ „
16	16·0	·5	„	„ „
17	16·3	·45	„	„ „
18	16·5	·45	„	„ „
19	15·0	·5	„	„ „
20	14·0	·45	„	„ „
21	13·0	·45	„	„ „ Pl. XIV. 5.
22	13·5	·45	„	„ „

No.	Wt.	Metal. Size.	Obverse.	Reverse.
		Æ *round*		
23	12·0	·45	As preceding.	As preceding. [Cunningham, 1894.]
24	11·0	·4	,,	,, ,,
25	11·0	·5	,,	,, ,,

? Connected with Acyuta dynasty.

Pṛ - - -

No.	Wt.	Metal. Size.	Obverse.	Reverse.
26	·46	·6	प्र (*pr*) in border of dots.	A 16-spoked wheel. [Cunningham, 1894.] **Pl. XIV. 6.**

No.	Wt.	Metal. Size.	Obverse.	Reverse.

ALMORĀ

Second—First Centuries B. C.

ŚIVADATTA

No.	Wt.	Metal. Size.	Obverse.	Reverse.
1	327	Æ base 1·1	 in centre. Around, bull before tree in railing; followed by legend 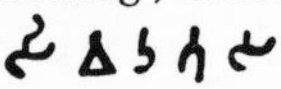 (*Sivadatasa*).	 [Clive-Bayley, 1889 **Pl. XIV. 7.**

P. E., i, p. 224, fig.

ŚIVAPĀLITA

No.	Wt.	Metal. Size.	Obverse.	Reverse.
2	281	1·0	Rude human figure in centre; bull before tree in railing; legend  (*Śivapālita*[*sa*]).	As preceding. [Clive-Bayley, 1889 **Pl. XIV. 8.**

HARIDATTA

No.	Wt.	Metal. Size.	Obverse.	Reverse.
3	304	1·1	 in centre. Around, bull before tree in railing; followed by legend 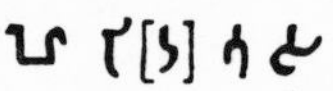 (*Haridatasa*).	As preceding. [Clive-Bayley, 1889 **Pl. XIV. 9.**

(The above three coins were found 'near Almorah in t Himalaya mountains' and presented to Sir Henry Elliot, fro whom they passed to the Clive-Bayley Collection.)

P. E., i, p. 224.

ĀRJUNĀYANA

Second Century B.C.

Var. *a*.

No.	Wt.	Metal. Size.	Obverse.	Reverse.
1	81	Æ ·65	Bull l. on hill (?).	Standing figure between  (lingam ?) and   (*Aj*(*u*)*nāyan*-) [Cunningham, 1894.] **Pl. XIV. 10.**

C., *C.A.I.*, Pl. VIII. 20.
(cf. *P.E.*, Pl. XLIV. 22).

Var. *b*.

No.	Wt.	Metal. Size.	Obverse.	Reverse.
2	53	1·25	Bull r. before tree in railing.	Bull r. before lingam. 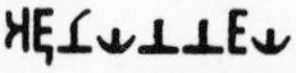 (*Ajunāyan*(*ā*)*n*(*āṁ*)*jaya*) [Cunningham, 1894.] **Pl. XIV. 11.**

Var. *c*.

No.	Wt.	Metal. Size.	Obverse.	Reverse.
3	104	·6	Much worn: bull?	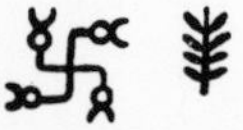 [-]  - (=*j*(*u*)*n*(*ā*)*y*(*a*)*n*-) [Eden, 1853.] **Pl. XIV. 12.**

No.	Wt.	Metal. Size.	Obverse.	Reverse.
			AUDUMBARA Second—First Centuries B. C.	
			ŚIVADĀSA	
		Æ *square*	Tree within enclosure on l. Forepart of elephant to l. on r. Undulating line below.	Two-storied domed stupa. Trident with axe on r.
1	45·0	·7	[illegible] - - - (*S*[*i*]*vadasasa*)	- - - [illegible] (- - *bar*[*a*]*sa*) [Whitehead, 1922. Pl. XV. 1.
2	33·0	·6	[illegible] - - -	- - [illegible] (- - *Sivadasasa*) [Whitehead, 1922.
			RUDRADĀSA	
3	36·8	·65 × ·5	As preceding. [illegible] - - - (*Rudradasasa*)	As preceding. [illegible] - - (*Odubarisa*) [Whitehead, 1922.
4	46·0	·65 × ·4	[illegible] - -	— ,,
5	36·0	·65	[illegible] - -	— ,, Pl. XV. 4.
6	40·0	·65	[- - - - -] [illegible] (*maha* - -) [illegible] (*Odubarisa*)	— [Whitehead, 1922 Pl. XV. 2.
7	35·0	·7	[illegible] - - -	[-] [illegible] [Irippal find, 1915.
8	31·0	·7	[illegible] - - (- - *sa raña Rudradasasa*)	— ,, Pl. XV. 10.

No.	Wt.	Metal. Size.	Obverse.	Reverse.
9	33·0	Æ *square* ·7	As preceding. 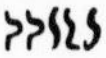 [- -]	As preceding.  [Irippal find, 1915.]
0	48·0	·65	- - -	- - - ,,
1	45·0	·65	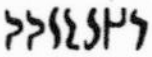	,, ,, **Pl. XV. 3.**

MAHĀDEVA

No.	Wt.	Metal. Size.	Obverse.	Reverse.
2	33·0	AR *round* ·65	Humped bull r.; lotus flower(?) in front.  around. (*Bhagavatamahadevasa*) Below 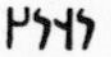 (*rajarañа*).	Elephant l.; trident on l. 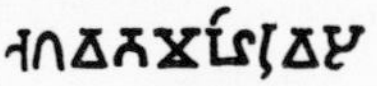 around. Below  (*rajarāja*). [Cunningham, 1894.] **Pl. XIV. 16.**
			C., *C.A.I.*, Pl. IV. 5.	
3	31·5	·65	Humped bull l.  on l.;  above. - - 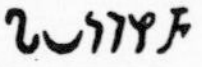 around. -  below.	As preceding. Traces of legend around. Below 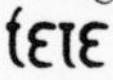 (*rājaraja*). [Gen. M. Clerk, 1920.] **Pl. XIV. 17.**
4	42·0	Æ *square* ·6	Tree in enclosure; forepart of elephant to l. on r. Top 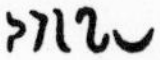 (*Mahadevasa* -) On r. - 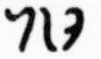 (*Odub* - -)	Stupa on l., trident with axe on r. On r. - - - 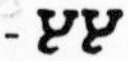 On l. 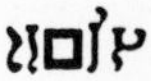 [Whitehead, 1922.] **Pl. XV. 5.**

No.	Wt.	Metal. Size.	Obverse.	Reverse.
15	42·0	Æ *square* ·65	 - - (- - *Mahadevasa*) - - 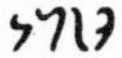	-  - - -  [Irippal find, 1915. **Pl. XV. 6.**
16	40·5	·7	- - -	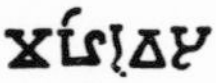  [Irippal find, 1915. **Pl. XV. 7.**
17	31·5	·6	—	 [Irippal find, 1915. **Pl. XV. 8.**
18	45·7	·7	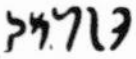	[- -] [Irippal find, 1915. **Pl. XV. 9.**
19	45·0	·65	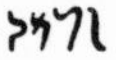 -	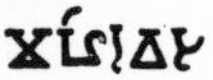  - - [Whitehead, 1922.
20	42·8	·7	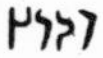 - -  - -	- -  [Irippal find, 1915.
			DHARAGHOṢA	
21	37·5	Æ *round* ·7	Viśvamitra standing facing with r. hand raised, traces of skin over l. arm. In front  (*Viśpamitra*) Around 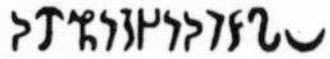 (*Mahadevasa raña Dharaghoṣasa*) Below 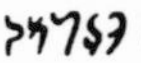 (*Odubarisa*)	Trident with axe on r.; tre in enclosure on l. Around 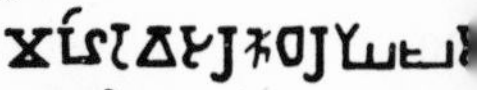 Below 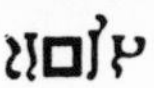 [Cunningham, 1894. **Pl. XIV. 14.**
			C., *C.A.I.*, Pl. IV. 1.	

No.	Wt.	Metal. Size.	Obverse.	Reverse.
22	43·7	Æ square ·6	Tree in enclosure; forepart of elephant. 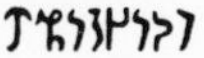 - - ([*Maha*]*devasa raña Dharaghoṣa*[*sa*])	Two-storied stupa; trident on r. -  [Whitehead, 1922.] **Pl. XIV. 15.**

RUDRAVARMA

No.	Wt.	Metal. Size.	Obverse.	Reverse.
23	—	Æ round ·7	Bull r., lotus in front. 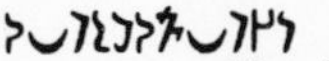 (*Raña Vamakisa Rudravarmasa*)  (*vijayata*)	Elephant r.; trident with axe on l. 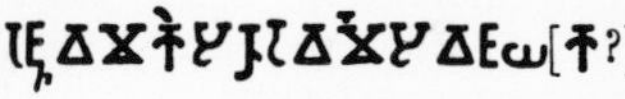 [Lahore Museum.] **Pl. XIV. 13.**

C., *C.A.I.*, Pl. IV. 6.
Panj. Mus. Cat., i, Pl. XVI. 137.

Uncertain

No.	Wt.	Metal. Size.	Obverse.	Reverse.
24	53·5	Æ round ·8	Tree in railing.  on r. cobra on l.	Stupa; traces of Brahmi legend. [J. P. Rawlins, 1922.] **Pl. XV. 11.**
25	27·0	·65	Similar.	” [J. P. Rawlins, 1922.] **Pl. XV. 12.**

ARYAMITRA

No.	Wt.	Metal. Size.	Obverse.	Reverse.
26	71·0	·7	Male figure standing to l., holding spear in r. hand. On l. - - 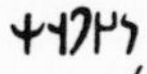 (*Raña Ajami* -)	Elephant to l.; tree on l.  (*Ajamitasa*) [Cunningham, 1894.] **Pl. XV. 13.**

C., *C.A.I.*, Pl. IV. 7.

No.	Wt.	Metal. Size.	Obverse.	Reverse.
27	52·0	Æ *round* ·7	As preceding.  (*Raña Ajamitrasa*)	As preceding. - 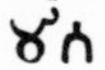 - [Rodgers, 1892. **Pl. XV. 14.**
28	54·5	·75	” - -]  [-]	Traces of legend. [Rodgers, 1892. **Pl. XV. 15.**
29	56·5	·7	” [-]	Elephant to l. with rider. 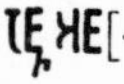[- -] [Whitehead, 1922. **Pl. XLIII. 1.**
30	23·0	·55	Elephant r.; traces of legend.	Tree in railing.  - - - 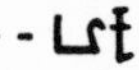 ? [A. Grant, 1885. **Pl. XV. 16.**

MAHIMITRA

No.	Wt.	Metal. Size.	Obverse.	Reverse.
31	51·0	·7	Standing figure as above. [-] (*Mah*(*i*)*mitrasa*)	Elephant to l. - - 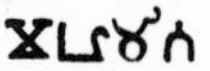 [-] [Cunningham, 1894.
			C., *C.A.I.*, Pl. IV. 9.	
32	35·5	·7	- -  ”	Traces of legend. [Cunningham, 1894. **Pl. XV. 17–18.**
33	34·0	·8	 - - - ”	” [- -] ” **Pl. XV. 19.**
			C., *C.A.I.*, Pl. IV. 8.	

No.	Wt.	Metal. Size.	Obverse.	Reverse.
34	31·0	Æ *round* ·65	As preceding. 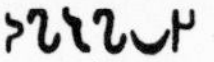 -	As preceding. [-] 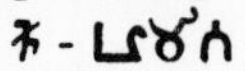 - - [J. P. Rawlins, 1922.] **Pl. XV. 20.**

BHĀNUMITRA

Var. *a.*

No.	Wt.	Metal. Size.	Obverse.	Reverse.
35	32·0	·55	Elephant to l.  (*Raña Bhānumitrasa*)	 [-] 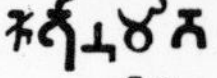 - - [Cunningham, 1894.] **Pl. XV. 21.**
			C., *C.A.I.*, Pl. IV. 12.	
36	28·7	·6	” - - 	” - - [J. P. Rawlins, 1922.]
37	25·0	·6	” 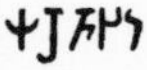	” -  - - ” **Pl. XV. 22.**
38	33·5	·65	”  -	” 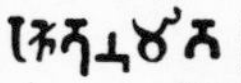 [- -] [J. P. Rawlins, 1922.] **Pl. XV. 19.**
39	37·0	·65	” - - -]  [-]	” - - [J. P. Rawlins, 1922.] **Pl. XV. 1.**
40	37·4	·6	” - -  -	” [-] 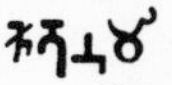 - [J. P. Rawlins, 1922.] **Pl. XVI. 2.**

No.	Wt.	Metal. Size.	Obverse.	Reverse.
41	23·5	Æ *round* ·5	As preceding. 	As preceding.  [J. P. Rawlins, 1922. **Pl. XVI. 3.**
42	32·5	·6	,, 	,, [- -] 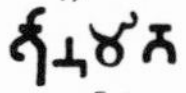 [-] [Cunningham, 1894.
43	31·6	·5	,, 	,, ,,
			Var. *b*.	
44	58·5	·75	Male figure standing to l., holding spear in r. hand; undulating line on r. Inscription illegible.	Elephant to l. with rider. [- -] 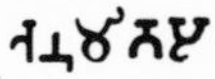 [Whitehead, 1922. **Pl. XLIII. 2.**
			Var. *c*.	
45	28·5	·55	Elephant to l. 	Elephant to r. before  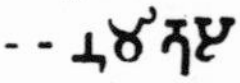 [Whitehead, 1922. **Pl. XLIII. 3.**

o.	Wt.	Metal. Size.	Obverse.	Reverse.

AYODHYĀ

Second Century B. C.

Cast coins: uninscribed

Type I.

| | 23·0 | Æ
round
·7 | Flower. | Plain.
[Cunningham, 1894.]
Pl. XVI. 6. |

C., *C.A.I.*, Pl. IX. 1.

Type II.

| | 34·0 | ·5 | Svastika. | [Cunningham, 1894.]
Pl. XVI. 7. |

C., *C.A.I.*, Pl. IX. 2.

Type III.

| | 36·0 | ·5 | Svastika over fish. | [Rodgers, 1894.]
Pl. XVI. 8.
(from Shahki Deri) |
| | 38·0 | ·5 | ,, | ,,
[Cunningham, 1894.]
Pl. XVI. 9. |

C., *C.A.I.*, Pl. IX. 3.

	26·8	·5	,,	,, [Lillie, 1893.] **Pl. XVI. 10.**
	30·0	·5	,,	,, [Eden, 1853.]
	36·0	·5	,,	,, [Cunningham, 1894.]

No.	Wt.	Metal. Size.	Obverse.	Reverse.
			MŪLADEVA Second—First Centuries B.C.	
8	56·0	Æ *square* ·85	Bull r.; uncertain object in front. 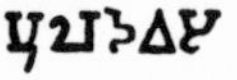 (*Mūladevasa*)	 (?) [Cunningham, 1894 **Pl. XVI. 11.**
			C., *C.A.I.*, Pl. IX. 4.	
9	42·0	·8	" " Inscription illegible.	" [Cunningham, 1894 **Pl. XVI. 12.**
10	45·0	·9 × ·6 *broken*	" "	" [Eden, 1853
			VĀYUDEVA Var. *a*.	
11	86·0	·8	Elephant l.; uncertain object in front. 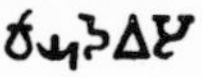 (*Vāyudevasa*)	 [Cunningham, 1894 **Pl. XVI. 13.**
			C., *C.A.I.*, Pl. IX. 5.	
12	86·6	·9	" " 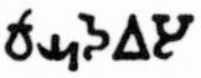	" [Cunningham, 1894

No.	Wt.	Metal. Size.	Obverse.	Reverse.
		Æ	Var. *b.*	
3	49·0	*square* ·8	Bull r. before  on r. (=) 	Standing figure in centre between two uncertain objects (probably *abhiṣeka* of Lakṣmī). [Eden, 1853.] **Pl. XVII. 8.**
4	36·5	·8	,,	,, [Cunningham, 1894.]
			VIŚĀKHADEVA	
			Var. *a.*	
			Lakṣmī standing facing. Elephants on either side standing on pedestals anointing her. 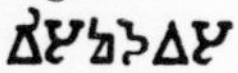 (*Viśākhadevasa*)	
5	45·0	·75	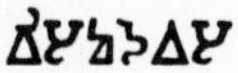	,, [Cunningham, 1894.] **Pl. XVI. 14.**
			C., *C.A.I.*, Pl. IX. 6.	
6	63·0	·8	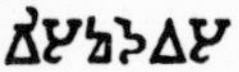	,, [Cunningham, 1894.] **Pl. XVI. 15.**
7	54·0	·8	- 	,, [Cunningham, 1894.]
8	68·0	·8	- - - - -	,, ,,

No.	Wt.	Metal. Size.	Obverse.	Reverse.
		Æ *square*	Var. *b*.	
19	55·0	·85	Bull l.; uncertain object in front. 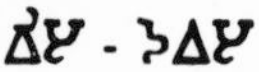	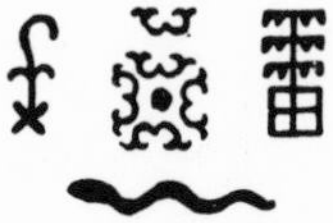 [Prinsep, 1847 Pl. XVI. 16.
20	22·5	·7	- - 	,, [Cunningham, 1894
			DHANADEVA	
			Var. *a*.	
			Bull. r. before  on r.  (*Dhanadevasa*)	Standing figure in centre; either side probably varian of  and 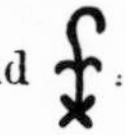. Three sma symbols above including  and 
21	43·5	·9 × ·8	,,	,, [Prinsep, 1837 Pl. XVI. 17.
22	70·5	·9 × ·8	,,	,, [Prinsep, 1837 Pl. XVI. 18.
23	38·0	·8	,,	,, [Cunningham, 1894 C., *C.A.I.*, Pl. IX. 8.

No.	Wt.	Metal. Size.	Obverse.	Reverse.
		Æ square	Var. *b*.	
24	103·0	·75	Bull l.; small uncertain object in front. 𑀥𑀦𑀤𑁂𑀯𑀲 (*Dhanadevasa*)	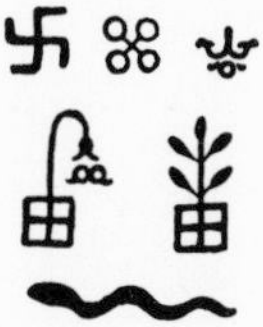 [Cunningham, 1894.] **Pl. XVIII. 1.**
			C., *C.A.I.*, Pl. IX. 9.	
25	107·0	·75	𑀥𑀦𑀤𑁂𑀯𑀲	" [Cunningham, 1894.] **Pl. XVIII. 2.**
26	80·5	·7	"	" [Cunningham, 1894.]
			ŚIVADATTA	
			Var. *a*.	
27	74·0	·9	Elephant l. Above 𑀲𑀺𑀯𑀤𑀢𑀲 (*Sivadatasa*)	Lakṣmī seated facing; elephants on either side sprinkling her; the whole enclosed in an oval. **Pl. XLIII. 4.**
28	49·5	·9	" 𑀲𑀺𑀯𑀤𑀢𑀲	" " **Pl. XLIII. 5.**
			Var. *b*.	
29	43·0	·55 *clipped*	" 𑀲𑀺𑀯𑀤𑀢𑀲	 between two uncertain symbols. [Temple, 1902.] **Pl. XVI. 7.**

No.	Wt.	Metal. Size.	Obverse.	Reverse.
		Æ square	Var. *c.*	
30	17·5	·55	As preceding. 	Group of uncertain symbo including  and a varie of tree in railing. **Pl. XVII. 3.**
31	9·5	·5	,, 	,, [Cunningham, 1894
32	12·5	·6	,, 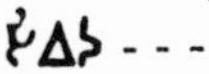	,, ,, **Pl. XVII. 4.**
			C., *C.A.I.*, Pl. IX. 11.	
			Var. *d.*	
33	24·7	·6	Bull to l. before  on l. 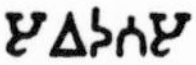	,, [Cunningham, 1894 **Pl. XVII. 5.**
34	11·0	·5	,, 	,, [Cunningham, 1894
35	9·5	·5	,, 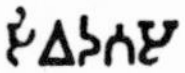	,, ,, **Pl. XVII. 6.**
			NARADATTA	
36	26·0	·6	Bull l. before  on l.  (*Naradatasa*)	Tree in centre.  on l.  (?) on r. [Cunningham, 1894 **Pl. XLIII. 6.**

o.	Wt.	Metal. Size.	Obverse.	Reverse.
		Æ *square*	**Uncertain**	
7	31·0	·55	Elephant l.; uncertain object in front. 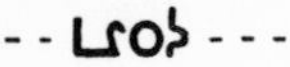	Tree in centre.  on r. Uncertain on r.  below. [Cunningham, 1894.] **Pl. XLIII. 7.**
8	40·0	·6	,, ,,	Tree in centre; other objects uncertain. [Cunningham, 1894.]
9	35·0	·55	Elephant r. before standard. 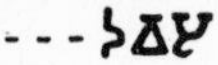	Tree in double square. [Cunningham, 1894.] **Pl. XLIII. 8.**
			SATYAMITRA First—Second Centuries A. D.	
0	136·5	*round* ·7	Bull to l.; standard on l. 𑀲𑀢𑁆𑀬𑀫𑀺𑀢𑀲 (*Satyamitasa*)	Cock to r.; palm tree on r. [H. N. Wright, Esq., Pres., 1915.]
1	123·0	·8	,, ,,	,, [Cunningham, 1894.] **Pl. XVII. 11** (*obv.*). C., *C.A.I.*, Pl. IX. 12.
2	122·5	·75	,, ,,	,, [C. M. Armstrong, Esq., Pres., 1890.] **Pl. XVII. 10.**
3	119·0	·7	,, ,,	,, [Cunningham, 1894.]

No.	Wt.	Metal. Size.	Obverse.	Reverse.
44	97·0	Æ *round* ·75	As preceding.  - -	As preceding. [Cunningham, 1894 **Pl. XVII. 12.**
45	117·0	·7	 - -	,, [Cunningham, 1894
46	110·0	·8		,, ,,
47	108·0	·7	 - -	,, [Grant, 1885
48	27·0	·45	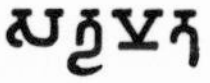 -	,, [Cunningham, 1894 **Pl. XVII. 13.**
			C., *C.A.I.*, Pl. IX. 13.	
49	29·0	·5	 - -	,, [Eden, 1853 **Pl. XVII. 14.**
50	17·0	·45	,,	,, [Major Hay, 1860
51	29·5	·5		,, [Cunningham, 189 **Pl. XVII. 15.**
52	23·0	·45	-  - - - -	,, [Cunningham, 189 **Pl. XVII. 16.**
53	26·0	·4	- -  -	,, [Cunningham, 189

o.	Wt.	Metal. Size.	Obverse.	Reverse.
		Æ *round*		
4	17·2	·4	As preceding.	As preceding. [Cunningham, 1894.]
5	26·0	·4	- - 𑀫𑀺𑀢𑀲	,, ,,
6	20·0	·4	𑀲𑀖𑀫𑀺𑀢	,, [Clive Bailey, 1889.]
7	26·5	·4	- 𑀖𑀫𑀺𑀢	,, [Major Hay, 1860.]

KUMUDASENA

o.	Wt.	Metal. Size.	Obverse.	Reverse.
8	120·0	·85	Bull l. before standard in railing. 𑀭𑀸𑀚𑁆𑀜 𑀓𑀼𑀫𑀼𑀤𑀲𑁂𑀦𑀲 (*Rajña Kumudasenasa*)	 in square. [H. N. Wright, Esq., Pres., 1900.] **Pl. XVII. 17.**

ĀRYAMITRA

o.	Wt.	Metal. Size.	Obverse.	Reverse.
9	96·0	·75	Bull l. before spear. 𑀅𑀬 - - -	Cock r. and tree. [Clive Bayley, 1889.]
0	105·0	·65	𑀅𑀬𑁆𑀬𑀫𑀺𑀢𑀲 (*Āyyamitasa*)	,, [Cunningham, 1894.] **Pl. XVII. 18.**
			C., *C.A.I.*, Pl. IX. 14.	
1	110·0	·6	- 𑀬 𑀢 -	,, [Eden, 1853.]
2	101·5	·6	𑀅𑀬𑀫𑀺𑀢𑀲	,, [I. O. C., 1882.]

No.	Wt.	Metal. Size.	Obverse.	Reverse.
63	105·0	Æ *round* ·7	As preceding.	As preceding. [Cunningham, 1894
64	106·0	·7		,, ,,
65	87·0	·5	[-]	,, ,,
66	120·5	·6	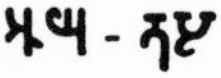	,, [Eden, 185
67	25·0	·4		,, [Cunningham, 1894 **Pl. XVII. 19.**

C., *C.A.I.*, Pl. IX. 15.

No.	Wt.	Metal. Size.	Obverse.	Reverse.
68	29·0	·4	[-]	,, [Eden, 185 **Pl. XVII. 20.**

SAṄGHA[MITRA]

No.	Wt.	Metal. Size.	Obverse.	Reverse.
69	123·0	·8	Bull l. Above  - -	 in square (?). [Cunningham, 1894 **Pl. XVII. 21.**

C., *C.A.I.*, Pl. IX. 16.

VIJAYAMITRA

Var. *a.*

No.	Wt.	Metal. Size.	Obverse.	Reverse.
70	32·0	·6	Bull l. before standard. 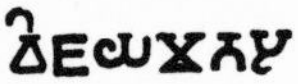 (*Vijayamitasa*)	Tree on l.; cock on r. [Cunningham, 189 **Pl. XVII. 22.**

No.	Wt.	Metal. Size.	Obverse.	Reverse.
		Æ *round*		
1	30·0	·6	As preceding. 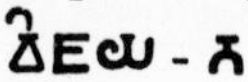	As preceding. [Cunningham, 1894.]
2	39·0	·6	„ 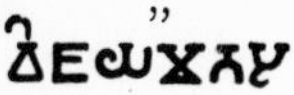	„ [Cunningham, 1894.] **Pl. XVIII. 1.**
3	30·0	·55	„	Cock on l.; tree on r. [Cunningham, 1894.] **Pl. XVIII. 2** (*obv.* and **3** *rev.*).
			C., *C.A.I.*, Pl. IX. 17.	
4	35·0	·6	„	„ [Cunningham, 1894.]
			Var. *b.*	
5	40·0	·55	Uncertain type. Around - - 	Bull l. on pedestal before standard. [Cunningham, 1894.] **Pl. XVIII. 5 and 2.**
			Var. *c.*	
6	46·0	·65	„ 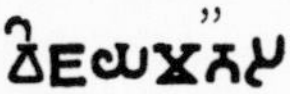	Stupa. [Cunningham, 1894.] **Pl. XVIII. 4.**
			C., *C.A.I.*, Pl. IX. 18.	
			Var. *d.*	
7	29·0	·55	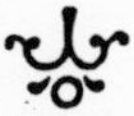  - - -	Bull on pedestal. [Cunningham, 1894.] **Pl. XVIII. 3 and 5.**
			C., *C.A.I.*, Pl. IX. 19.	
8	39·0	·5	„	„ [Eden, 1853.]

No.	Wt.	Metal. Size.	Obverse.	Reverse.
			ERAN	
			Inscribed	
			DHARMAPĀLA	
			Third Century B. C.	
1	179·0	Æ *square* ·95	 (*Dhamapālasa*)	Plain. [Cunningham, 1894. **Pl. XVIII. 6.**
			C., *C.A.I.*, Pl. XI. 18.	
			Uninscribed	
			Var. *a*.	
2	98·5	·8 × ·6	Elephant r.	Tree in railing. [Cunningham, 1894 **Pl. XIX. 1.**
			C., *C.A.I.*, Pl. XI. 13.	
			Var. *b*.	
3	160·0	·9		Bull to r.  on l. [Cunningham, 1894 **Pl. XVIII. 16.**
			C., *C.A.I.*, Pl. XI. 8.	
			Var. *c*.	
4	64·0	·65		Plain. [Cunningham, 1894 **Pl. XVIII. 23.**
			C., *C.A.I.*, Pl. XI. 11.	

No.	Wt.	Metal. Size.	Obverse.	Reverse.
		Æ *square*	Var. *d.*	
5	100·0	·85		Plain. [Cunningham, 1894.] **Pl. XVIII. 13.**
			C., *C.A.I.*, Pl. XI. 2.	
6	92·5	·85	,, ,,	,, [Cunningham, 1894.] **Pl. XVIII. 15.**
			C., *C.A.I.*, Pl. XI. 7.	
			Var. *e.*	
7	192·0	1·1		Plain. [Cunningham, 1894.] **Pl. XVIII. 11.**
			C., *C.A.I.*, Pl. XI. 1.	
8	135·0	1·0	,, ,,	,, [Cunningham, 1894.]
			Var. *f.*	
9	192·0	·95		Plain. [Cunningham, 1894.] **Pl. XVIII. 14.**
			Var. *g.*	
10	98·0	·85		Plain. [Cunningham, 1894.] **Pl. XVIII. 7.**
11	96·5	·75	,, ,,	,, [Cunningham, 1894.]

No.	Wt.	Metal. Size.	Obverse.	Reverse.
12	92·0	Æ *square* ·8	As preceding.	As preceding. [H. Nelson Wright, Esq., Pres. **Pl. XVIII. 17.**
13	89·0	·9	"	" [J. Gibbs, 1881.
14	73·5	·65	"	" [Cunningham, 1894.
15	79·0	·75	"	" " **Pl. XVIII. 18.**
			Var. *k*.	
16	52·0	·8		" [Cunningham, 1894. **Pl. XVIII. 20.**
17	56·5	·8	" "	" [Cunningham, 1894. **Pl. XVIII. 12.**
			C., *C.A.I.*, Pl. XI. 6.	
18	62·0	·75	" "	" [Cunningham, 1894.
19	79·0	·75		" " **Pl. XVIII. 22.**
			C., *C.A.I.*, Pl. XI. 10.	
			Var. *i*.	
20	121·0	·8		" [Cunningham, 1894

No.	Wt.	Metal. Size.	Obverse.	Reverse.
		Æ	Var. *j.*	
21	73·0	*square* ·65		Plain. [Cunningham, 1894.] **Pl. XVIII. 10.**
			C., *C.A.I.*, Pl. XI. 5.	
22	84·0	·8	,, ,,	,, [Cunningham, 1894.]
23	77·0	·6	,, ,,	,, ,, **Pl. XVIII. 19.**
24	82·0	·75	,, ,,	,, [Cunningham, 1894.] **Pl. XVIII. 8.**
			C., *C.A.I.*, Pl. XI. 4.	
25	55·0	·6	,, ,,	,, [Cunningham, 1894.]
			Var. *k.*	
26	112·0	·85	 river with fishes and tortoises.	,, ,, **Pl. XVIII. 9.**
			C., *C.A.I.*, Pl. XI. 3.	
27	62·5	·7	,, ,,	,, [Cunningham, 1894.] **Pl. XVIII. 21.**

No.	Wt.	Metal. Size.	Obverse.	Reverse.
		Æ *square*	Var. *l.*	
28	58·0	·7		Plain. [Cunningham, 1894.
29	51·0	·7	"	 [Cunningham, 1894.
			C., *C.A.I.*, Pl. XI. 9.	
30	21·0	·65	"	" " **Pl. XIX. 7.**
			Var. *m.*	
31	77·0	·8	 standing figure in centre; river with fishes below.	 with  in angles. [Cunningham, 1894. **Pl. XLIII. 9.**
			C., *C.A.I.*, Pl. XI. 12.	
			Var. *n.*	
32	74·0	·7	 standing figure in centre; river below with fishes.	 [Cunningham, 1894. **Pl. XIX. 3.**
			C., *C.A.I.*, Pl. XI. 16.	
			Var. *o.*	
33	36·0	·5		 [Cunningham, 1894. **Pl. XIX. 10.**

Wt.	Metal. Size.	Obverse.	Reverse.
		KĀḌA	
		Third Century B. C.	
	Æ *round cast*	Var. *a*.	
116·0	·9	Large rayed circle (sun).	Tree in railing in centre; uncertain rectangular object on l. On r. 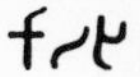 (*Kāḍasa*). **Pl. XIX. 14.**
		C., *C.A.I.*, Pl. V. 6.	
		Var. *b*.	
124·0	·95	Undulating line. 	As obverse. [Rodgers, 1892.] **Pl. XIX. 15.**
164·0	·95	,,	,, [Rodgers, 1883.]
166·0	·9	,,	,, [Thomas, 1850.] **Pl. XIX. 16.**
157·0	·9	,,	,, [Thomas, 1850.]
125·0	·9	,,	,, [Cunningham, 1894.]
		C., *C.A.I.*, Pl. II. 21.	

No.	Wt.	Metal. Size.	Obverse.	Reverse.
		Æ *round cast*		Var. *c.*
7	143·0	·95	 undulating line below.	Rude figure on r. holding st[...] in l. hand; uncertain obje[...] on l., ? kalaśa with flowers. 卐 below on l. [Rodgers, 188[...] **Pl. XIX. 19.**
8	166·0	·85	,, ,,	,, [Cunningham, 189[...] **Pl. XIX. 17.**
			C., *C.A.I.*, Pl. II. 22.	
		square cast		Var. *d.*
9	181·0	1·0	Undulating line. 	Elephant l. [Thomas, 185[...] **Pl. XIX. 18.**
10	211·0	1·0	,,	,, [Whitehead, 192[...]
			White King 5218.	
				Var. *e.*
11	52·0	·5		? Kalaśa with flowers. [Thomas, 185[...] **Pl. XIX. 20.**
				Var. *f.*
12	76·0	·7	Rayed circle (sun) as on no. 1.	Horse r. [Eden, 185[...] **Pl. XLIII. 10.**
13	69·0	·8	,, ,,	,, [Thomas, 185[...]
14	64·0	·65	,, ,,	,, [Prinsep, 1837 **Pl. XLIII. 11.**

No.	Wt.	Metal. Size.	Obverse.	Reverse.
			KANAUJ (?)	
			BRAHMAMITRA	
		Æ *round*		
1	96·5	·8	  (*Brahmamitasa*)	 [Thomas, 1850.] **Pl. XIX. 11.**
			SŪRYAMITRA	
2	52·0	·65	 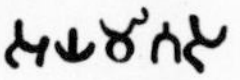 (*Sūyamitasa*)	Illegible. [Thomas, 1853.] **Pl. XIX. 12.**
			VIṢṆUDEVA	
3	65·0	·8	 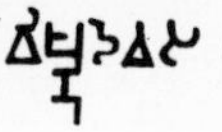 (*Viṣṇudevasa*)	Horse l. before yūpa? [Prinsep, 1847.] **Pl. XIX. 13.**
			P.E., I, p. 115.	

No.	Wt.	Metal. Size.	Obverse.	Reverse.
			KAUŚĀMBĪ	
			Early uninscribed cast coins.	
			Third Century B. C.	
			Var. *a*.	
			Humped bull to l. before   above.	Leafy tree in three-barred rai ing ;  below.  over wheel on l.  卐 on r.
1	152·5	Æ *round* ·1	,, ,,	,, [Cunningham, 189
2	116·0	1·0	,, ,,	,, ,,
3	104·0	1·0	,, ,,	,, ,, **Pl. XX. 14.**
			C., *C.A.I.*, Pl. V. 7.	
4	96·0	1·0	,, ,,	,, [Cunningham, 189 **Pl. XXI. 1.**
5	86·5	·95	,, ,,	,, [Cunningham, 189
6	77·5	·9	,, ,,	,, ,,

o.	Wt.	Metal. Size.	Obverse.	Reverse.
		Æ round		
7	76·0	·95	As preceding.	As preceding. [H. Nelson Wright, Esq., Pres., 1902.] **Pl. XX. 13.**
8	90·0	·9	”	” [Cunningham, 1894.] **Pl. XXI. 2.**
9	88·0	·95	”	” [I. O. C., 1882.]
0	75·0	1·0	”	” [Cunningham, 1894.]
1	76·0	1·0	”	” ”
			Var. *b*.	
2	29·0	·7	” but wheel in place of 	Bull r. before tree in railing. [H. Nelson Wright, Esq., Pres., 1904.] **Pl. XXI. 3.**
			Var. *c*.	
3	100·0	1·1	Lakṣmī standing facing, being sprinkled by elephants.	Tree (more conventional) in railing.  on r.  on l.  [Cunningham, 1894.] **Pl. XX. 15.**

C., *C.A.I.*, Pl. V. 9.

No.	Wt.	Metal. Size.	Obverse.	Reverse.
			Second Century B.C.	
			SUDEVA (?)	
14	190·0	Æ *round* 1·0	Elephant l. on  before pillar.  ([*Sudeva*]*sa*)	Tree in railing on r.; illegib symbols on l. [Cunningham, 189 **Pl. XX. 11.**
			C., *C.A.I.*, Pl. V. 10.	
			BṚHASPATIMITRA I	
15	·68	1·0	Horse r.;  over square containing an uncertain symbol in front. 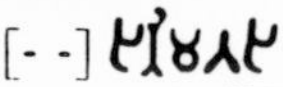 ([*Baha*]*satim*[*i*]*tasa*)	Elephant r. on ; tree railing behind.  above on l. [Cunningham, 189 **Pl. XX. 1.**
			C, *C.A.I.*, Pl. V. 8.	
			PARVATA	
16	12·0	·45	Bull r.	 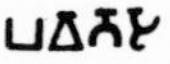 (*Pavatasa*) [H. Nelson Wright, Esq., Pre 190 **Pl. XX. 10.**
16*a*	7·0	·4	,,	,, [Cunningham, 189
			AŚVAGHOṢA	
17	21·0	·65	Bull r.; uncertain object (trisul ?) in crescent above.	Tree in railing; uncertain o jects on r. and l. -  - ([*A*]*śvaghoṣ*[*as* [Cunningham, 189 **Pl. XX. 6.**
			C., *C.A.I.*, Pl. V. 14.	

BṚHASPATIMITRA II

Late Second Century B.C.

No.	Wt.	Metal. Size.	Obverse.	Reverse.
			Bull r. before   above.	Tree in railing in centre.  on l.  on r.  𑀩𑀳𑀲𑀢𑀺𑀫𑀺𑀢𑀲 (*Bahasatimitasa*)
	98·0	Æ *round* ·75	,,	𑀩𑀳𑀲𑀢𑀺𑀫𑀺 - - [Cunningham, 1894.] **Pl. XX. 2.**
			C., *C.A.I.*, Pl. V. 11.	
	121·0	·75	,,	,, ,, - - - 𑀢𑀺𑀫𑀺𑀢𑀲 [Cunningham, 1894.]
	109·0	·75	,,	,, ,, 𑀩𑀳𑀲𑀢𑀺 - - [Clive Bayley, 1889.]
	110·0	·75	,,	,, ,, - 𑀳𑀲 - - - [Eden, 1853.]
	60·0	·6	,,	 on l. 𑀩𑀳𑀲𑀢𑀺𑀫𑀺𑀢𑀲 [Clive Bayley, 1889.] **Pl. XX. 3.**

No.	Wt.	Metal. Size.	Obverse.	Reverse.
23	60·0	Æ *round* ·6	As preceding.	As preceding. 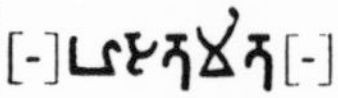 [Cunningham, 1894
24	23·0	·45	Bull l.;  above.	,,  on l.; on r. 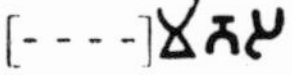 [Cunningham, 1894
25	16·8	·4	Bull r.	,,  on r. [H. Nelson Wright, Esq., Pres 1904

Countermarked series.

No.	Wt.	Metal. Size.	Obverse.	Reverse.
26	121·0	·7	Type of Bṛhaspatimitra, countermarked tree in railing.	As No. 18. [Cunningham, 1894 **Pl. XX. 4.**

C., *C.A.I.*, Pl. V. 13.

No.	Wt.	Metal. Size.	Obverse.	Reverse.
26*a*	74·0	·7	,, ,,	,, [Cunningham, 1894
27	116·0	·8	,, ,, countermark trisul.	Traces of type. [Cunningham, 1894 **Pl. XXI. 18.**
28	110·0	·8	,, ,,	,, [Cunningham, 1894 **Pl. XXI. 16.**
29	120·0	·75	,, ,,	,, [Cunningham, 1894 **Pl. XXI. 17.**

No.	Wt.	Metal. Size.	Obverse.	Reverse.
		Æ *round*		
0	95·0	·7	As preceding.	As preceding. [Cunningham, 1894.]
1	120·0	·75	,,	,, ,,
2	·95	·75	,,	,, ,,
			C., *C.A.I.*, Pl. V. 12.	
			First Century B. C.—First Century A. D.	
			DHANADEVA	
3	60·0	·8	Bull l.; trident behind.  in front.	Tree in railing. 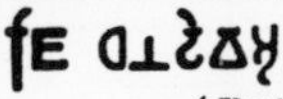 (*Rāja Dhanadevasya*) [Cunningham, 1894.] **Pl. XX. 12.**
			C., *C.A.I.*, Pl. V. 18.	
			AGNIMITRA	
4	112·0	·8	Bull r. before   above, countermarked with trisul.	[?] on l.; tree in railing;  on r. 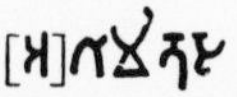 ([*A*]*gimitasa*) [H. Nelson Wright, Esq., Pres., 1904.] **Pl. XX. 5.**
a	22·0	·4	Bull l. before 	Similar, but  on r. 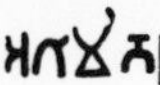[-] [Cunningham, 1894.] **Pl. XXVIII. 15.**
			C., *C.A.I.*, Pl. VII. 16.	

No.	Wt.	Metal. Size.	Obverse.	Reverse.
		Æ *round*	**JEṬṬHAMITRA**	
35	127·0	·7	Bull l.	Tree in railing. 𑀚𑁂𑀣𑀫𑀺𑀢𑀲 (*J*(*e*)*thamitasa*) [Cunningham, 189 **Pl. XX. 9.**
			C., *C.A.I.*, Pl. V. 16.	
36	59·0	·6	As preceding.	𑀚𑁂𑀣𑀫𑀺𑀢𑀲  [Cunningham, 1894 **Pl. XX. 7.**
			C., *C.A.I.*, Pl. V. 17.	
37	89·0	·7	Horse to l.;  in front.	Standing figure. On r. 𑀚𑁂𑀣𑀫𑀺𑀢𑀲 [Cunningham, 189 **Pl. XX. 8.**
			C., *C.A.I.*, Pl. V. 15.	
			Incomplete legends.	
38	64·5	·75	Bull r.	Spear; tree in railing: *chowr* 𑀦𑀯𑀲 (- - *navasa*) [Prinsep, 184 **Pl. XXI. 4.**
39	66·5	·75	,, wheel above.	,, [Prinsep, 184
40	62·5	·75	,,	,, ,, **Pl. XXI. 6.**

o.	Wt.	Metal. Size.	Obverse.	Reverse.
	68·0	Æ *round* ·75	As preceding.	As preceding. [Cunningham, 1894.] **Pl. XXI. 7.**
2	67·5	·75	„	„ [Cunningham, 1894.]
3	68·5	·75	„	„ „
	71·5	·75	„	„ „
	61·0	·7	„	„ „ **Pl. XXI. 8.**
	33·0	·6	„	„ [Cunningham, 1894.]
	33·5	·6	„	„ „
	33·0	·68	„	„ „ } on r.
	37·0	·5	„	„ „
	21·0	·65	„	„ „ **Pl. XXI. 5.**
	19·0	·48	„	„ [Cunningham, 1894.]

No.	Wt.	Metal. Size.	Obverse.	Reverse.
52	66·0	Æ *round* ·75	Bull r.; trident behind.	Tree in railing. 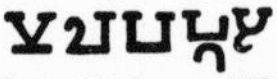 [H. Nelson Wright, Esq., Pres 1904 **Pl. XXI. 9.**
53	65·0	·75	,,	,, [Prinsep, 1847
54	65·0	·75	,,	,, ,,
55	65·0	·75	,,	,, [Clive Bayley, 1889 **Pl. XXI. 10.**
56	60·0	·6	,,	,, [Clive Bayley, 1889
57	55·0	·75	,,	,, [Cunningham, 1894
58	63·0	·7	,,	,, ,, **Pl. XXI. 11.**
59	45·0	·7	Elephant r.	Tree in railing;  on r.  [Eden, 1853 **Pl. XXI. 12.**
60	45·0	·65	,,	,, -  [H. Nelson Wright, Esq., Pre 1904

No.	Wt.	Metal. Size.	Obverse.	Reverse.
61	46·0	Æ *round* ·65	As preceding.	As preceding.  [Cunningham, 1894.]
62	40·0	·7	Bull (?) r.	,, 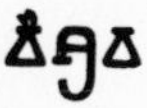 [Eden, 1853.]
63	45·0	·6	,,	,, 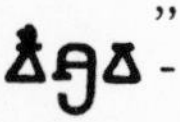 [Cunningham, 1894.]
64	45·0	·6	Bull l.	,, 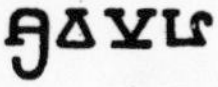 [Eden, 1853.] **Pl. XXI. 13.**
65	62·0	·65	Elephant r.	,, but  on l.  [Cunningham, 1894.]
66	40·0	·6	,,	,, 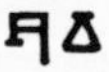 [Cunningham, 1894.]
67	45·0	·6	Bull l. (?)	,,  [Govt. U. P., 1904.]
68	44·5	·65	Bull r.	; tree in railing ;   [Cunningham, 1894.]
69	51·0	·65	,,	,, ,, 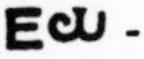 [Cunningham, 1894.]

No.	Wt.	Metal. Size.	Obverse.	Reverse.
70	80·0	Æ *round* ·7	As preceding.	As preceding. 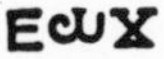 [Cunningham, 1894.]
71	84·5	·8	Bull r.	Similar.  [Cunningham, 1894.]
72	57·0	·8	,,	,, 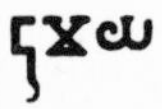 [Cunningham, 1894.] Pl. XXI. 14.
73	74·0	·8	Bull r.; trident behind.	Illegible. Pl. XXI. 15.

KULŪTA

. First Century A. D.

VĪRAYAŚAḤ

No.	Wt.	Metal. Size.	Obverse.	Reverse.
1	75·7	·75	Wheel surrounded by a circle of dots. Around 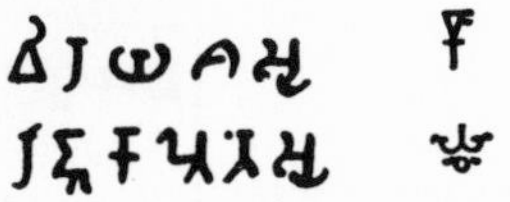 (*Vīrayaśasya rājña kulūtasya*)	 (*raña*) [Cunningham, 1894.] Pl. XVI. 4.

C., *C.A.I.*, Pl. IV. 14.

KUṆINDA

AMOGHABHŪTI

First Century B.C.

Silver.

Var. *a.*

No.	Wt.	Metal. Size.	Obverse.	Reverse.
			Deer to r.; female figure (? Lakṣmī) standing (sometimes on lotus) facing, holding flower in uplifted r. hand.  above back of deer.  above horns of deer.  below deer. 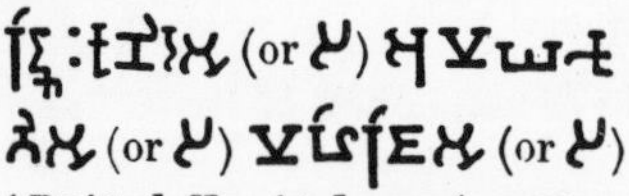 (*Rājñaḥ Kuṇiṁdasya* (or *sa*) *Amoghabhutisya* (or *sa*) *Mahārājasya* (or *sa*))	 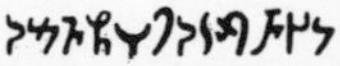 (*Raña Kuṇidasa Amoghabhutisa*) around.  (*Maharajasa*) below.
1	34·0	Æ round ·7	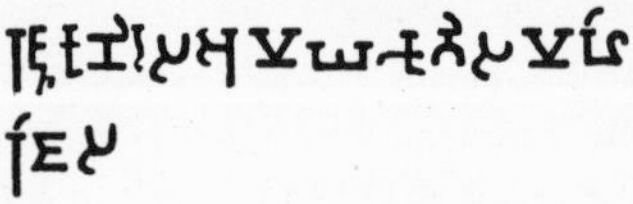	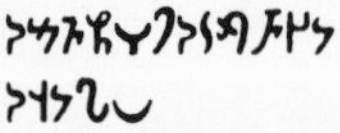 [Cunningham, 1894.] **Pl. XXII. 1.**
			C., *C.A.I.*, Pl. V. 1.	
2	29·2	·65	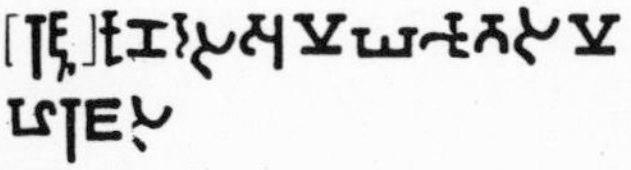	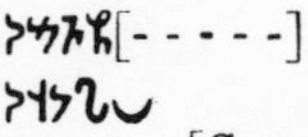 [Cunningham, 1894.]
3	29·0	·7	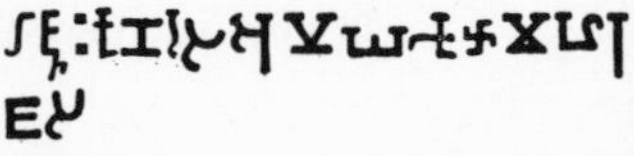	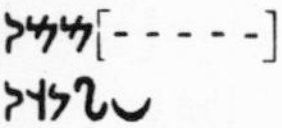 [Shaw, 1889.]

No.	Wt.	Metal. Size.	Obverse.	Reverse.
4	32·7	Æ round ·65	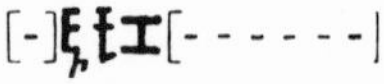	Traces of legend. [Cunningham, 1894. Pl. XXII. 7.
5	29·0	·65		,, [Whitehead, 1922.
6	30·0	·65	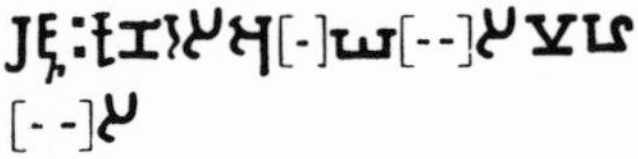	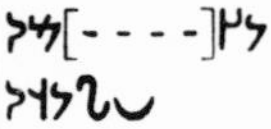 [Whitehead, 1922.
			Var. b.	
7	34·4	·7	As preceding, but  below deer and  between deer and figure and 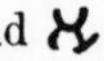 for  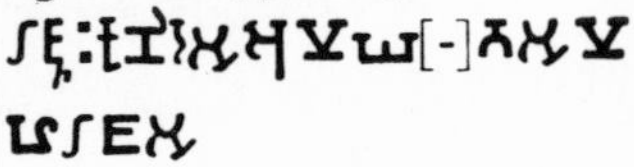	As preceding.  [Shaw, 1889. Pl. XXII. 2.
			Var. c.	
8	38·0	·7	As No. 1, but nothing below deer. 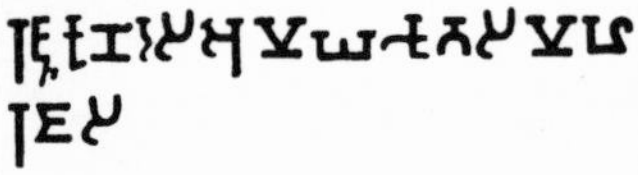	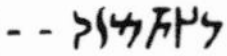 [Thomas, 1850. Pl. XXII. 3.
9	34·0	·7	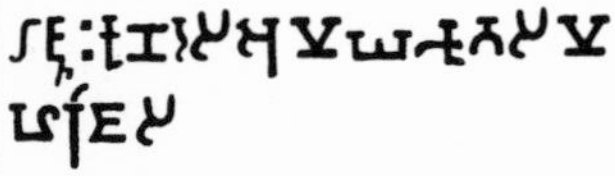	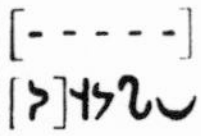 [Cunningham, 1894. C., *C.A.I.*, Pl. V. 2.
10	33·8	·65	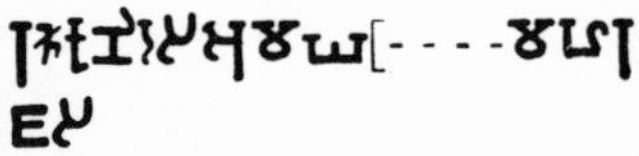	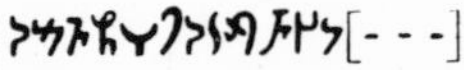 [Cunningham, 1894. Pl. XXII. 6.

o.	Wt.	Metal. Size.	Obverse.	Reverse.
		Æ round		
1	22·7 much worn	·65	Traces of legend.	[script] [- - -] [script] [Prinsep, 1837.]
2	30·8	·7	[script] [- - - - - - -] [script] [- -]	[- - -] [script] [- -] [script] [Thomas, 1850.] Pl. XXII. 8.
3	34·5	·65	[- - - - -] [script] [script] [-]	[script] [- - - -] [script] [script] [Cunningham, 1894.]
4	28·7	·65	[script] [script]	[script] [- -] [script] [Cunningham, 1894.]
5	34·6	·8	[script] [- -] [script] [script]	[script] [script] [Cunningham, 1894.] Pl. XXII. 5.
6	21·0 much worn	·65	[script] [script]	[- -] [script] [- - - -] [script] [- - -] [Cunningham, 1894.] Pl. XXII. 4.

Var. *d.*

| 7 | 26·5 base | ·65 | As preceding, but ℱ below horse ; traces of legend. | As preceding ; traces of legend. [Cunningham, 1894.] Pl. XXIII. 6. |

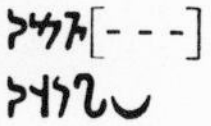

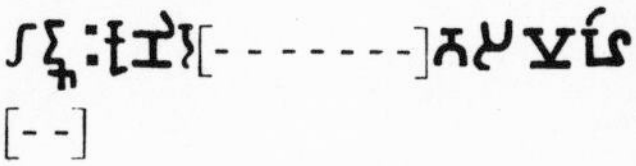

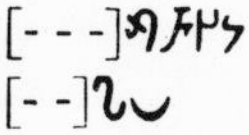

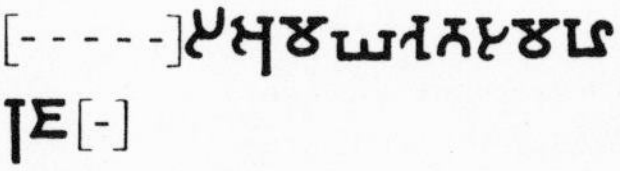

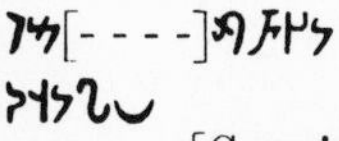

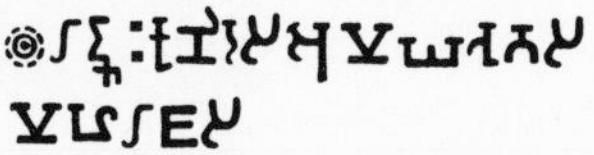

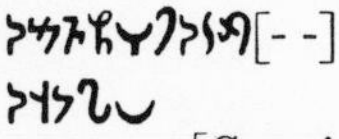

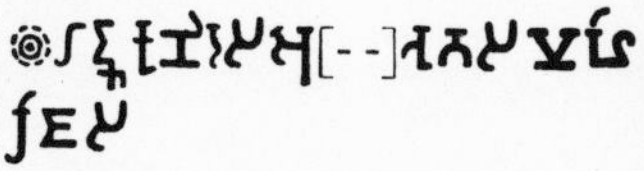

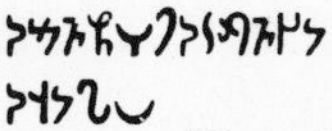

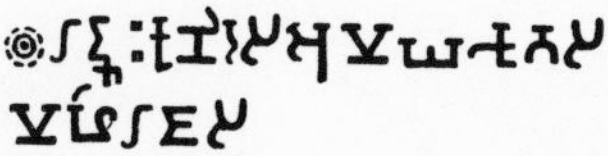

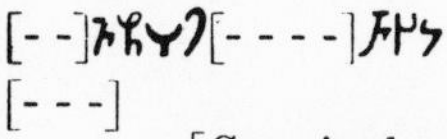

No.	Wt.	Metal. Size.	Obverse.	Reverse.
			Copper	
			Class I: neat fabric with good legends.	
			Deer r.; Lakṣmī facing, holding flower as in No. 1.  above deer.  above its horns. 𑀭𑀸𑀚𑁆𑀜𑀓𑀼𑀡𑀺𑀤𑀲𑀅𑀫𑁄𑀖𑀪𑀽𑀢𑀺𑀲𑀫𑀳𑀸 𑀭𑀸𑀚𑀲 (*Rājña(ḥ) Kunindasa Amogha bhūt*[*i*]*sa mahārājasa*)	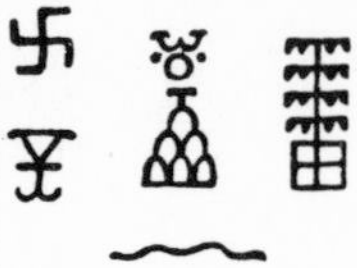 Border of dots (no legend).
18	58·0	Æ *round* ·85	𑀭𑀚𑁆𑀜𑀓𑀼𑀡𑀺𑀤𑀲𑀅𑀫𑁄𑀖𑀪𑀽𑀢𑀺𑀲𑀫𑀳𑀸 𑀭𑀸𑀚𑀲	,, [Cunningham, 1894. **Pl. XXIII. 1.**
19	62·0	·75	𑀭𑀸𑀚𑁆𑀜𑀓𑀼𑀡𑀺𑀤[- - -]𑀪𑀽𑀢𑀺𑀲𑀫𑀳𑀸𑀭𑀸𑀚 𑀲	,, [Cunningham, 1894.
20	46·0	·8	𑀭𑀸𑀚𑁆𑀜𑀓𑀼𑀡𑀺𑀤𑀲𑀅𑀫[- - - - - -]𑀳𑀸𑀭𑀸 𑀚𑀲	,, ,, **Pl. XXII. 14.** [Cunningham, 1894. C., *C.A.I.*, Pl. V. 3.
21	43·0	·75	Trace of legend.	,, ,,
22	47·5	·7	𑀭𑀸𑀚 𑀓𑀼𑀡𑀺𑀤[- - - - -]𑀳𑀸𑀭𑀸[- - -]	,, [Cunningham, 1894. **Pl. XXII. 16.**
23	46·5	·7	[- - -]𑀫𑀳𑀸𑀭𑀸𑀚[-]	,, [Thomas, 1850. **Pl. XXII. 15.**

No.	Wt.	Metal. Size.	Obverse.	Reverse.
		Æ *round*		
4	41·5	·7	[- - -]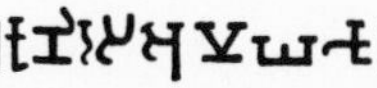[- -]	As preceding. [Thomas, 1850.]
5	42·0	·6	Trace of legend.	„ [Cunningham, 1894.] **Pl. XXIII. 4.**
			Class II: coarse fabric and very incomplete legends.	
			As in Class I, but legend usually very fragmentary.	As in Class I.
6	162·0	1·1	Traces of legend.	„ [Prinsep, 1837.] **Pl. XXII. 9.**
7	130·0	·95	„	„ [Cunningham, 1894.] **Pl. XXII. 10.**
8	125·0	·9	[- - - -]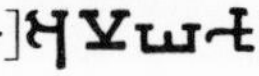[- - - -]	„ [Elliot, 1886.]
9	102·5	·95	Traces of legend.	„ [Cunningham, 1894.]
0	120·0	·9	„	„ „
1	115·0	·95	„	„ [Thomas, 1850.]
2	125·0	·8	„	„ [Cunningham, 1894.]

No.	Wt.	Metal. Size.	Obverse.	Reverse.
		Æ *round*		
33	97·0	·9	Traces of legend.	As preceding. [Cunningham, 1894
34	110·0	·8	,,	,, ,,
35	99·0	·85		,, ,, **Pl. XXII. 12.**
36	95·0	·85		,, [Cunningham, 1894
37	96·5	·8	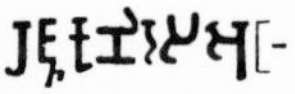	,, [Clive Bayley, 1889
38	70·0	·8		,, [Thomas, 1850
39	97·0	·8	Traces of legend.	,, [Bush, 1865 **Pl. XXIII. 9.**
40	75·0	·7	,,	,, [Thomas, 1850 **Pl. XXIII. 10.**
41	94·0	·8	,,	,, [Major R. C. Temple, Pres 1892
42	59·5	·8	,,	,, [Cunningham, 1894
43	60·0	·8	,,	,, —

o.	Wt.	Metal. Size.	Obverse.	Reverse.
		Æ *round*		
4	57·0	·9	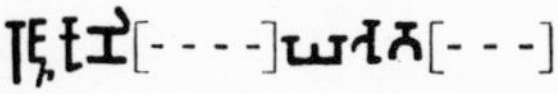	As preceding. [Cunningham, 1894.]
5	55·0	·9	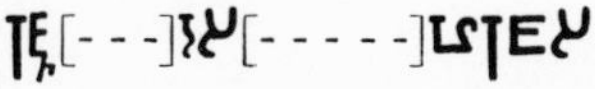	,, [Thomas, 1850.] **Pl. XXII. 11.**
6	49·4	·9	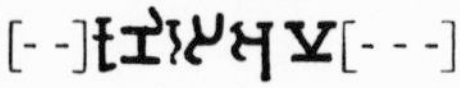	,, [Cunningham, 1894.] **Pl. XXII. 13.**
7	66·0	·8	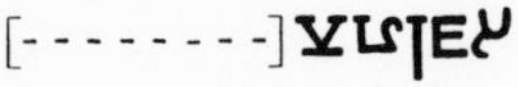	,, [Thomas, 1850.]
8	57·0	·75	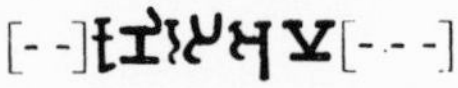	,, [Cunningham, 1894.]
9	46·0	·75	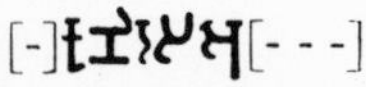	,, ,,
0	50·0	·7	Traces of legend.	,, ,,
1	56·0	·7	,,	,, [Thomas, 1850.]
2	47·0	·7	,,	,, [Cunningham, 1894.]
3	41·0	·65	,,	,, ,,
4	40·0	·7	,,	,, ,,
5	36·0	·6	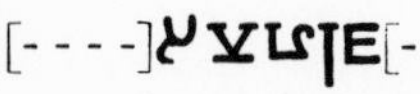	,, [Thomas, 1850.]

No.	Wt.	Metal. Size.	Obverse.	Reverse.
56	42·0	Æ *round* ·6	Traces of legend.	As preceding. [Thomas, 1850.
57	41·0	·6	"	" [Prinsep, 1837.
58	38·0	·5	"	" [Cunningham, 1894.
59	37·0	·6	"	" "
60	30·5	·6	"	" "
61	35·0	·6	[- - -]	" "
62	27·0	·65	Traces of legend.	" [Elliot, 1886.
63	26·0	·75	"	" [Cunningham, 1894.
64	24·0	·6	"	" " **Pl. XXIII. 7.**
65	28·0	·55	"	" [Cunningham, 1894. **Pl. XXIII. 8.**
66	25·0	·6	[- -][- -]	" [Cunningham, 1894.
67	26·0	·55	[- - -]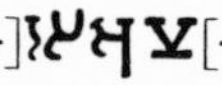[- - - -]	" "

o.	Wt.	Metal. Size.	Obverse.	Reverse.
		Æ *round*		
8	22·0	·6	[- - -][- - -]	As preceding. [Cunningham, 1894.]
9	9·5	·5	[- - - -]	,, ,, **Pl. XXIII. 5.**
			ANONYMOUS Second Century A. D. Var. *a.*	
			Male figure (Śiva) standing facing, holding trident with axe on shaft in r. hand; flower or star behind over his left shoulder. 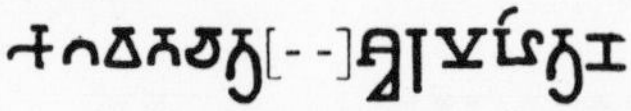 (*Bhāgavata Catr(? tu ? kra)* [- -] *śvara-Mahātraṇa*)	Deer l.  above horns.  behind.  in front.  below deer.  above. below. Border of dots.
0	277·0	1·0	- - - 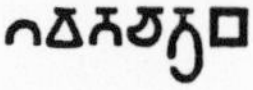	,, [H. Nelson Wright, Esq., Pres., 1915.] **Pl. XXIII. 12.**
)a	265·0	1·0	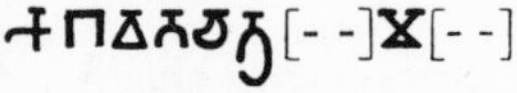	Similar, but  below deer. [Spink, 1928.] **Pl. XLIII. 13.**
1	280·0	1·0	- - 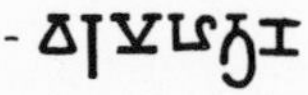	Similar with  above. [Rodgers, 1892.]
2	291·0	1·0		Similar to 70. [Cunningham, 1894.] **Pl. XXIII. 14.**
			C., *C.A.I.*, Pl. V. 5.	

No.	Wt.	Metal. Size.	Obverse.	Reverse.
		Æ round		
73	289·0	1·0	- - - -] 	Similar. [Cunningham, 1894 **Pl. XXIII. 13.**
74	249·0	·95	[- - -]  [- - -]	,, without  [Cunningham, 1894 **Pl. XLIII. 12.**
75	280·0	1·0	Traces of inscription.	,,  below deer. [Rodgers, 1892
76	131·0	·85	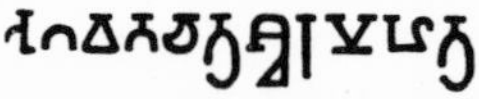	,,  and star above deer. [Rodgers, 1892 **Pl. XXIII. 15.**
77	131·0	·85	-]  [-	,, [Cunningham, 1894
				C., *C.A.I.*, Pl. V. 4.
			Var. *b.*	
78	212·0	1·0	As in Var. *a*. Traces of inscription.	Deer l.  on r.  }  above.  belo **Pl. XXIII. 11.**
			Var. *c.*	
79	274·0	1·0	As in Var. *a*. Traces of inscription.	Deer r.  on l.  on r. [Rodgers, 1892 **Pl. XLIII. 14.**

No.	Wt.	Metal. Size.	Obverse.	Reverse.

MATHURA

Late Third Century B.C.

GOMITRA I

No.	Wt.	Metal. Size.	Obverse.	Reverse.
			 in centre. [𑀕]𑁄𑀫𑀺𑀢𑀲 (*Gomitasa*) above. 𑀬𑀸𑀭𑀸𑀡𑀸𑀬𑀸𑀁 (*-yārāṇāyāṁ ?*) below.	Tree in railing in square of dots.
	89·0	Æ *square* ·7	" "	" [Cunningham, 1894.] **Pl. XXIV. 21.**
	76·0	·75	[-]𑀫𑀺𑀢𑀲[-𑀭𑀸𑀡𑀸]	" [Cunningham, 1894.] **Pl. XXIV. 20.**

C., *C.A.I.*, Pl. VIII. 10.

No.	Wt.	Metal. Size.	Obverse.	Reverse.
	66·0	·6	[-𑀭𑀸𑀡]	" [Cunningham, 1894.]
	68·5	·65	Traces of legend.	" "

? Another Gomitra of different dynasty.

No.	Wt.	Metal. Size.	Obverse.	Reverse.
	25·8	·65	Rude figure with arms uplifted; 𑀫 on r. 𑀕𑁄𑀫𑀺𑀢𑀲	Three-branched tree in railing. [Clive Bayley, 1889.] **Pl. XXV. 3.**

c. 200–50 B.C.

GOMITRA II

Var: *a*.

Square, of rude fabric.

No.	Wt.	Metal. Size.	Obverse.	Reverse.
		Æ *square*	Standing female figure of goddess (Lakṣmī) facing, holding lotus in uplifted r. hand. On l.   on r.  below. 𑀕𑁄𑀫𑀺𑀢𑀲 (*Gomitasa*) (The whole in a circular die)	Three elephants with ride holding goads, the centre o facing, other two three-quarte to l.
6	100·0	·95	𑀕𑁄𑀫𑀺𑀢𑀲	,, [Bhagvanlal, 1889
7	115·0	·95	,,	,, [Hay, 1860
8	107·0	·8	𑀕𑁄𑀫𑀺𑀢[-]	,, [Johnson, n.d
9	120·0	·7	Almost illegible.	,, [Cunningham, 1894
10	100·0	·7	𑀕𑁄𑀫𑀺𑀢𑀲	,, [Clive Bayley, 1889 **Pl. XXV. 1.**
11	102·0	·55	No trace of legend.	,, [Clive Bayley, 1889 **Pl. XXV. 2.**

Wt.	Metal. Size.	Obverse.	Reverse.
	Æ round	Round, of neat fabric.	
122·0	·8	𑀕𑁄𑀫𑀺𑀢𑀲	As preceding. [For the type cf. **Pl. XLIV. 6** from no. 13.] [H. Nelson Wright, Pres., 1918.]
110·5	·8	"	" [Clive Bayley, 1889.] **Pl. XXV. 5–6.**
110·5	·6	"	" [Bhagvanlal, 1889.]
101·5	·7	"	" [Clive Bayley, 1889.]
89·0	·65	No traces of inscription.	" " **Pl. XXV. 7.**
		Var. *b*.	
83·5	·7	Type similar except that goddess holds lotus in l. hand. 𑀕𑁄𑀫𑀺𑀢𑀲	? Traces of above type. [Rodgers, 1883.] **Pl. XXV. 4.**
		Var. *c*.	
51·0	·7	Goddess facing on l.; tree in centre.  below tree. 𑀕𑁄𑀫𑀺𑀢𑀲 reading downwards on r.	Illegible. [Rodgers, 1883.] **Pl. XLV. 1.**

No.	Wt.	Metal. Size.	Obverse.	Reverse.
			Var. *d*.	
			Bull r. before tree in railing.  at end of legend. 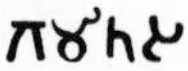	Plain.
19	32·0	Æ *round* ·5		,, [Thomas, 185 Pl. XXV. 8.
20	44·0	·5		,, [Thomas, 185
21	46·0	·6	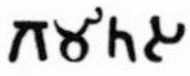	,, [Rodgers, 189 Pl. XXV. 9.
22	42·0	·5		,, [Thomas, 185 Pl. XXV. 11.
23	39·0	·5	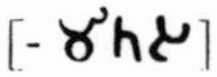	,, [Thomas, 185 Pl. XXV. 10.
24	46·0	·6	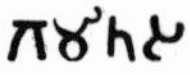	,, [Thomas, 185
25	40·0	·6	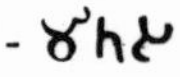	,, ,,

No.	Wt.	Metal. Size.	Obverse.	Reverse.
			BRAHMAMITRA	
			Var. *a.*	
			Lakṣmī standing facing, holding lotus in l. hand.  on l.  on r.  (*Brahmamitasa*)	Three elephants with riders; the central one facing, others to r. and l. respectively.
6	85·0	Æ *round* ·75	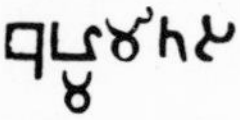	,, [H. Nelson Wright, Esq., Pres., 1885.] **Pl. XXV. 12.**
7	87·5	·85	,, ,,	,, [Cunningham, 1894.]
8	73·0	·7	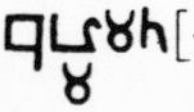[-]	,, ,,
			C., *C.A.I.*, Pl. VIII. 12.	
9	84·5	·6	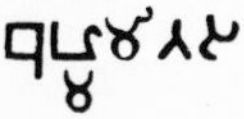	,, [Thomas, 1850.] **Pl. XXV. 14.**
0	83·5	·65	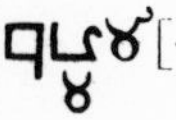[- -]	,, [Cunningham, 1894.]
			Var. *b.*	
1	82·5	·8	As above, but  in place of  on l. 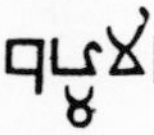[- -]	Illegible. [Thomas, 1850.] **Pl. XXV. 13.**

No.	Wt.	Metal. Size.	Obverse.	Reverse.
		Æ round	**GOṢADATTA**	
31*a*	75·0	·8	Traces of type as on no. 6. 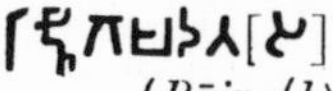 (*Rājna*(*ḥ*) *Goṣadata*(*sa*))	Traces of three elephants typ[e]. [S. C. Pears, Esq., Pres., 1904.] (from the Kurram valley) **Pl. XLIII. 18.**
			DṚDHAMITRA	
32	51·5	·6	Lakṣmī standing facing, holding lotus in uplifted r. hand.  on l.  on r.  (*Dadh*[*a*]*mitasa*)	Traces of three elephants typ[e]. [Gen. M. Clerk, 1920.] **Pl. XLIII. 16.**
			SŪRYAMITRA	
			Lakṣmī standing facing as before, between  on l. and   on r.  (*Sūyamitasa*)	Three elephants with rider[s] with goads; the central on[e] facing, other two to r. and l. [For the type cf. **Pl. XLIV. 9** from no. 35.]
33	130·0	·8	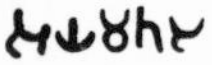	,, [Thomas, 1850.]
34	125·0	·7		,, [Clive Bayley, 1889.] **Pl. XXV. 21** (*rev.*).
35	106·0	·8	[-]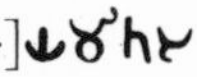	,, [Thomas, 1850.] **Pl. XXV. 17.**

No.	Wt.	Metal. Size.	Obverse.	Reverse.
36	117·5	Æ round ·75		As preceding. [H. Nelson Wright, Esq., Pres., 1915.] **Pl. XXV. 18.**
37	115·0	·8		,, [Clive Bayley, 1889.] **Pl. XXV. 19–20.**

VIṢṆUMITRA

No.	Wt.	Metal. Size.	Obverse.	Reverse.
			Lakṣmī standing facing as before, between  on l. and  on r.  (*Viṣṇumitasa*)	Three elephants with riders as above.
8	81·5	·7		,, [Bhagvanlal, 1889.] **Pl. XXV. 15.**
9	75·0	·7	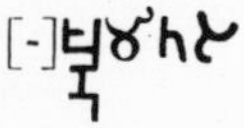	,, [Rodgers, 1883.] **Pl. XXV. 16.**
0	79·0	·7	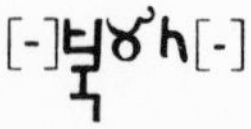	,, [Thomas, 1850.]
	68·0	·7	,, ,,	,, ,,

No.	Wt.	Metal. Size.	Obverse.	Reverse.
42	79·0	Æ round ·7	[-]𑀱𑁆𑀞[- - -]	As preceding. [Thomas, 1850
43	66·0	·7	𑀚𑁂𑀱𑁆𑀞𑀫[- -]	,, ,,

PURUṢADATTA

No.	Wt.	Metal. Size.	Obverse.	Reverse.
			Lakṣmī standing facing as before.  on l.  on r. 𑀧𑀼𑀭𑀼𑀱𑀤𑀢𑀲 (*Puruṣadatasa*)	Degenerate copy of thr elephants type.[1] [For the type cf. **Pl. XLIV. 1** from no. 44.]
44	93·5	·8	𑀧𑀼𑀭𑀼𑀱𑀤𑀢𑀲	,, **Pl. XXIV. 1.**
45	98·0	·75	[- - - -]𑀢𑀲	,, [Swiney, 186 **Pl. XXIV. 3.**
46	86·0	·35	𑀧𑀼𑀭𑀼𑀱[- - -]	,, [Cunningham, 189
47	90·0	·9	𑀧𑀼𑀭𑀼𑀱𑀤𑀢𑀲	,, [Thomas, 185
48	81·0	·8	𑀧𑀼𑀭𑀼𑀱[- - -]	,, [Cunningham, 189

[1] The gradual corruption of this type is illustrated on Pl. XLIV. 8–12.

No.	Wt.	Metal. Size.	Obverse.	Reverse.
49	75·0	Æ *round* ·75	[- - -]	As preceding. [Cunningham, 1894.] **Pl. XXIV. 2.**
50	88·0	·8	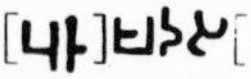[- -]	,, [Cunningham, 1894.] **Pl. XXIV. 4.**
51	42·0	·6	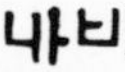[- - -]	,, [Thomas, 1850.]

UTTAMADATTA

No.	Wt.	Metal. Size.	Obverse.	Reverse.
			Lakṣmī standing facing as before on  between  on l. and  on r. 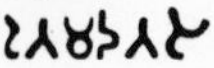 (*Utamadatasa*)	Elephant r.
52	103·5	·8	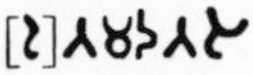	,, [Cunningham, 1894.] **Pl. XXIV. 15.**
53	67·0	·7	- - 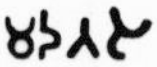	,, [Clive Bayley.] **Pl. XXIV. 17.**
54	51·0	·6	[- -]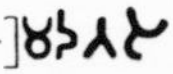	,, [Thomas, 1850.] **Pl. XXIV. 16.**

No.	Wt.	Metal. Size.	Obverse.	Reverse.
			BALABHŪTI	
			Var. *a.*	
			Lakṣmī standing facing; objects on either side not clear. 𑀭𑀚𑁆𑀜𑀩𑀮𑀪𑀽𑀢𑀺𑀲 (*Rājña*[*ḥ*] *Balabhūtisa*)	Degenerate copy of thre elephants type.
55	81·0	Æ *round* ·65	𑀩𑀮𑀪𑀽𑀢𑀺[-]	,, [Cunningham, 1894. **Pl. XXV. 22.**
			C., *C.A.I.*, Pl. VIII. 8.	
56	66·5	·7	[-]𑀮𑀪𑀽𑀢𑀺𑀲	,, [Cunningham, 1894. **Pl. XXV. 23.**
57	59·0	·65	,, ,, [-][𑀮]𑀪𑀽[𑀢𑀺𑀲]	,, [Major R. C. Temple, Pres. 1892. **Pl. XXV. 24.**
			Var. *b.*	
			? Another Balabhūti of different dynasty.	
			Standing figure holding uncertain object in raised r. hand. [𑀭]𑀚𑁆𑀜𑀩𑀮𑀪𑀽𑀢𑀺𑀲 (*Rājña*[*ḥ*] *Balabhūtisa*)	Tree in railing.
58	33·0	·65	- - 𑀚𑁆𑀜𑀩𑀮𑀪𑀽[-]	,, [Cunningham, 1894.] **Pl. XLIII. 19.**
			C., *C.A.I.*, Pl. VIII. 9.	
59	30·0	·65	- -]𑀮𑀪𑀽𑀢𑀺[- -]	,, [Cunningham, 1894.] **Pl. XLIII. 20.**

Wt.	Metal. Size.	Obverse.	Reverse.
		RAMADATTA	
		Lakṣmī standing facing as before on , between  on l. and  on r. 𑀭𑀸𑀫𑀤𑀢𑀲 (*Rāmadatasa*)	Degenerate copy of three elephants type.
107·0	Æ *round* ·9	𑀭𑀸𑀫𑀤𑀢[-]	,, [Thomas, 1850.]
101·7	·9	𑀭𑀸𑀫𑀤[- -]	,, [Eden, 1853.]
107·0	**·9**	[- - -]𑀢𑀲	,, [H. Nelson Wright, Esq., Pres., 1915.]
106·0	·9	[-]𑀫𑀤𑀢𑀲	,, ,, **Pl. XXIV. 5.**
100·0	·9	[-]𑀫𑀤𑀢𑀲	,, [Bhagvanlal, 1889.]
90·0	·75	𑀭𑀸𑀫𑀤𑀢[-]	,, [Cunningham, 1894.] **Pl. XXIV. 6.**
		C., *C.A.I.*, Pl. VIII. 16.	
86·5	·75	𑀭𑀸𑀫𑀤𑀢𑀲	,, [Thomas, 1850.] **Pl. XXIV. 7.**

No.	Wt.	Metal. Size.	Obverse.	Reverse.
67	107·5	Æ *round* ·75	[𑀭𑀸𑀫𑀤𑀢𑀲]	As preceding. [Clive Bayley, 188
68	116·5	1·0	𑀭𑀸𑀫𑀤𑀢𑀲	,, [Prinsep, 184 **Pl. XXIV. 8.**
69	110·5	1·0	[-]𑀫𑀤𑀢𑀲	,, [Cunningham, 189
			Var. *b*.	
70	57·0	·55	As preceding, but arranged in incuse square. 𑀭𑀸𑀫𑀤𑀢𑀲	As preceding. [Indian Museum, 188 **Pl. XXIV. 12.**
			Var. *c*.	
			Similar to Var. *a*, but legend 𑀭𑀸𑀚𑁆𑀜𑀭𑀸𑀫𑀤𑀢𑀲 *Rājña*[*ḥ*] *Rāmadatasa*	As preceding.
71	116·5	·85	𑀭𑀸𑀚𑁆𑀜𑀭𑀸[𑀫𑀤]𑀤𑀢𑀲	,, [Clive Bayley, 189
72	59·0	·55	[-]𑀚𑁆𑀜𑀭𑀸𑀫𑀤𑀢𑀲	,, ,, **Pl. XXIV. 13.**
			C., *C.A.I.*, Pl. VIII. 15.	

No.	Wt.	Metal. Size.	Obverse.	Reverse.
			Var. *d*.	
			Lakṣmī standing facing as before on  between  on l. and  on r.  below. 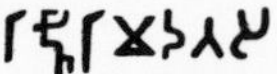 (*Rājña*[*ḥ*] *Rāmadatasa*) All in incuse square.	Very degenerate copy of three elephants type. [For the type cf. **Pl. XLIV. 11** and **12**, from nos. 73 and 77.
3	137·3	Æ *round* ·8	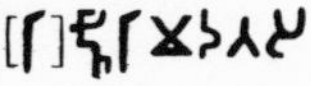	„ **Pl. XXIV. 10.**
4	125·5	·8	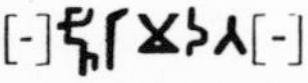	„ **Pl. XXIV. 9.**
5	122·3	·9	No traces of inscription, but types very clear.	„ **Pl. XXIV. 11.**
6	123·0	·7	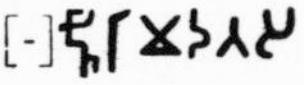	„ [Cunningham, 1894.]
			C., *C.A.I.*, Pl. VIII. 13.	
7	136·0	·75	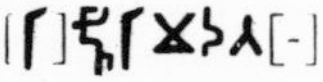	„ [Bhagvanlal, 1889.] **Pl. XXIV. 14.**
8	96·0	·7	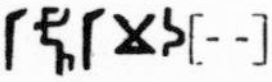	„ [Cunningham, 1894.]

No.	Wt.	Metal. Size.	Obverse.	Reverse.
			KĀMADATTA	
79	98·5	Æ *round* ·7	Lakṣmī as before on  between  on l. and probably  on r. 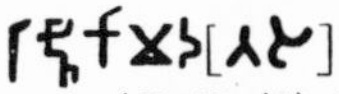 (*Rājña*(*ḥ*) *Kāmada*(*tasa*))	Illegible. [Clive Bayley, 1889 **Pl. XXIV. 18.**
			Uncertain: with title *Mahārāja*.	
			Lakṣmī as on above coins, standing facing on ;  on r. - - - 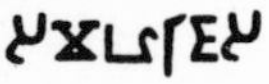	Three elephants type.
80	95·0	·7	- 	,, [H. Nelson Wright, Esq., Pres 1915 **Pl. XXIX. 24.**
81	97·0	·65	[- - - -]	,, [Eden, 1853
82	80·5	·65	[- - - - - -]	,, [Thomas, 1850
83	58·5	·6	- - - 	,, ,,
84	61·5	·6	,,	,, ,,

No.	Wt.	Metal. Size.	Obverse.	Reverse.
			ŚIVADATTA (*c.* 60–50 B.C.)	
5	65·0	Æ round ·7	Lakṣmī standing facing;  below;  on l.;  on . 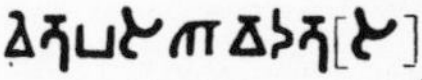[ ] (*Khatapasa Śivadatasa*)	Horse l. [Purcha d, 848.] **Pl. XXV. 26.**
			HAGĀMAṢA (*c.* 50–40 B.C.)	
			Lakṣmī standing facing on 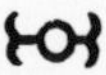, holding flower in uplifted r. hand, between  on l. and  on r. 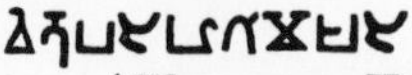 (*Khatapasa Hagāmaṣasa*)	Horse l.
6	91·0	·8	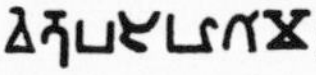[- -]	,, [Prinsep, 1847.]
7	65·0	·8	[- - -]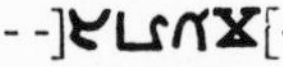[-]	,, [Bhagvanlal, 1889.] **Pl. XXVI. 1.**
8	49·0	·8	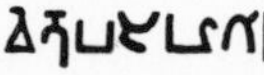[- - -]	,, ,, **Pl. XXVI. 2.**
9	71·0	·7	[- -]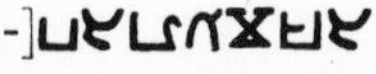	,, [Cunningham. 1894.]
			C., *C.A.I.*, Pl. VIII, 6.	

No.	Wt.	Metal. Size.	Obverse.	Reverse.
90	102·0	Æ *round* ·75		As preceding. [I. O. C., 1882 **Pl. XXVI. 3.**
91	105·0	·8		,, [Thomas, 1850 **Pl. XXVI. 5.**
92	80·0	·8		,, [Clive Bayley, 1889 **Pl. XXVI. 4.**
93	53·0	·7		,, [Clive Bayley, 1889
94	66·0	·7	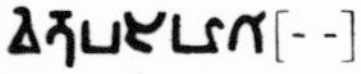	,, [Cunningham, 1894
95	65·0	·7		,, [Thomas, 1850
96	66·0	·75		,, [Cunningham, 1894

HAGĀMAŚA and HAGĀNA

97	67·5	·75	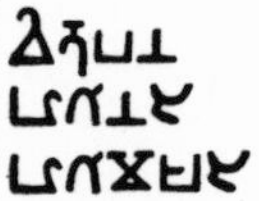  (*Khatap*[*ā*]*na Hagānasa Hagāmaṣasa*)	Horse l. [Clive Bayley, 1889 **Pl. XXVI. 6.**

No.	Wt.	Metal. Size.	Obverse.	Reverse.
			RĀJUVULA (Rañjubula, Rājūla) (*c.* 40–20 B.C.) Class I.	
			Bust of the king r., diademed. ΒΑCΙΛΕΩC ΒΑCΙΛΕѠΝ CѠΤΗΡΟC ΡΑΙΥ (much blundered).	Pallas l., holding in l. hand aegis and hurling thunderbolt in r. [Kharoshthi] [Kharoshthi] Varying letters in field. (*Apratihatacakrasa Chhatrapasa Rajuvulasa*)
98[1]	38·0	Æ *base round* ·55	Portions of above inscription.	On l. [Kharoshthi] On r., read outwardly, [Kharoshthi] Below [Kharoshthi] [Kharoshthi] on l., [Kharoshthi] on r. in field. [Cunningham, 1894.] **Pl. XXVI. 7.**
99	36·8	·55	” ”	[Kharoshthi][- -][Kharoshthi] [Kharoshthi] [[Kharoshthi]] on l., [Kharoshthi] on r. in field. [Cunningham, 1894.]
00	36·6	·55	” ”	Traces of inscription. [Cunningham, 1894.] **Pl. XXVI. 8.**
01	36·4	·55	” ”	Traces of inscription around. [- -][Kharoshthi] below. [Kharoshthi] on l., [Kharoshthi] on r. in field. [Cunningham, 1894.] **Pl. XXVI. 11.**
02	36·0	·55	” ”	Similar. [Cunningham, 1894.]

[1] Nos. 98–105 are B.M. *Cat. Gk. and Scyth. Kings*, p. 67, nos. 1–8.

No.	Wt.	Metal. Size.	Obverse.	Reverse.
103	30·8	Æ base round ·55	As preceding.	Similar, but [illegible] on l., [illegible] on r. in field. [Cunningham, 1894.]
104	35·2	·5	,,	,, ,,
105	35·8	·5	,,	,, ,,
106	30·0	·65	,,	,, ,, **Pl. XXVI. 9.**
			C., *C.A.I.*, Pl. VIII. 1.	
107	33·0	·55	,,	[illegible] on l., [illegible] on r. in field. [Cunningham, 1894.]
108	36·0	·6	,,	[illegible] on l., [illegible] on r. in field. [Bhagvanlal, 1889.]
109	36·0	·55	,,	,, in field. [Cunningham, 1894.] **Pl. XXVI. 10.**
			C., *C.A.I.*, Pl. VIII. 3.	
110	37·0	Æ round ·5	Similar, but ruder.	As preceding, but ruder fabric [illegible][- - -] [illegible] [illegible] on l., [illegible] on r. in field. [J. P. Rawlins, 1922.]
111	39·5	·5	,,	- -][illegible][,, in field. [Col. Shepherd, Pres., 1903.]
112	34·5	·5	,,	][illegible][- -] ,, in field. [Col. Shepherd, Pres., 1903]

No.	Wt.	Metal. Size.	Obverse.	Reverse.
			Class II.	
			Lakṣmī standing facing between  on l. and  on r. 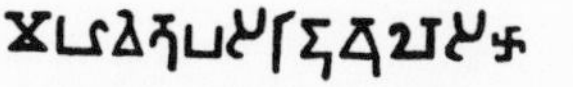 (*Mahākhatapasa Rājuvulasa*)	Abhiṣeka of Lakṣmī; the goddess standing in centre being sprinkled by elephants on pedestals on either side.
13	92·0	Æ round ·7	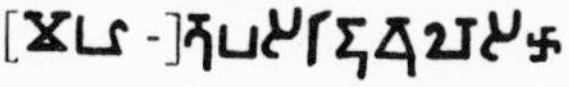	" (traces only) [Cunningham, 1894.] **Pl. XXVI. 12.**
			C., *C.A.I.*, Pl. VIII. 4 (*obv.*).	
14	90·0	·7		" [Cunningham, 1894.] **Pl. XXVI. 13.**
			C., *C.A.I.*, Pl. VIII. 4 (*rev.*).	
			Class III.	
			Lion r.;  above. Traces of legend; probably in corrupt Greek.	Hercules standing to l. with r. hand out and club and lion-skin on l. arm. 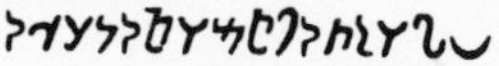 (*Mahakhatapasa apratichakrasa Rajulasa*)
			Var. *a.*  on l. in field.	
15	145·0	·85	No trace of legend.	No trace of legend. [W. S. Talbot, Esq., Pres., 1903.] **Pl. XLIII. 21.**

No.	Wt.	Metal. Size.	Obverse.	Reverse.
		Æ *round*	Var. *b.* 卐 on l. in field.	
116	129·0	·8	Traces of legend.	On r. - - [Kharoshthi] - - Below [- - -][Kharoshthi] [J. P. Rawlins, 1922.] **Pl. XLIII. 22.**
117	102·5	·7	,,	On l. [Kharoshthi] - - - - [Kharoshthi] - - [C. J. Rodgers, 1894.]
118	111·5	·65	,,	On l. - - [Kharoshthi] - [Indian Museum, 1885.] **Pl. XLIV. 1.**
			(from Hoshiārpur)	
119	130·0	·75	,,	- - [Kharoshthi] - - - - - - [Clive Bayley, 1889.
120	86·5	·7	,,	- - - [Kharoshthi] - - [Indian Museum, 1889. **Pl. XLIV. 2.**
			(from Amritsar)	
			Var. *c.* Ч on l., Π on r. in field.	
121	100·0	·65	As preceding.	On l. - - [Kharoshthi] - - - [W. S. Talbot, Esq., Pres 1903
122	85·0	·6	,,	[Kharoshthi] - - - - - [J. P. Rawlins, 1922
123	80·0	·6	,,	- [Kharoshthi] - - - [R. B. Whitehead, 1922 **Pl. XLIV. 3.**

No.	Wt.	Metal. Size.	Obverse.	Reverse.
		Æ *round*		
24	77·5	·65	As preceding.	
25	73·0	·65	,,	 [R. B. Whitehead, 1922.]
26	77·0	·65	,,	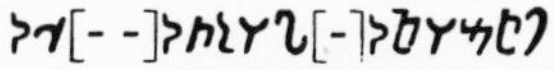 [J. P. Rawlins, 1922.] **Pl. XLIV. 4.**
27	66·5	·65	,,	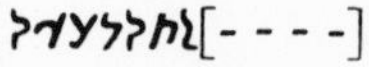 [Col. Massy, Pres., 1889.]
28	60·0	·6	,,	 [W. S. Talbot, Esq., Pres., 1903.]
29	61·5	·55	,,	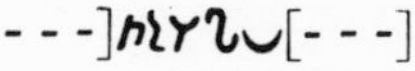 [J. P. Rawlins, 1922.]
30	55·0	·55	,,	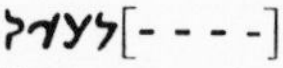 [W. S. Talbot, Esq., Pres., 1903.]
31	58·5	·6	,,	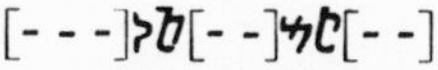 [R. B. Whitehead, 1922.]
32	50·0	·6	,,	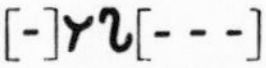 [R. B. Whitehead, 1922.]
33	40·0	·5	,,	Traces of inscription. [R. B. Whitehead, 1922.] **Pl. XLIV. 5.**
34	39·0	·6	,,	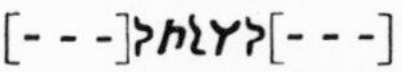 [R. R. Whitehead, 1922.]

ŚOḌĀSA

(*c.* 20–10 B.C.)

Var. *a.*

(son of the Mahākṣatrapa)

No.	Wt.	Metal. Size.	Obverse.	Reverse.
			Lakṣmī standing facing between  on l. and  on r. 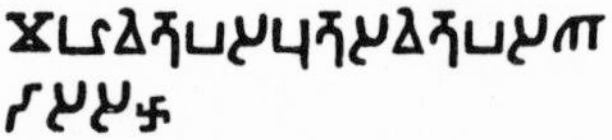 (*Mahakhatapasa putasa khatapasa Śoḍāsasa*)	Abhiṣeka of Lakṣmī; the goddess standing facing between two elephants mounted on pedestals and sprinkling her.
135	116·0	Ꞵ *round* ·7	[- - - - - - - -]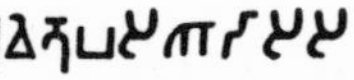	,, [Prinsep. **Pl. XXVI. 16.**
			(*J.A.S.B.*, iii, Pl. 18, no. 4.)	
136	87·5	·7	[- - - -]	,, [Thomas, 1853. **Pl. XLIII. 17.**
137	80·5	·6		,, [Eden, 1853.
138	130·0	·7		,, [Clive Bayley, 1889. **Pl. XXVI. 17.**
139	50·0	Æ *round* ·65	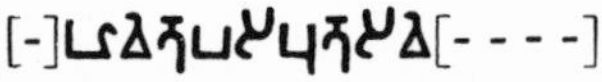	,, [Cunningham, 1894. **Pl. XXVI. 14.**
			C., *C.A.I.*, Pl. VIII. 5.	

o.	Wt.	Metal. Size.	Obverse.	Reverse.
0	47·0	Æ round ·65	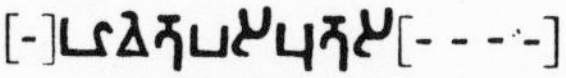	As preceding. [Cunningham, 1894.] **Pl. XXVI. 15.**
			C., *C.A.I.*, Pl. VIII. 5.	
1	30·5	·6	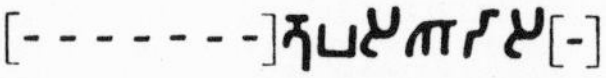	,, [Thomas, 1850.]
2	58·0	·6	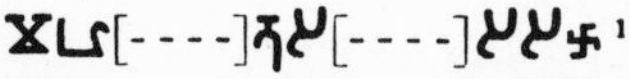 [1]	,, [Bhagvanlal, 1889.] **Pl. XXV. 25.**

Var. *b*.

(son of Rājuvula)

			As no. 135, but legend  (*Rājuvulaputasa Khatapasa Śoḍasasa*)	Abhiṣeka of Lakṣmī as before.
3	40·5	·55	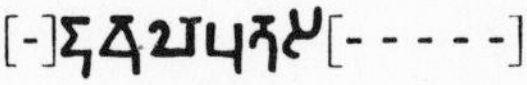	,, [Bhagvanlal, 1889.]
4	30·5	·6		,, [Clive Bayley, 1889.]
5	27·0	·6	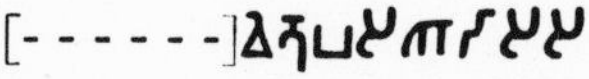	,, ,, **Pl. XXVI. 18.**

Var. *c* (without patronymic).

6	35·0	·55	As above, but legend  (*Mahākhatapasa Śoḍasasa*)	As above. [Major R. C. Temple, Pres., 1892.] **Pl. XLIII. 15.**

[1] This is the coin read 'Mevaku' by Bhagvanlal.

No.	Wt.	Metal. Size.	Obverse.	Reverse.

PAÑCĀLA

[VIŚVA ?]PĀLA

No.	Wt.	Metal. Size.	Obverse.	Reverse.
1	58·0	Æ *round* ·65	 [𑀯𑀺𑀰𑁆𑀯]𑀧𑀸𑀮𑀲 ([*Viśva* ?]*pālasa*) All in incuse square.	Illegible. [Cunningham, 1894 **Pl. XXVII. 4.**

C., *C.A.I.*, Pl. VII. 18.

RUDRAGUPTA

No.	Wt.	Metal. Size.	Obverse.	Reverse.
			 𑀭𑀼𑀤𑁆𑀭𑀕𑀼𑀧𑁆𑀢𑀲 (*Rudraguptasa*) All in incuse square.	Railing with three pilla above; uncertain objects top of each.
2	78·0	·75	𑀭𑀼𑀤𑁆𑀭𑀕𑀼𑀧𑁆𑀢𑀲	,, [Cunningham, 1894 **Pl. XXVII. 1.**

C., *C.A.I.*, Pl. VII. 1.

No.	Wt.	Metal. Size.	Obverse.	Reverse.
3	81·5	·85	[-]𑀤𑁆𑀭𑀕[- -]	,, [Cunningham, 1894
4	58·5	·75	𑀭𑀼𑀤𑁆𑀭𑀕[- -]	,, ,,
5	40·5	·6	𑀭𑀼𑀤𑁆𑀭𑀕𑀼𑀧𑁆𑀢𑀲	,, ,,
6	32·0	·55	[-]𑀤𑁆𑀭𑀕𑀼𑀧𑁆𑀢[-]	,, ,, central object a trident. **Pl. XXVII. 2.**

SŪRYAMITRA

o.	Wt.	Metal. Size.	Obverse.	Reverse.
		Æ round	 𑀲𑀼𑀬𑀫𑀺𑀢𑁆𑀭𑀲 (*Suyamitrasa*)	Sun over  between pillars on railing.
7	243·0	1·0	𑀲𑀼𑀬𑀫𑀺𑀢𑁆𑀭[-]	,, [Da Cunha, 1890.]
8	228·0	·8	𑀲𑀼[- -]𑀢𑁆𑀭𑀲	,, [Cunningham, 1894.]
			C., *C.A.I.*, Pl. VII. 4.	
9	170·0	·85	𑀲𑀼𑀬𑀫𑀺𑀢𑁆𑀭𑀲	,, [H. Rivett-Carnac, Esq., Pres., 1881.] **Pl. XXVII. 8.**
0	178·0	·9	𑀲𑀼𑀬𑀫𑀺𑀢𑁆𑀭𑀲	,, [Cunningham, 1894.]
1	202·0	·9	[-]𑀬[-]𑀢𑁆𑀭𑀲	,, ,, **Pl. XXVII. 9.**
2	106·0	·75	𑀲𑀼𑀬𑀫𑀺𑀢𑁆𑀭[-]	,, [Cunningham, 1894.] **Pl. XXVII. 10.**
3	91·0	·75	𑀲𑀼𑀬𑀫𑀺𑀢𑁆𑀭𑀲	,, [Cunningham, 1894.]

PHALGUNIMITRA

No	Wt.	Metal. Size.	Obverse.	Reverse.
14	267·0	Æ round 1·0	 𑀨𑀕𑀼𑀦𑀺𑀫𑀺𑀢𑁆𑀭𑀲 (*Phagunimitrasa*) 𑀨𑀕𑀼𑀦𑀺𑀫𑀺𑀢𑁆𑀭	Female deity standing facin on lotus, holding uncertai object in raised r. hand.  on l.; star above head. ,, [Da Cunha, 1890. **Pl. XXVII. 11.**
15	273·0	1·0	,,	,, [Cunningham, 1894.
16	243·0	1·0	,,	,, ,,
17	230·0	·95	,,	,, ,,
18	215·0	1·0	,,	,, ,,
19	194·0	1·0	,,	,, [H. D. Willock, Esq., Pres 1885. **Pl. XXVII. 12.**
20	186·0	1·0	,,	,, [Cunningham, 1894. **Pl. XXVII. 13.**
			C., *C.A.I.*, Pl. VII. 5.	
21	170·0	1·0	,,	,, [H. Rivett Carnac, Esq., Pres.

No.	Wt.	Metal. Size.	Obverse.	Reverse.
22	113·0	Æ *round* ·95	As preceding.	As preceding. [Cunningham, 1894.]
23	85·0	·8	[-]𑀕𑀼𑀦𑀺𑀫𑀺𑀢𑁆𑀭𑀲	” ”
24	86·5	·75	𑀨𑀕𑀼𑀦𑀺𑀫𑀺𑀢𑁆𑀭𑀲	” [H. Rivett-Carnac, Esq., Pres.]
25	95·0	·8	”	” [Clive Bayley, 1889.] **Pl. XXVII. 14.**
26	46·5	·75	”	” [Cunningham, 1894.]

BHĀNUMITRA

Var. *a*.

No.	Wt.	Metal. Size.	Obverse.	Reverse.
			 𑀪𑀸𑀦𑀼𑀫𑀺𑀢𑁆𑀭𑀲 (*Bhanumitrasa*)	Sun between pillars on railed pedestal.  on r. and l.
7	182·0	·65	𑀪𑀸𑀦𑀼𑀫𑀺𑀢𑁆𑀭𑀲	” [Cunningham, 1894.]
			C., *C.A.I.*, Pl. VII. 6.	
8	216·0	1·0	”	” [H. Rivett-Carnac, Esq., Pres., 1881.] **Pl. XXVII. 16.**
9	130·0	·8	[- -]𑀫𑀺𑀢𑁆𑀭𑀲	” [H. D. Willock, Esq., Pres.]

No.	Wt.	Metal. Size.	Obverse.	Reverse.
30	52·5	Æ *round* ·55	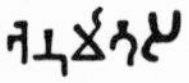	As preceding. [Cunningham, 1894
31	45·0	·6	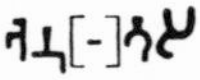	,, [Cunningham, 1894 **Pl. XXVII. 17.**
32	27·5	·45	,,	,, [Cunningham, 1894
33	14·5	·45	,,	,, ,,
34	16·0	·45	,,	,, ,,
			C., *C.A.I.*, Pl. IV. 13.	
35	18·0	·5	,,	,, ,, **Pl. XXVII. 15.**
			C., *C.A.I.*, Pl. VII. 9.	
36	15·0	·45	,,	,, [Cunningham, 1894 **Pl. XXVII. 18.**
37	12·5	·45	,,	,, [Cunningham, 1894 **Pl. XXVII. 19.**
38	13·5	·45	,,	,, [Cunningham, 1894 **Pl. XXVII. 20.**

o.	Wt.	Metal. Size.	Obverse.	Reverse.
			Var. *b*.	
		Æ *round*	 on obverse obliterated by countermark 	
9	246·0	1·0	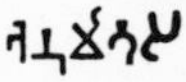 countermark 	Sun between pillars on railed pedestal. [Cunningham, 1894.]
			C., *C.A.I.*, Pl. VII. 7.	
a	247·0	1·0	,,	,, [Spink, 1928.]
0	195·0	1·05	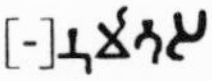	,, [Da Cunha, 1889.]
1	93·0	·85	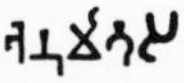	,, [Cunningham, 1894.]
			BHADRAGHOṢA	
			 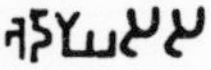 (*Bhadraghosasa*)	Female deity standing facing on lotus.  on l.; star above;  on r.
2	252·0	1·05	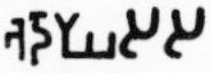	,, [Cunningham, 1894.] **Pl. XXVIII. 1.**
			C., *C.A.I.*, Pl. VII. 10.	
3	240·0	1·1	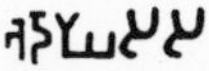 countermark 	,, [H. Rivett-Carnac, Esq., Pres.] **Pl. XXVIII. 2.**
4	235·0	1·05	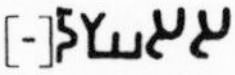 countermark 	,, [Da Cunha, 1890.]
5	16·0	·4	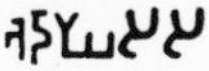	,, [Cunningham, 1894.] **Pl. XXVIII. 3.**
			C., *C.A.I.*, Pl. VII. 11.	

No.	Wt.	Metal. Size.	Obverse.	Reverse.
			BHŪMIMITRA	
			  (*Bhūmimitrasa*)	Male figure with flaming ha standing facing between tw pillars on railing.
46	241·0	Æ *round* 1·0	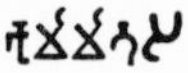	,, [Cunningham, 1894 **Pl. XXVIII. 4.**
47	230·0	1·05	,,	,, [H. Rivett-Carnac, Esq., Pre 1881 **Pl. XXVIII. 6.**
48	237·0	1·0	,,	,, [Da Cunha, 1890
49	252·0	1·0	,,	,, [Cunningham, 1894
50	198·0	·85	,,	,, ,, **Pl. XXVIII. 7.**
			C., *C.A.I.*, Pl. VII. 12.	
51	189·0	1·05	,,	,, [Clive Bailey, 188 **Pl. XXVIII. 5.**
52	125·0	·8	,,	,, [Cunningham, 189

o.	Wt.	Metal. Size.	Obverse.	Reverse.
			DHRUVAMITRA	
				As No. 2.
		Æ	𑀥𑁆𑀭𑀼𑀯𑀫𑀺𑀢𑁆𑀭𑀲 (*Dhruvamitrasa*)	
3	53·0	*round* ·7	𑀥𑁆𑀭𑀼𑀯𑀫𑀺[- -]	„ [Cunningham, 1894.] **Pl. XXVII. 5.**
			C., *C.A.I.*, Pl. VII. 3.	
4	58·5	·7	𑀥𑁆𑀭𑀼𑀯𑀫𑀺[-]𑀲	„ [Cunningham, 1894.]
5	57·0	·75	𑀥𑁆𑀭𑀼𑀯𑀫𑀺𑀢𑁆𑀭𑀲	„ „ **Pl. XXVII. 6.**
6	59·0	·65	„	„ [Cunningham, 1894.]
7	41·0	·6	𑀥𑁆𑀭𑀼𑀯𑀫𑀺[- -]	„ „ **Pl. XXVII. 7.**
8	20·5	·65	𑀥𑁆𑀭𑀼𑀯 [- - -]	„ [Cunningham, 1894.]
			AGNIMITRA	
				Male figure (Agni) with flaming hair, standing facing on platform between two pillars.
			𑀅𑀕𑀺𑀫𑀺𑀢𑁆𑀭𑀲 (*Agimitrasa*)	
9	291·0	·9	𑀅𑀕𑀺𑀫𑀺𑀢𑁆𑀭𑀲	„ [Cunningham, 1894.]
			C., *C.A.I.*, Pl. VII. 13.	

No.	Wt.	Metal. Size.	Obverse.	Reverse.
60	292·0	Æ *round* 1·0	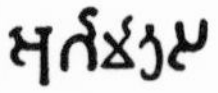	As preceding. [Cunningham, 1894 **Pl. XXVIII. 8.**
61	283·0	1·0	,,	,, [Da Cunha, 1890
62	274·0	1·05	,,	,, [H. Nelson Wright, Esq., Pre 1915
63	285·0	1·0	,,	,, [H. Rivett-Carnac, Esq., Pre 1881
64	259·0	1·05	,,	,, [Cunningham, 1894
65	91·0	·7	,,	,, ,, **Pl. XXVIII. 9.**
66	88·0	·65	,,	,, [Parkes Weber Gift, 1906
67	92·0	·7	,,	,, [Cunningham, 1894
68	89·0	·65	,,	,, ,,
			C., *C.A.I.*, Pl. VII. 15.	
69	80·0	·7	,,	,, [Thomas, 1850 **Pl. XXVIII. 12.**

o.	Wt	Metal. Size.	Obverse.	Reverse.
0	90·0	Æ *round* ·7	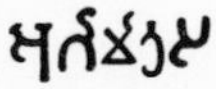	As preceding. [Thomas, 1850.] **Pl. XXVIII. 11.**
1	96·0	·7	,,	,, [Cunningham, 1894.]
2	117·5	·7	,,	,, ,,
3	81·5	·65	,,	,, ,,
4	57·0	·6	,,	,, [H. Rivett-Carnac, Esq., Pres., 1881.]
5	34·0	·6	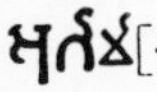[- -]	,, [Cunningham, 1891.]
6	34·0	·45	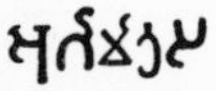	,, ,, **Pl. XXVIII. 13.**
			C., *C.A.I.*, Pl. VII. 14.	
7	32·0	·5	,,	,, [H. Nelson Wright, Esq., Pres., 1915.]
8	32·0	·5	,,	,, [Cunningham, 1891.] **Pl. XXVIII. 14.**
9	73·0	·85	As above, but  obliterated by countermark standing female figure.	,, [H. Rivett-Carnac, Esq., Pres., 1889.] **Pl. XLVI. 16.**
)	120·0	·85	,, countermark lion l.	,, [Clive Bayley, 1889.] **Pl. XLVI. 15.**

No.	Wt.	Metal. Size.	Obverse.	Reverse.
			VIṢNUMITRA	
			 𑀯𑀺𑀱𑁆𑀡𑀼𑀫𑀺𑀢𑁆𑀭𑀲 (*Viṣṇumitrasa*)	Facing deity holding uncertai objects in either outstretche hand.
81	60·0	Æ *round* ·55	𑀯𑀺𑀱𑁆𑀡𑀼𑀫𑀺𑀢𑁆𑀭𑀲	„ [Cunningham, 1894. **Pl. XXIX. 6.**
			C., *C.A.I.*, Pl. VII. 21.	
82	59·0	·65	„	„ [Cunningham, 1894
83	68·0	·6	„	„ [Ibbetson, 1920
84	59·0	·6	„	„ [H. Nelson Wright, Esq., Pres **Pl. XXIX. 8.**
85	62·0	·8	„	„ [H. Nelson Wright, Esq., Pres **Pl. XXIX. 9.**
86	48·0	·6	„	„ [Cunningham, 1894
			JAYAGUPTA	
			 𑀚𑀬𑀕𑀼𑀧𑁆𑀢𑀲 (*Jayaguptasa*)	 on l. Standing deity i archway.
87	86·5	·5	𑀚𑀬𑀕𑀼𑀧𑁆𑀢𑀲	„ **Pl. XXVII. 19.**
88	23·0	·45	„	„ **Pl. XXVII. 3.**

No.	Wt.	Metal. Size.	Obverse.	Reverse.
			JAYAMITRA	
			 𑀚𑀬𑀫𑀺𑀢𑁆𑀭𑀲 (*Jayamitrasa*)	Standing deity facing below pillars on pedestal.
89	77·0	Æ *round* ·7	𑀚𑀬𑀫𑀺𑀢𑁆𑀭𑀲	" [Cunningham, 1894.]
90	65·0	·6	"	" " **Pl. XXVIII. 17.** C., *C.A.I.*, Pl. VII. 17.
91	69·0	·7	"	" [Cunningham, 1894.]
92	69·0	·7	"	" [H. Nelson Wright, Esq., Pres.] **Pl. XXVIII. 20.**
93	69·0	·7	"	" [H. Nelson Wright, Esq., Pres.] **Pl. XXVIII. 21.**
94	71·0	·7	"	" [H. Nelson Wright, Esq., Pres.] **Pl. XXVIII. 18.**
			INDRAMITRA	
			 𑀇𑀁𑀤𑁆𑀭𑀫𑀺𑀢𑁆𑀭𑀲 (*Iṁdramitrasa*)	Standing deity facing on pedestal, holding uncertain object in r. hand.
95	83·0	·65	𑀇𑀁𑀤𑁆𑀭𑀫𑀺𑀢𑁆𑀭𑀲	" [Cunningham, 1894.] **Pl. XXIX. 2.**

No.	Wt.	Metal. Size.	Obverse.	Reverse.
96	78·0	Æ *round* ·65	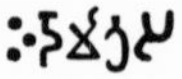	As preceding. [Cunningham, 1894.]
97	76·0	·65	,,	,, ,,
98	66·0	·6	,,	,, ,,
			C., *C.A.I.*, Pl. VII. 19.	
99	65·0	·65	,,	,, [H. Rivett-Carnac, Esq., Pres., 1881.] **Pl. XXIX. 1.**
99*a*	64·0	·6	,,	,, [Spink, 1928.]
100	54·0	·5	,,	Deity in archway;  on l. [Cunningham, 1894.]
			C., *C.A.I.*, Pl. VII. 20.	
101	45·0	·5	,,	,, ,,
102	45·0	·5	,,	,, [H. Nelson Wright, Esq., Pres.
103	38·0	·5	,,	,, [Cunningham, 1894. **Pl. XXIX. 3.**
104	32·5	·5	,,	,, [Cunningham, 1894.
105	37·0	·5	,,	,, [H. Nelson Wright, Esq., Pres **Pl. XXIX. 5.**

No.	Wt.	Metal. Size.	Obverse.	Reverse.
			PURĪ	
			Var. *a*.	
			Rude figure of king standing facing with head to l. and r., hand outstretched as if sprinkling incense on altar and l. arm raised as if holding sceptre (the type goes back to a Kushan obverse like B.M.C., Pl. XXVIII. 2).	Rude figure of deity standing to l. with r. arm outstretched and l. arm bent resting on hip (this type goes back to a Kushan reverse like B.M.C., Pl. XXVIII. 1, 3, 4).
	132·0	Æ *round* ·9	,, (from Purī)	,, [As. Soc. Bengal Pres., 1895.] **Pl. XXX. 1.**
	151·5	·9	,, ,,	,, [As. Soc. Bengal Pres., 1895.]
	135·0	·9	,, ,,	,, ,, **Pl. XXX. 2.**
	145·5	·95	,, ,,	,, [As. Soc. Bengal Pres., 1895.]
	145·0	·9	,, ,,	,, ,,
	114·0	·9	,, ,,	,, ,,
			Var. *b*.	
	145·0	·95	Similar. (from Purī)	Similar, but both arms outstretched at angle of 45°. Crescent on l. above. [As. Soc. Bengal Pres., 1895.] **Pl. XXX. 3.**

No	Wt.	Metal. Size.	Obverse.	Reverse.
		Æ round	Var. *c*.	
8	146·7	·95	Similar, but crescent above on l. (from Purī)	Similar, but r. arm raised 45 above shoulder and l. ar outstretched 45° below. [As. Soc. Bengal Pres., 1895. **Pl. XXX. 4.**
9	156·5	·9	,, ,,	,, [As. Soc. Bengal Pres., 1895
			Var. *d*.	
10	120·0	·9	As preceding. (from Purī)	Similar, but position of arm reversed. [As. Soc. Bengal Pres., 1895 **Pl. XXX. 7.**
			Var. *e*.	
11	132·0	·9	Similar, but position of arms reversed; crescent above on r. (from Purī)	As in Var. *c*. [As. Soc. Bengal Pres., 1895 **Pl. XXX. 10.**
12	151·0	·9	,, ,,	,, [As. Soc. Bengal Pres., 1895
13	150·0	·9	,, ,,	,, ,,
14	125·0	·9	,, ,,	,, ,,
			Var. *f*.	
15	120·0	·9	Similar, but smaller, even cruder figure; Kushan dress still obvious; both arms outstretched, and like the legs and feet represented by thick semicircles. (from Purī)	Similar to obverse. [As. Soc. Bengal Pres., 1895 **Pl. XXX. 5.**

o.	Wt.	Metal. Size.	Obverse.	Reverse.
		Æ *round*	Var. *g*.	
6	150·0	·9	Similar to Var. *f*.	Similar to Var. *f*, with addition of semicircle above on l. [As. Soc. Bengal Pres., 1895.]
			Var. *h*.	
7	141·5	·0	Similar to Var. *f*, but r. arm horizontal and l. raised 45°. (from Purī)	Similar figure to l. with both arms outstretched to l. so that little is seen of the right one; crescent above on l. [As. Soc. Bengal Pres., 1895.] **Pl. XXX. 8.**
8	147·5	·9	,, ,,	,, [As. Soc. Bengal Pres., 1895.]
9	152·0	·9	,, ,,	,, ,,
0	145·0	·9	,, ,,	,, ,,
1	147·0	·9	,, ,,	,, ,,
2	137·5	·9	,, ,,	,, ,,
3	135·0	·9	,, ,,	,, ,,
4	125·0	·9	,, ,,	,, ,,
5	125·0	·9	,, ,,	,, ,, **Pl. XXX. 9.**

No.	Wt.	Metal. Size.	Obverse.	Reverse.
26	163·0	Æ *round* ·95	As preceding.	As preceding. [As. Soc. Bengal Pres., 1895.
27	147·0	·9	,,	,, ,,
28	128·0	·85	,,	,, ,,
29	91·0	·85	,, (from Bhanjakia)	,, [The Maharaja of Mayurbhan Pres., 1928
30	87·5	·85	,,	,, ,,
31	85·0	·8	,, ,,	,, ,, **Pl. XLIV. 14.**
32	81·5	·85	,, ,,	,, [The Maharaja of Mayurbhar Pres., 1928
33	78·5	·85	,, ,,	,, ,,
34	76·0	·85	,, ,,	,, ,, **Pl. XLIV. 15.**
35	79·0	·7	,, ,,	,, [The Maharaja of Mayurbhar Pres., 1928
36	71·5	·8	,, ,,	,, ,,
37	69·5	·8	,, ,,	,, ,,
38	62·0	·8	,, ,,	,, ,,

No.	Wt.	Metal. Size.	Obverse.	Reverse.
		Æ round	Var. *i*.	
39	130·0	·9	Similar to Var. *h*, but crescent above on l. (from Purī)	Similar to Var. *h*. [As. Soc. Bengal Pres., 1895] **Pl. XXX. 11.**
			Var. *j*.	
40	160·0	·9	Similar, but r. arm horizontal and l. at angle of 45°; crescent above on r. (from Purī)	Similar, but both arms outstretched at angle of 45°; crescent above on l. [As. Soc. Bengal Pres., 1895.] **Pl. XLIV. 16.**
			Var. *k*.	
41	132·0	·9	Similar, but r. arm raised 45° from shoulder and l. 45° below—apparently walking to l.; crescent above on r. (from Purī)	As Var. *e*. [As. Soc. Bengal Pres., 1895.] **Pl. XXX. 12.**
			Var. *l*.	
42	130·0	·9	As Var. *f*. (from Purī)	As Var. *k*. [As. Soc. Bengal Pres., 1895.]

No.	Wt.	Metal. Size.	Obverse.	Reverse.
			RĀJANYA	
			Type I.	
			Brahmi Inscriptions.	
			CLASS 1.	
			Deity (? Lakṣmī) facing, holding lotus (?) in r. hand; closely resembling Mathurā deity. 𑀭𑀸𑀚𑀜𑀚𑀦𑀧𑀤𑀲 (*Rājaña janapadasa*)	Bull l. in rayed circle.
			Var. *a*.	
1	†121·0	Æ *round* ·7	𑀭𑀚𑀜𑀚𑀦𑀧𑀤𑀲	Bull l. in rayed circle. [Cunningham, 1894. **Pl. XXIX. 15.**
			C., *C.A.I.*, Pl. I. 2.	
2	77·0	·7	𑀭𑀚𑀜𑀚 - - -	,, [Rodgers, 1893. **Pl. XXIX. 23.**
			Var. *b*: ruder fabric.	
3	60·0	·65	[-]𑀚𑀜𑀚𑀦𑀧𑀤𑀲	Bull l. in rayed circle. [Clive Bayley, 1889. **Pl. XXIX. 16.**
4	33·0	·65	,,	,, [J. P. Rawlins, 1922. **Pl. XXIX. 17.**
5	41·5	·6	[- -]𑀜𑀚𑀦𑀧[- -]	,, [J. P. Rawlins, 1922.

o.	Wt.	Metal. Size.	Obverse.	Reverse.
		Æ *round*		
6	33·5	·65	𑀭𑀚𑀜[- -]𑀧[- -]	As preceding. [J. P. Rawlins, 1922.]
7	30·0	·65	𑀭𑀚𑀜𑀚𑀦𑀧[- -]	„ „
8	30·0	·65	[- - -]𑀚𑀦𑀧𑀤𑀲	„ „ **Pl. XXIX. 19.**
9	38·0	·65	𑀭𑀚𑀜𑀚𑀦𑀧𑀤𑀲	„ [Indian Museum, 1889.] **Pl. XXIX. 18.**
0	25·5	·5	[-]𑀚𑀜𑀚[- - - -]	„ [Thomas, 1850.]
			Var. *c*.	
1	31·4	·7	As above, but very crudely represented. - - - - 𑀚𑀦 on r. 𑀧𑀤𑀲 on l.	Bull l. in rayed circle. [J. P. Rawlins, 1922.] **Pl. XXIX. 22.**
			CLASS 2. Kharoṣṭhī Inscriptions.	
			Goddess (Lakṣmī) standing facing, holding lotus in r. hand as on coins of Mathurā. 𐨪𐨗𐨙𐨗𐨣𐨤𐨡𐨯 (*Rajaña janapadasa*)	Bull l. in rayed circle.
2	55·0	·7	𐨪𐨗𐨙𐨗𐨣𐨤𐨡𐨯	„ [J. P. Rawlins, 1922.] **Pl. XXIX. 13.**

No.	Wt.	Metal. Size.	Obverse.	Reverse.
		Æ *round*		
13	37·0	·75	[- - -]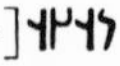	As preceding. [J. P. Rawlins, 1922 **Pl. XXIX. 21.**
14	32·0	·65	[- - -]	,, [J. P. Rawlins, 1922
15	26·0	·7	- - - -][- -]	,, ,,
16	15·0	·5	[- - -]	,, ,, **Pl. XXIX. 20.**
			Type II.	
17	41·5	·65	Standing figure facing l.; r. hand raised; on l. traces of inscription.	 in rayed circle. [J. P. Rawlins, 1922 **Pl. XXIX. 11.**
			Type III.	
18	111·3	·8	Stupa; traces of inscription.	Tree in railing. [J. P. Rawlins, 1922 **Pl. XXIX. 12.**
			Type IV.	
19	43·0	·7	Four-tiered stupa; traces of Kharoṣṭhī legend on r.	 above.  in centre. 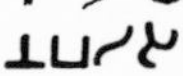 (*Trakatajanapadas* [J. P. Rawlins, 1922 **Pl. XXIX. 10.**

No.	Wt.	Metal. Size.	Obverse.	Reverse.
		Æ	**Type V.**	
20	52·0	*square* ·8	Type not clear; probably standing figure on railed pedestal. 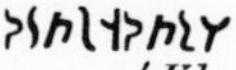 (*Khatapasa janapadasa*)	Horse l. in double square; the interstices filled with semi-circles. [Rodgers, 1892.] **Pl. XLIV. 13.**
			Type VI.	
21	82·0	*round* ·7	Types uncertain; include  Below, -]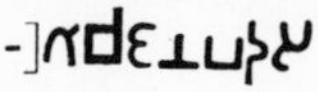	 [H. Nelson Wright, Esq., Pres. 1915.] **Pl. XLIV. 6.**
22	75·0	·7	Similar. -]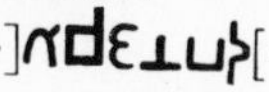[-]	Illegible. **Pl. XLIV. 7.**

No.	Wt.	Metal. Size.	Obverse.	Reverse.
			TAXILA	
			Inscribed Coins.	
			CLASS 1.	
			Var. *a.*	
1	80·0	Æ *square* ·65 × ·8	𑀦𑁂𑀕𑀫 (*Negama*)	𑀢𑀸𑀮𑀺𑀫[𑀢 or 𑀲] (*Tālima*[*ta* or *sa* ?]) [Cunningham, 1857.] **Pl. XXXI. 1.**
			C., *C.A.I.*, Pl. III. 8.	
			Var. *b.*	
2	107·0	·9	𑀦𑁂𑀕𑀫𑀸 (*Negamā*)	𑀤𑁄𑀚𑀓 (*Dojaka*)  [Cunningham, 1894. **Pl. XXXI. 2.**
			C., *C.A.I*, Pl. III. 9.	
3	112·5	·85	"	" [Cunningham, 1894. **Pl. XXXI. 3.**
4	123·0	·9 × ·6	"	" [Cunningham, 1894 **Pl. XXXI. 4.**
5	73·0	·8 *broken*	"	- - 𑀓 [Cunningham, 189
6	41·0	·5 *broken*	𑀦𑁂𑀕 -	Illegible. [Cunningham, 185

o.	Wt.	Metal. Size.	Obverse.	Reverse.
		Æ square	Var. *c.*	
7	90·0	·85	 (*Negamā*)	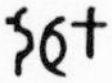 (*Dojaka*) [Cunningham, 1894.] **Pl. XXXI. 6.**
			C., *C.A.I.*, Pl. III. 10.	
8	79·5	·75		,, [Cunningham, 1894.] **Pl. XXXI. 5.**
9	62·0	·9	,,	,, [Hay, 1860.]
			Var. *d.*	
0	66·0	·8	 (*Negamā*)	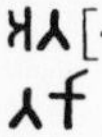[-] (*At*[-]*takā*) [Cunningham, 1894.] **Pl. XXXI. 7.**
			C., *C.A.I.*, Pl. III. 11.	
1	77·0	·8	,,	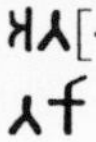[-] [Hay, 1860.] **Pl. XXXI. 8.**
			Var. *e.*	
2	97·0	·6	 (*Negamā*) 	Illegible. [Cunningham, 1894.] **Pl. XXXI. 10.**
			Var. *f.*	
3	113·5	·9	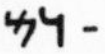 - - (- - *dare*)  (- - *kame*)	Illegible. [Cunningham, 1894.] **Pl. XXXI. 9.**
			C., *C.A.I.*, Pl. III. 12.	

No.	Wt.	Metal. Size.	Obverse.	Reverse.
			CLASS 2.	
			Var. a.	
			Sixteen-spoked wheel; - - - around;  above.	 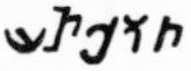 (*Paṁcanekame*)
14	87·0	Æ *square* ·8	,,	,, [I. O. C. **Pl. XXXI. 16.**
15	83·0	·8	,,	,, [W. S. Talbot, Esq., Pres 1903
16	82·0	·8	,,	,, [Cunningham, 1894
17	81·5	·8	,,	,, [W. S. Talbot, Esq., Pres 1903 **Pl. XXXI. 12.**
18	81·5	·8	,,	,, [Whitehead, 1922
19	77·5	·75	,,	,, [Cunningham, 1894
			C., *C.A.I.*, Pl. III. 13.	
20	77·0	·8	,,	,, ,,

No.	Wt.	Metal. Size.	Obverse.	Reverse.
21	68·5	Æ *square* ·8	As preceding.	As preceding. [W. S. Talbot, Esq., Pres., 1903.]
22	60·0	·85	,,	,, [Cunningham, 1894.] **Pl. XXXI. 14.**
23	66·5	·8	,,	,, [Cunningham, 1894.]
24	56·5	·75	,,	,, ,,
25	58·5	·8	,,	,, ,,
26	58·0	·7	,,	,, [J. P. Rawlins, 1922.] **Pl. XXXI. 13.**
27	58·5	·8	,,	,, [W. S. Talbot, Esq., Pres., 1903.] **Pl. XXXI. 11.**
28	56·0	·7	,,	,, [Stubbs, 1865.]
29	55·5	·8	,,	,, [Whitehead, 1922.]
30	48·0	·7	,,	,, [Cunningham, 1894.]
31	37·0	·7	,,	,, ,,

No.	Wt.	Metal. Size.	Obverse.	Reverse.
32	40·5	Æ *square* ·7	As preceding.	As preceding. [Stubbs, 1865.
33	31·0	·8	,,	,, [Whitehead, 1922.

Var. *b*.

No.	Wt.	Metal. Size.	Obverse.	Reverse.
34	56·0	·85	Wheel and other symbols uncertain; traces of Kharoṣṭhī inscription.	Uncertain symbols; traces c Brāhmī inscription. [Cunningham, 1894. **Pl. XXXI. 17.**

C., *C.A.I.*, Pl. III. 14.

CLASS 3.

Var. *a*.

No.	Wt.	Metal. Size.	Obverse.	Reverse.
			Elephant standing facing.  on l. Palm-tree on r.	Horse to l.  above on r.  in front on l. 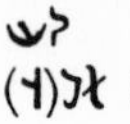 (*Hidu-jasame*)
35	121·0	·8	,,	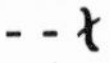 [Cunningham, 1894
36	118·0	·7	,,	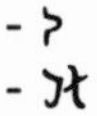 ,, **Pl. XXXIV. 7.**
37	115·0	·8	,,	 [W. S. Talbot, Esq., Pres 1903
38	130·0	·9	,,	,, [Whitehead, 1922 **Pl. XXXIV. 6.**

o.	Wt.	Metal. Size.	Obverse.	Reverse.
			Var. *b*.	
		Æ *square*	As preceding.	As above, but different uncertain inscription.
9	88·0	·8	,,	,, [Chanda Mall, 1889.] **Pl. XXXIV. 3.**
0	88·0	·95	,,	,, [Cunningham, 1894.] **Pl. XXXIV. 4.**
			C., *C.A.I.*, Pl. III. 5.	
1	60·0	·85	,,	,, [Cunningham, 1894.]
2	73·0	·85	,,	,, ,,

Uninscribed.

CLASS 1.

Var. *a*.

o.	Wt.	Metal. Size.	Obverse.	Reverse.
			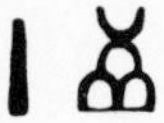	Plain.
3	164·0	·9 × ·8	,,	,, [Cunningham, 1894.] **Pl. XXXII. 2.**
			C., *C.A.I.*, Pl. II. 6.	
4	133·5	·9 × ·8	,,	,, [Cunningham, 1894.] **Pl. XXXII. 1.**
5	136·0	1·0 × ·6	,,	,, [Stubbs, 1865.]
6	133·0	·9 × ·6	,,	,, [Hay, 1860.]

No.	Wt.	Metal. Size.	Obverse.	Reverse.
			Var. *b*.	
47	164·0	Æ *square* ·8		Plain. [Cunningham, 1894 **Pl. XXXII. 3.**
			C., *C.A.I.*, Pl. II. 7.	
			Var. *c*.	
48	174·0	·8		Plain. [Cunningham, 1894 **Pl. XXXII. 4.**
			C., *C.A.I.*, Pl. II. 8.	
			Var. *d*.	
49	150·0	·8		Plain. [Cunningham, 1894 **Pl. XXXII. 11.**
			C., *C.A.I.*, Pl. II. 12.	
			Var. *e*.	
50	144·0	·75	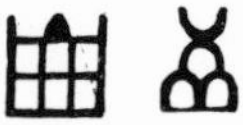	Plain. [Cunningham, 1894 **Pl. XXXII. 12.**
			C., *C.A.I.*, Pl. II. 13.	
51	145·0	·85	,,	,, [Cunningham, 1894 **Pl. XXXII. 13.**
			Var. *f*.	
52	115·0	·8		Plain. [Cunningham, 1894 **Pl. XXXII. 14.**
			C., *C.A.I.*, Pl. II. 10.	

No.	Wt.	Metal. Size.	Obverse.	Reverse.
			Var. *g*.	
53	86·0	Æ *square* ·7		Plain. [Capt. W. F. Temple, Pres., 1902.]
			Var. *h*.	
				Plain.
54	175·0	·95	”	” [Cunningham, 1894.]
55	170·0	·95	”	” ”
			C., *C.A.I.*, Pl. II. 14.	
56	160·0	·95	”	” [I. O. C.]
57	159·0	·95	”	” [Brereton, 1859.] **Pl. XXXII. 5.**
58	143·0	·9	”	” [Lady Sale, 1857.] **Pl. XXXII. 6.**
59	141·0	1·0 × ·6	”	” [Lady Sale, 1857.]
60	123·0	·9	”	” ”

No.	Wt.	Metal. Size.	Obverse.	Reverse.
			Var. *i*.	
				Plain.
61	166·7	Æ *square* 1·0 × ·9	”	” [Cunningham, 1894.] **Pl. XXXII. 10.**
62	160·0	1·0 × ·6	”	” [Hay, 1860.]
63	155·0	·75	”	” [Cunningham, 1894.] C., *C.A.I.*, Pl. II. 9.
64	126·0	·8	”	” ” **Pl. XXXII. 9.**
65	127·0	·8	”	” [Hay, 1860.]
66	137·0	·9	”	” [I. O. C., 1882.]
67	110·0	·9	”	” [Parkes Weber Gift, 1906.]
68	95·0	·85	”	” [Cunningham, 1894.]
			Var. *j*.	
				Plain.
69	151·5	·9	”	” [I. O. C., 1882.] **Pl. XXXII. 7.**

o	Wt.	Metal. Size.	Obverse.	Reverse.
0	152·5	Æ *square* ·5	As preceding.	As preceding. [Cunningham, 1894.]
			C., *C.A.I.*, Pl. II. 11.	
1	122·0	·9	,,	,, ,, **Pl. XXXII. 8.**
2	200·0	1·1 × ·7	,, countermark 	,, [Valentine, 1921.]

CLASS 2.

Var. *a*.

o	Wt.	Metal. Size.	Obverse.	Reverse.
			Elephant to r.  above.	Lion to l.  on l. 卐 above (in incuse square).
3	226·0	1·2 × ·8	,,	,, [Lady Sale, 1844.] **Pl. XXXII. 17.**
4	218·0	1·0 × ·7	,,	,, [Stubbs, 1885.] **Pl. XXXII. 19.**
5	210·0	·8	,,	,, [Cunningham, 1894.]
6	201·0	·9 × ·8	,,	,, [Thomas, 1850.]
7	200·0	·9	,,	,, [Cunningham, 1894.]

No.	Wt.	Metal. Size.	Obverse.	Reverse.
78	203·8	Æ *square* ·8	As preceding.	As preceding. [Cunningham, 1894 **Pl. XXXII. 21.**
79	199·0	·9	,,	,, [Lady Sale, 1844
80	196·5	·8	,,	,, [Parkes Weber Gift, 1908
81	193·0	·9 × ·6	,,	,, [Thomas, 1850 **Pl. XXXII. 18.**
82	192·0	·9 × ·8	,,	,, [Thomas, 1850
83	182·5	·85	,,	,, ,,
84	180·0	·75	,,	,, [Cunningham, 1894
85	167·0	·8	,,	,, [E. I. C
86	154·5	·8	,,	,, [Eden, 1853
87	104·0	·7	,,	,, [Cunningham, 1894
88	100·0	·8	,,	,, ,,

o.	Wt.	Metal. Size.	Obverse.	Reverse.
9	71·5	Æ *round* ·8 × ·7	As preceding.	As preceding. [Cunningham, 1857.] **Pl. XXXII. 20.**
0	66·5	·8	,,	,, [Brereton, 1859.]
1	68·0	·6	,,	,, [Cunningham, 1894.] **Pl. XXXIII. 1.**
				Var. *b.*
2	139·0	1·0 × ·6	Elephant r. [symbol] above.	Lion to r. [symbol] on r. 卐 above. [Thomas, 1850.]
3	142·5	·8	,,	,, [Cunningham, 1894.]
4	116·0	·9	,,	,, [Stubbs, 1865.]
				Var. *c.*
5	200·0	1·0 × ·7	Elephant to l. [symbol] above.	Lion to r. [symbol] on r. 卐 above. [1850.]
6	190·0	·85	,,	,, [Cunningham, 1894.] **Pl. XXXII. 22.**
				C., *C.A.I.*, Pl. III. 1.
				Var. *d.*
7	134·0	·8	Elephant to l. [symbol] above.	Lion to r. 卐 above. [symbol] on r. [Cunningham, 1894.]

No.	Wt.	Metal. Size.	Obverse.	Reverse.
		Æ *round*	Var. *e.*	
98	70·0	·75	Elephant to l.  above.	Lion to l. 卐 above. [Prinsep, 1837
			Var. *f.*	
			Elephant to r. before  on r.	Horse l.; star above.
99	215·5	·8 × ·5	”	” [Cunningham, 1894 **Pl. XXXIII. 5.**
100	129·5	·7	”	” [I. O. C **Pl. XXXIII. 2.**
101	175·5	·7	”	” [Stubbs, 1865 **Pl. XXXIII. 3.**
102	168·5	·75	”	” [Cunningham, 1894 **Pl. XXXIII. 4.**
103	163·5	·8 × ·6	”	” [Cunningham, 1894
			C., *C.A.I.*, Pl. III. 3.	
104	151·5	·75	”	” ” **Pl. XXXIII. 6.**
			C., *C.A.I.*, Pl. III. 4.	

No.	Wt.	Metal. Size.	Obverse.	Reverse.
05	115·0	Æ *round* ·7	As preceding.	As preceding. [Cunningham, 1894.]
06	70·0	·65	,,	,, ,,

Var. *g*.

07	166·0	·9 × ·8	Elephant to l.	Horse to l.; star above.  below. [Brereton, 1859.] **Pl. XXXIII. 7.**

CLASS 3.

Var. *a*.

08	100·0	*square* ·9	,,	,, [Cunningham, 1894.] **Pl. XXXIII. 13.**

C., *C.A.I.*, Pl. III. 6.

09	97·0	1·0	,,	,, [Cunningham, 1894.]
10	71·0	·9	,,	,, ,, **Pl. XXXIII. 10.**
11	66·0	·8	,,	,, [W. S. Talbot, Esq,, Pres., 1903.] **Pl. XXXIII. 12.**

No.	Wt.	Metal. Size.	Obverse.	Reverse.
112	65·0	Æ *square* ·8	As preceding.	As preceding. [Cunningham, 1894 **Pl. XXXIII. 14.**
113	65·0	·9	,,	,, [Cunningham, 1894
114	51·5	·9	,,	,, ,,
115	49·5	·8	,,	,, [W. S. Talbot, Esq., Pres 1903
115 *a*	40·0	·8	,,	,, [Mrs. J. P. Rawlins, 1928
116	30·0	·75	,,	,, [I. O. C., 1882 **Pl. XXXIII. 15.**
117	36·0	·7	,,	,, [W. S. Talbot, Esq., Pres 1903
118	29·5	·7	,,	,, ,,
119	29·5	·7	,,	,, ,,
120	30·0	1·0	,,	,, [C. W. Simson, Esq., Pres 1921. **Pl. XXXIII. 11.**
121	28·0	·65	,,	,, [Cunningham, 1894.
121 *a*	28·0	·6	,,	,, [Mrs. J. P. Rawlins, 1928

).	Wt.	Metal. Size.	Obverse.	Reverse.
			Var. *b*.	
			Head facing.  above.  on l.	
2	141·0	Æ *square* 1·0 × ·7	,,	,, [Col. H. E. Deane, Pres., 1923.] **Pl. XXXIV. 2.**
3	105·0	·9	,,	,, [Thomas, 1850.] **Pl. XXXIV. 3.**
4	75·0	·98	,,	,, [Cunningham, 1894.] **Pl. XXXIV. 1.**
5	66·0	·7	,,	,, [Cunningham, 1894.]
			Var. *c*.	
			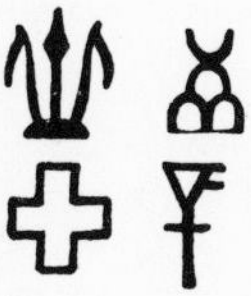	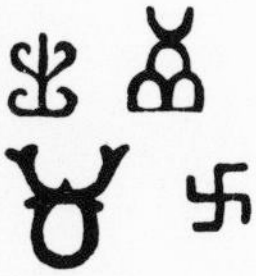
6	159·0	*round* ·9	,,	,, [Cunningham, 1894.]
			C., *C.A.I.*, Pl. II. 20.	
7	156·0	·95	,,	,, [Col. H. E. Deane, Pres., 1923.]

No.	Wt.	Metal. Size.	Obverse.	Reverse.
128	152·0	Æ *round* ·9	As preceding.	As preceding. [Thomas, 1850 **Pl. XXXV. 4.**
129	151·0	·9	,,	,, [Bush, 1865
			Var. *d*.	
			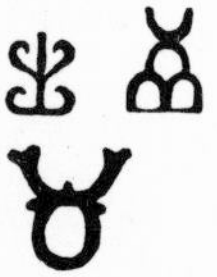	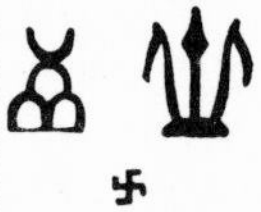
130	70·0	*square* ·6	,,	,, [Hay, 1860 **Pl. XXXIV. 9.**
131	53·0	·6	,,	,, [Parry, 1922 **Pl. XXXIV. 8.**
132	44·0	·6	,,	,, —
133	27·0	·5	,,	,, [Hay, 1860
			CLASS 4. Var. *a*.	
			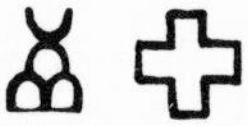	Plain.
134	176·0	*round* ·95	,,	,, [Cunningham, 1894 **Pl. XXXV. 2.**
			C., *C.A.I.*, Pl. IV. 16.	

.	Wt.	Metal. Size.	Obverse.	Reverse.
5	155·0	Æ *round* ·95	As preceding.	As preceding. [Cunningham, 1894.]
6	153·0	·9	„	„ „
7	141·0	·9	„	„ „ **Pl. XXXV. 3.**
8	140·0	·9	„	„ [Cunningham, 1894.]
9	140·0	·9	„	„ [Stubbs, 1865.]
0	104·0	·8	„	„ [Thomas, 1850.]
1	75·0	·8	„	„ [Cunningham, 1894.]
			Var. *b.*	
2	305·0	1·3		 in relief. [Cunningham, 1894.] **Pl. XXXV. 7.**
			C., *C.A.I.*, Pl. II. 15.	
			Var. *c.*	

3	34·0	·55	„	„ [Eden, 1853.] **Pl. XXXIV. 12.**

No.	Wt.	Metal. Size.	Obverse.	Reverse.
144	29·0	Æ *round* ·5	As preceding.	As preceding. [Thomas, 185 **Pl. XXXIV. 13.**
145	28·0	·5	,,	,, [Eden, 185
146	22·5	·55	,,	 [Clive Bayley, 188 **Pl. XXXIV. 15.**
			Var. *d.*	

147	24·0	·55	,,	,, [J. P. Rawlins, 192 **Pl. XXXIV. 10.**
148	37·0	·65	,,	,, [J. P. Rawlins, 192 **Pl. XXXIV. 11.**
			Var. *e.*	

149	40·0	·55	,,	,, [Thomas, 185 **Pl. XLIV. 17.**
150	31·0	·55	,,	,, [Eden, 185
			Var. *f.*	
151	42·0	·6		 [Col. Lafon **Pl. XXXIV. 14.**

o.	Wt.	Metal. Size.	Obverse.	Reverse.
		Æ	Var. *g*.	
2	71·5	*round* ·8		 [Cunningham, 1894.] **Pl. XXXV. 1.**
			C., *C.A.I.*, Pl. II. 19.	
2	90·0	·7	,,	,, [Mrs. J. P. Rawlins, 1928.]
			Var. *h*.	
3	60·0	*square* ·65		 [Cunningham, 1894.] **Pl. XIX. 2.**
			C., *C.A.I.*, Pl. XI. 15.	
			Var. *i*.	
4	66·5	·7		 [H. Nelson Wright, Esq., Pres., 1915.] **Pl. XXXV. 5.**
4	54·0	·65	,,	,, [C. J. Rodgers, 1892.]
			Var. *j*.	
5	18·5	·6		Plain. [J. P. Rawlins, 1921.] **Pl. XXXV. 6.**
5	19·5	·6	,,	,, [Mrs. J. P. Rawlins, 1928.]
			Var. *k*.	
6	20·0	·8		Plain. [Eden, 1853.] **Pl. XXXV. 10.**

No.	Wt.	Metal. Size.	Obverse.	Reverse.
			CLASS 5.	
			Var. *a*.	
157	10·5	Æ *round* ·45	Elephant l.	 [Rawlins, 192 **Pl. XXXIV. 17.**
			Var. *b*.	
158	44·0	*round* ·6	Elephant r.	 [Cunningham, 189 **Pl. XXXIV. 16.**
			Var. *c*.	
159	123·0	*square* ·95	Elephant to l.	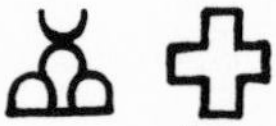 [Cunningham, 189 **Pl. XXXIII. 9.**
			Var. *d*.	
160	39·5	·6 × ·4	Elephant to l.  on r.  above.	Plain. [Thomas, 185 **Pl. XLIV. 20.**
			Var. *e*.	
161	39·0	·7	Lion to l.  in front.  above.	Plain. [Stubbs, 186 **Pl. XXXIII. 8.**
162	42·0	·75	,,  above.  in front.	,, **Pl. XLIV. 18.**

No.	Wt.	Metal. Size.	Obverse.	Reverse.
		Æ round	Var. *f.*	
3	38·0	·6	Bull l.  above and below.	Plain. [Thomas, 1850.] **Pl. XXXV. 13** (*a*).
			Var. *g.*	
4	32·0	·6	Bull. r.  below.  above.	Plain. [Thomas, 1850.] **Pl. XXXV. 13** (*b*).
			Var. *h.*	
5	21·0	·5	Two bulls facing each other.  above.  below.	As obverse. [Cunningham, 1894.] **Pl. XLIV. 26.**
			Var. *i.*	
6	47·0	·6	Bull to l.  above on r.	Lion l. on pedestal. [J. P. Rawlins, 1922.] **Pl. XXXV. 9.**
			Var. *j.*	
7	32·0	·5	As Var. *g.*	Lion to r. before tree in railing. [H. Nelson Wright, Esq., Pres., 1915.] **Pl. XXXV. 8.**
			Var. *k.*	
8	28·5	·55	Lion to l. before tree in railing.	 [W. S. Talbot, Esq., Pres., 1903.] **Pl. XLIV. 19.**

No.	Wt.	Metal. Size.	Obverse.	Reverse.
			CLASS 6.	
			Var. a.	
169	33·5	AV *round* ·4	Bull l.  in front.	 [I. O. C., 1882 **Pl. XXXV. 11.**
			Var. b.	
170	61·0	Æ *round* ·7		 in circle. [Cunningham, 1894 **Pl. XXXV. 12.**
			C., *C.M.I.*, Pl. I. 1.	
			CLASS 7.	
171	50·5	·75	Tree in railing.  on l.  on r	Plain. [W. S. Talbot, Esq., Pre 190 **Pl. XXXII. 16.**

Wt.	Metal. Size.	Obverse.	Reverse.
		TAXILA	
		Attribution doubtful.	
	Æ	Var. *a*. Miscellaneous.	
67·5	*round* ·7		Plain. [J. Burgess, 1890.] **Pl. XLIV. 21.**
22·5	·45	Hunting scene; king r. on horseback with slain animal below; behind him a lion.	Tree in centre; standing figure on either side. [Whitehead, 1922.] **Pl. XLV. 1.**
		White King, no. 5232.	
15·5	·5	Tree in railing in centre; on l. figure on elephant to r.; on r. lion r. (?) with  above; at top  and uncertain object.	 [Mrs. J. P. Rawlins, 1928.] **Pl. XLV. 2.**
18·0	*square* ·5	Steelyard.	Altar with  above. [Messrs. Spink, Pres., 1920.] **Pl. XLV. 3.**
		Var. *b*.	
84·0	·8	Lion r. in circular incuse.	Plain. [Thomas, 1850.]
59·5	·6 × ·3	Lion l. in circular incuse.	,, [Eden, 1853.]
		Var. *c*.	
82·0	·6	Lion (?) l. before  on l.	Plain. [Cunningham, 1894.] **Pl. XLV. 4.**
		C., *C.A.I.*, Pl. II. 5.	

No.	Wt.	Metal. Size.	Obverse.	Reverse.
		Æ *square*		
8	45·0	·7 × ·35	As preceding.	As preceding. [H. Nelson Wright, Esq., Pre 1915 **Pl. XLV. 5.**
9	43·5	·7 × ·3	,,	,, [H. Nelson Wright, Esq., Pre 1915
10	39·0	·7 × ·3	,,	,, [Cunningham, 1894 **Pl. XLV. 6.**
			C., *C.A.I.*, Pl. H. 4.	
11	34·0	·65 × ·3	Lion r. before  on r.	,, [Cunningham, 1894 **Pl. XLV. 7.**
			C., *C.A.I.*, Pl. II. 3.	
			Var. *d.* Perhaps weights.	
12	79·5	·6		Plain. [Cunningham, 1894 **Pl. XLIV. 24.**
			C., *C.A.I.*, Pl. I. 23.	
13	57·0	*round* ·6	Svastika with  in each angle.	Plain. [Cunningham, 1894 **Pl. XLIV. 25.**
14	43·0	·6	,,	,, [Cunningham, 1894
15	35·0	·5	,,	,, ,,
16	129·0	·8	Cross with pellet in each angle.	,, [Thomas, 185

TRIPURĪ

Third Century B.C.

No.	Wt.	Metal. Size.	Obverse.	Reverse.
		Æ round	  on r. 𑀢𑀺𑀧𑀼𑀭𑀺 (*Tipuri*) on l.	Plain.
1	115·0	·85	”	” [Bhagvanlal, 1889.] **Pl. XXXV. 14.**
2	118·0	·85	”	” [Bhagvanlal, 1889.] **Pl. XXXV. 15.**

J.R.A.S., 1894, p. 554, Pl. no. 15.

No.	Wt.	Metal. Size.	Obverse.	Reverse.
3	123·0	·85	”	” [Cunningham, 1894.]

No.	Wt.	Metal. Size.	Obverse.	Reverse.
			UDDEHIKÂ	
			Var. *a.*	
1	80·0	Æ *square* ·8	 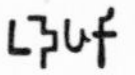 (*Udehàki*)	 over bull r. [Bush, 1865 **Pl. XXXV. 16.**
			Var. *b.* With name Suryamitra.	
2	53·5	·75	 [-] (*Udeha*[-])  [- -] (*Suyami*[*tasa*])  [- -]	Elephant to l.; traces of oth symbols; countermark  [C. B. Armstrong, Esq., Pre 1890 **Pl. XXXV. 17.**

UJJAYINĪ

CLASS 1.

Var. *a*.

No.	Wt.	Metal. Size.	Obverse.	Reverse.
			 River with fishes below.	
1	99·0	Æ *round* ·7	,,	,, [Prinsep, 1847.] **Pl. XXXVI. 20.**
2	97·0	·7	,,	,, [Prinsep, 1847.]
3	84·0	·7	,,	,, ,, **Pl. XXXVI. 21.**
4	63·0	·8	,,	,, [Prinsep, 1847.] **Pl. XXXVI. 18.**
5	82·5	·6	,,	,, [Malcolm, 1868.] **Pl. XXXVI. 17.**
6	72·5	·6	,,	,, [Brind, 1859.] **Pl. XXXVI. 19.**

No.	Wt.	Metal. Size.	Obverse.	Reverse.
		Æ *round*		
7	77·0	·7	As preceding.	As preceding. [Prinsep, 1847.
8	76·5	·6	,,	,, [Cunningham, 1894.
9	67·0	·7	,,	,, ,,
10	80·0	·7	,,	,, ,,
			C., *C.A.I.*, Pl. X. 15.	
11	74·0	·6	,,	,, ,,
12	68·0	·6	,,	,, [Eden, 1853.
13	60·5	·6	,,	,, [Cunningham, 1894.
14	32·5	·55	,,	,, ,,
			Var. *b*.	
			 River with fishes below.	
		square		
15	80·0	·8	,,	,, [Bhagvanlal, 1889.
16	52·0	·6	,,	,, ,, **Pl. XXXVII. 4.**

No.	Wt.	Metal. Size.	Obverse.	Reverse.
		Æ *square*	Var. *c.*	
17	62·0	·55		 [Cunningham, 1894.]
			Var. *d.*	
18	32·5	·5	 over horse l. on r. Tree in railing on l.	 [Cunningham, 1894.] **Pl. XXXVII. 17.**
			Var. *e.*	
19	50·0	·6	Lingam between two different trees in railings.   above.	 [Bhagvanlal, 1889.] **Pl. XXXVI. 15.**
			Var. *f.*	
20	41·5	·5		 **Pl. XXXVI. 16.**
			Var. *g.*	
21	25·0	·4	 ; uncertain border.	Plain. [Cunningham, 1894.] **Pl. XXXVI. 22.**
			C., *C.A.I.*, Pl. X. 9.	
			Var. *h.*	
22	57·0	·65		 [Bhagvanlal, 1889.] **Pl. XXXVI. 11.**

No.	Wt.	Metal. Size.	Obverse.	Reverse.
			Var. *i.*	
23	59·0	Æ *square* ·6	 River below.	 Hand (?) [Cunningham, 1894.] **Pl. XXXVI. 10.**
			C., *C.A.I.*, Pl. XI. 19.	
			Var. *j.*	
24	53·0	·6		 [Bhagvanlal, 1889.] **Pl. XXXVII. 2.**
			Var. *k.*	
			 River with fishes around.	 with 卐 in angles.
25	58·0	·75	,,	,, [Cunningham, 1894. **Pl. XXXVII. 1.**
			C., *C.A.I.*, Pl. X. 16.	
26	78·0	·75	,,	,, [Cunningham, 1894

No.	Wt.	Metal. Size.	Obverse.	Reverse.
			CLASS 2.	
			Var. a.	
			  or  (Kārttikeya standing facing, holding spear in r. and uncertain bag-like object in l.)  above on l. On l. tree in railing.  On r.  with  above on r. of head.	
7	155·0	Æ *round* ·8	„	„
8	137·0	·65	„	„ [Cunningham, 1894.]
9	119·0	·7	„	„ „ Pl. XXXVIII. 1. C., *C.A.I.*, Pl. X. 2.
0	98·0	·7	„	„ [Cunningham, 1894.] Pl. XXXVIII. 3.
1	90·0	·75	„	„ [Cunningham, 1894.]
2	109·0	·7	„	„ [Prinsep, 1847.]

No.	Wt.	Metal. Size.	Obverse.	Reverse.
33	102·0	Æ *round* ·7	As preceding.	As preceding. [Prinsep, 1847 **Pl. XXXVIII. 4.**
34	110·0	·7	,,	,, [Prinsep, 1847
35	114·0	·75	,,	,, ,,
36	97·0	·6	,,	,, ,,
37	110·0	·6	,,	,, [Cunningham, 1894 **Pl. XXXVIII. 7.**
38	80·0	·6	,,	,, [Cunningham, 1894
39	74·0	·6	,,	,, ,,
40	70·0	·65	,,	,, ,,
			Var. *b.*	
			Similar, with addition of  on r. below 	
41	124·0	·8	,,	,, [Eden, 1853 **Pl. XXXVIII. 2.**

No.	Wt.	Metal. Size.	Obverse.	Reverse.
2	100·0	Æ *round* ·7	As preceding.	As preceding. [Eden, 1853.] **Pl. XXXVIII. 5.**
3	60·0	·55	„	„ [Cunningham, 1894.] **Pl. XXXVIII. 6.**
4	56·0	·6	„	„ [Cunningham, 1894.]
5	56·0	·6	„	„ „ **Pl. XXXVIII. 8.**
6	63·0	·6	„	„ [Eden, 1853.] **Pl. XXXVIII. 9.** (double-struck)
			Var. *c*.	
7	77·0	·6	Similar, but deity better executed, standing facing with empty hands by side.  above peacock on l.  on r. with  above.	 [Cunningham, 1894.]
			Var. *d*.	
8	51·0	·55	Similar, deity standing facing, but head to r.  over  on r. Objects on l. uncertain.	 [Sir Walter Elliot, 1886.] **Pl. XXXVIII. 13.**

No.	Wt.	Metal. Size.	Obverse.	Reverse.
		Æ *round*	Var. *e*.	
49	55 ·0	·5	Similar, deity facing with head to r. as in preceding.  above  on r.  on l.	 [Steuart, 1848 **Pl. XXXVIII. 10.**
			Var. *f*.	
			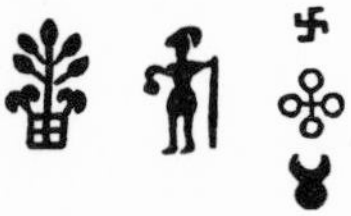	
50	25·0	·45	,,	,, [Cunningham, 1894 **Pl. XXXVIII. 11.**
			C., *C.A.I.*, Pl. X. 4.	
51	21·0	·4	,,	,, [Bhagvanlal, 1889 **Pl. XXXVIII. 12.**
			Var. *g*.	
			 River below.	
52	50·0	·5	,,	,, [Prinsep, 1847 **Pl. XXXVIII. 14.**
53	37·0	·5	,,	,, [Bhagvanlal, 1889
54	27·5	·5	,,	,, [Prinsep, 1847
55	38·0	·5	,,	,, ,,

o.	Wt.	Metal. Size.	Obverse.	Reverse.
			Var. *h*.	
			Deity standing facing, holding staff and pouch as on var. *a*, with head to r. as on var. *d–g*.  on r.  l. with  and 卐 above. River with fishes below.	
6	80·0	Æ *round* ·7	”	” [Cunningham, 1894.] **Pl. XXXVIII. 15.**
			C., *C.A.I.*, Pl. X. 3.	
7	73·0	·7	”	” [Cunningham, 1894.] **Pl. XXXVIII. 16.**
			Var. *i*.	
8	98·0	·75	Deity standing facing with spear in r. hand and bag in l.  on r.  on l.  below.	 with 卐 in each angle. [Cunningham, 1894.] **Pl. XXXVIII. 17.**
			C., *C.A.I.*, Pl. X. 1.	
			Var. *j*.	
9	52·0	·75	Standing deity; tree on r.; river with fishes below; other symbols uncertain.	 [Cunningham, 1894.]
			C. *C.A.I.*, Pl. X. 7.	

No.	Wt.	Metal. Size.	Obverse.	Reverse.
			Var. *k.*	
			 Kārttikeya standing facing, holding spear in r. hand and bag (?) in l.   on l.  on r.	
60	79·0	Æ *square* ·65	,,	,, [Cunningham, 1894 Pl. **XXXVII. 19.**
			C., *C.A.I.*, Pl. X. 5.	
61	67·0	·65	,,	,, [Cunningham, 1894 Pl. **XXXVII. 20.**
62	60·0	·75	,,	,, [Bhagvanlal, 1894
63	67·5	·6	,,	 [Prinsep, 1847 Pl. **XXXVII. 21.**
			Var. *l.*	
			 Kārttikeya, six-headed (*ṣaṇmukha*) standing in centre, holding staff in r. hand and bag (?) in l.   on l.  on r.	
64	76·0	*round* ·7	,,	,, [Cunningham, 1894
65	81·0	·6	,,	,, [Prinsep, 1847 Pl. **XXXVIII. 22.**

Wt.	Metal. Size.	Obverse.	Reverse.
		Var. *m.*	
		Similar, but  on l. and  on r. 	 in border of river with fishes.
62·0	Æ *round* ·6	,,	,, [Cunningham, 1894.] **Pl. XXXVIII. 19.**
		C., *C.A.I.*, Pl. X. 6.	
60·0	·6	,,	,, [Bhagvanlal, 1889.]
36·0	·5	,,	,, — **Pl. XXXVIII. 20.**
36·0	·5	,,	,, [Cunningham, 1894.] **Pl. XXXVIII. 21.**
		Var. *n.*	
		As preceding.	
26·0	·5	,,	,, [Cunningham, 1894.] **Pl. XXXVIII. 18.**
36·0	·45	,,	,, [Cunningham, 1894.]

No.	Wt.	Metal. Size.	Obverse.	Reverse.
		Æ	Var. *o*.	
72	55·0	*round* ·55	As preceding.	Bull r. over  [Prinsep, 1847
			Var. *p*.	
			Female deity (Lakṣmī) seated facing on lotus.  over  on l.  on r.	 with 卐 in ea angle.
73	59·0	·5	,,	,, [Cunningham, 1894 **Pl. XXXVIII. 23.**
			C., *C.A.I.*, Pl. X. 10.	
74	46·0	·5	,,	,, [Bhagvanlal, 188 **Pl. XXXVIII. 24.**
75	50·0	·5	,,	,, but  in angles in place of [Clive-Bayley, 188
75*a*	44·5	·5	,,	,, [—]
			Var. *q*.	
76	82·0	·6	Lakṣmī seated facing on lotus. Uncertain border.	 [Cunningham, 1894
77	57·0	·6	Lakṣmī seated facing on lotus.	 [Cunningham, 189 **Pl. XXXVIII. 25.**

o.	Wt.	Metal. Size.	Obverse.	Reverse.
			CLASS 3.	
			Var. a.	
			  below.	
8	63·0	Æ *square* ·65	,,	,, [Cunningham, 1894.] **Pl. XXXVII. 7.**
			C., *C.A.I.*, Pl. X. 14.	
9	84·0	·65	,,	,, [Cunningham, 1894.] **Pl. XXXVII. 6.**
			C., *C.A.I.*, Pl. X. 13.	
0	36·0	·5	,,	,, [Cunningham, 1894.] **Pl. XXXVII. 5.**
1	41·0	·5	,,	,, [Cunningham, 1894.]
			Var. b.	
			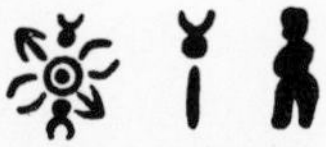 Border 	
2	67·0	·7	,,	,, [Steuart, 1884.]

No.	Wt.	Metal. Size.	Obverse.	Reverse.
83	84·5	Æ *square* ·6	As preceding.	As preceding. [Prinsep, 1837
84	56.0	·65	”	” [Cunningham, 1894
			C., *C.A.I.*, Pl. X. 11.	
			Var. *c.*	
85	74·5	·75		 [Rev. H. R. Scott, Pres., 1903
			Var. *d.*	

86	30·0	·55	”	” [Cunningham, 1894 **Pl. XIX. 6.**
87	48·0	·45	”	” [Cunningham, 1894. **Pl. XIX. 8.**
88	32·5	·5	”	” [Cunningham, 1894
89	54·0	·5	”	”

No.	Wt.	Metal. Size.	Obverse.	Reverse.
			Var. *e.*	
0	46·5	Æ *square* ·55	  border.	 [Cunningham, 1894.] **Pl. XIX. 5.**
			C., *C.A.I.*, Pl. XI. 20.	
			Var. *f.*	
			 River with fishes below.	
1	24·5	·45	”	” [Cunningham, 1894.] **Pl. XIX. 9.**
2	22·0	·4	”	” [Cunningham, 1894.]
			Var. *g.*	
3	39·0	·5	  below.	 [Cunningham, 1894.] **Pl. XIX. 4.**
			C., *C.A.I.*, Pl. XI. 17.	
			Var. *h.*	
				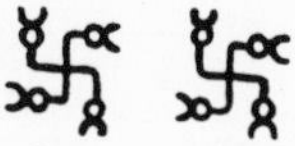
4	29·2	·5	”	” [Rev. H. R. Scott, Pres., 1903.]

No.	Wt.	Metal. Size.	Obverse.	Reverse.
95	23·0	Æ square ·45	As preceding.	As preceding. [Rev. H. R. Scott, Pres., 1903
96	17·2	·4	,,	,,
97	15·0	·4	,,	,, ,,

CLASS 4.

Var. *a.*

			Lakṣmī seated facing, being sprinkled (*abhiṣeka*) by elephants standing on pedestals on either side. At top 卐 on r. and l.	
98	102·0	·6	,,	,, [Cunningham, 1894 Pl. **XVIII.** 24.

C., *C.A.I.*, Pl. XI. 14.

99	85·0	·6	,,	,, [Cunningham, 1894 Pl. **XXXVI.** 5.
100	55·0	·6	,,	,, [Cunningham, 1894 Pl. **XXXVI.** 4.

No.	Wt.	Metal. Size.	Obverse.	Reverse.
			Var. *b*.	
			Two draped female figures standing facing; one on l. holds uncertain object in raised r. hand. River with fishes below.	
01	59·5	Æ *square* ·7	”	” [Clive Bayley, 1889.] **Pl. XXXVI. 1.**
02	49·0	·7 × ·6	”	” [H. Nelson Wright, Esq., Pres., 1915.] **Pl. XXXVI. 2.**
03	55·0	·6	”	” [Bhagvanlal, 1889.] **Pl. XXXVI. 3.**
			Var. *c*.	
04	38·5 *broken*	*round* ·7	Two (of three) figures standing facing; cf.  on silver punch-marked coins (pp. 26, 27).	 [Cunningham, 1894.] **Pl. XLIV. 22.**
			Var. *d*.	
05	70·5	*square* ·65	Standing female figure. 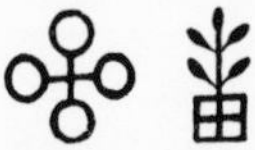 River with fishes below.	Plain. [Bhagvanlal, 1889.] **Pl. XXXVII. 8.**

No.	Wt.	Metal. Size.	Obverse.	Reverse.
			CLASS 5.	
			Var. *a*.	
			 Bull r. before tree in railing.	
		Æ *round*	Countermarked: standing deity (Kārttikeya) and 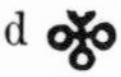	
106	77·0	·6	”	” [Eden, 1853. **Pl. XXXVIII. 26.**
107	65·0	·6	”	” [Prinsep, 1837. **Pl. XXXVIII. 27.**
108	76·0	·6	”	” [Thomas, 1850. **Pl. XXXVIII. 28.**
			Var. *b*.	
			 Bull r. before tree in railing.	 with 卐 in each angle.
			C., *C.A.I.*, Pl. I. 30.	
109	75·0	·7	”	” [Cunningham, 1894. **Pl. XXXVII. 9.**
110	101·5	·7	”	” — **Pl. XXXVII. 10.**

o.	Wt.	Metal. Size.	Obverse.	Reverse.
1	84·0	Æ *round* ·7	As preceding.	As preceding. [Prinsep, 1847.]
2	81·0	·7	,,	,, ,,
3	24·0	·4	,,	,, [Cunningham, 1894.] **Pl. XXXVII. 11.**
			C., *C.A.I.*, Pl. X. 18.	
			Var. *c.*	
			Bull r. and 卐 before tree in railing.	 with 卐 in each angle.
4	67·0	*square* ·8	,,	,, — **Pl. XXXVI. 13.**
5	40·0	·55	,,	,, [Cunningham, 1894.] **Pl. XXXVI. 12.**
6	19·0	·4	,,	,, with  in each angle. [Cunningham, 1894.]
			Var. *d.*	
7	16·0	·45	Bull before tree in railing.  above.	 [Cunningham, 1894.] **Pl. XXXVI. 14.**
			C., *C.A.I.*, Pl. X. 17.	

No.	Wt.	Metal. Size.	Obverse.	Reverse.
			Var. *e*.	
118	36·5	Æ *round* ·7	Bull r. before tree in railing.  behind.	 [Cunningham, 1894
			C., *C.A.I.*, Pl. X. 12.	
			Var. *f*.	
			Bull r. before tree in railing.   above.	Standing deity (Kārttikeya … on 27 ff.) and 
119	71·6	·6	,,	,, [Prinsep, 1847 **Pl. XXXVII. 18.**
120	52·0	·75	,,	,, countermarked  [Prinsep, 1847 **Pl. XXXVII. 3.**
			Var. *g*.	
121	27·0	*square* ·5		Plain. [Cunningham, 1894
			CLASS 6.	
			Var. *a*.	
			 Lion l. 	
122	75·0	·6	,,	,, [Prinsep, 1847

o.	Wt.	Metal. Size.	Obverse.	Reverse.
3	66·0	Æ *square* ·55	As preceding.	As preceding. [Bhagvanlal, 1889.] **Pl. XXXVII. 13.**
4	63·0	·55	,,	,, [Bhagvanlal, 1889.]
			Var. b.	
			Elephant to r. before tree in railing.  above. River with fishes below.	
5	80·0	·7	,,	,, — **Pl. XXXVI. 6.**
6	92·5	·8	,,	,, [Cunningham, 1894.]
7	84·0	·7	,,	,, [Bhagvanlal, 1889.] **Pl. XXXVI. 7.**
8	60·0	·6	,,	,, [Cunningham, 1894.] **Pl. XXXVI. 8.**
9	52·0	·55	,,	,, [Cunningham, 1894.]
0	57·0	·7	,,	,, — **Pl. XXXVI. 9.**

No.	Wt.	Metal. Size.	Obverse.	Reverse.
			Var. *c.*	
131	117·0	Æ *square* ·9 × ·8	Elephant l.	 Pl. **XLIV. 23.**
			Var. *d.*	
132	64·0	·65	Elephant l.	 [Cunningham, 1894
			Var. *e.*	
133	13·0	·4	Elephant r.  above.	 with  in each angle [Cunningham, 1894 Pl. **XXXVII. 12.**
			CLASS 7. Inscribed.	
			 Elephant r.	 and hand over  (*Ujaniyi*)
134	64·0	·55	,,	,, [Cunningham, 1894 Pl. **XXXVII. 14.**
135	54·0	·5	,,	,, —
136	71·0	·5	,,	,, — Pl. **XXXVII. 15.**
137	62·0	·55	,,	,, [Cunningham, 1894 Pl. **XXXVII. 16.**
			C., *C.A.I.*, Pl. X. 20.	

No.	Wt.	Metal. Size.	Obverse.	Reverse.
			UPAGODA	
1	185·0	Æ *round* 1·0	 (*Upagodasa*)	Plain. [Clive Bayley, 1889.] **Pl. XXXV. 18.**
			J.R.A.S., 1900, p. 102, Pl. no. 3.	
			UPĀTIKYĀ	
1	37·0	·55	 (*Upātikyā*)	Plain. [Cunningham, 1894.] **Pl. XXXV. 19.**
			C., *A.S.R.*, III, p. 14 and *C.A.I.*, Pl. VIII. 2.	

VATAŚVAKA

No.	Wt.	Metal. Size.	Obverse.	Reverse.
		Æ round	  (*Vaṭasvaka*) on l.	Plain.
1	144·0	·9	”	” [Cunningham, 1894. **Pl. XXXIX. 2.**
2	141·0	1·0	”	” [I. O. C., 1882. **Pl. XXXIX. 3.** *Ar. Ant.*, Pl. XV. 30.
3	138·0	·9	”	” [Whitehead, 1922. **Pl. XXXIX. 4.** White King, no. 5217.
4	140·0	·85	”	” [Cunningham, 1894
5	140·0	·85	”	” ”
6	135·0	·85	”	” ” **Pl. XXXIX. 1.** C., *C.A.I.*, Pl. II. 17.

YAUDHEYA

CLASS 1.

Var. *a*.

No.	Wt.	Metal. Size.	Obverse.	Reverse.
				Plain.
	17·5	Potin *round* ·4	,,	,, [Prinsep, 1847.]
	14·0	·4	,,	,, ,,
	13·6	·4	,,	,, [Thomas, 1850.]
	10·0	·4	,,	,, ,,

Var. *b*.

No.	Wt.	Metal. Size.	Obverse.	Reverse.
				Plain.
	27·4	·4	,,	,, [Prinsep, 1847.] **Pl. XXXIX. 6.**
	24·2	·5	,,	,, [Cunningham, 1894.]
	18·0	·4		,, [Thomas, 1850.]

No.	Wt.	Metal. Size.	Obverse.	Reverse.
			Var. *c*.	
		Æ *round*		Plain.
8	42·5	·6	,,	,, [Prinsep, 184 **Pl. XXXIX. 5.**
9	35·5	·6	,, overstruck with 	,, [Prinsep, 184 **Pl. XXXIX. 7.**
			Var. *d*.	
10	16·5	·5	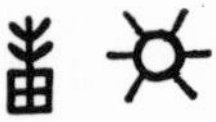	Plain. [Prinsep, 184
			Var. *e*.	
11	32·0	·6	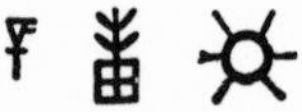  (*Mahārājasa*)	 **Pl. XXXIX. 10.**
12	21·6	·7	,, 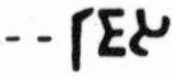	,, [Cunningham, 189 C., *C.A.I.*, Pl. VI. 10.
13	25·5	·7	,, 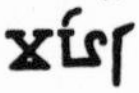 [- -]	,, [Thomas, 185
14	20·5	·5	,, 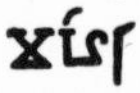 - -	,, ,,
15	22·0	·5	,, [-]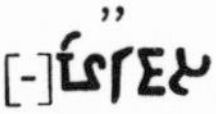	,, [Eden, 18

o.	Wt.	Metal. Size.	Obverse.	Reverse.
			CLASS 2.	
			Var. *a*.	
		Potin *round*	Bull r. before  on r. 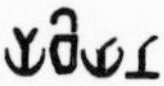 (*Yaudheyānāṁ*) above. Uncertain inscription below.	Elephant r.  above. Uncertain pennon-like object behind.
	26·5	·5	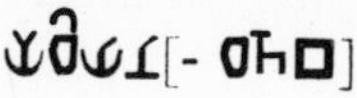	,, [Prinsep, 1847.] **Pl. XXXIX. 11.**
	22·5	·5	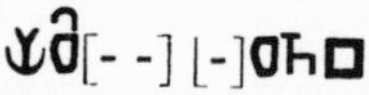	,, [Eden, 1853.]
	17·6	·6	Traces of inscription.	,, [Prinsep, 1847.]
	14·5	·6	,,	,, ,,
	16·0	·6		,, [Eden, 1853.]
	17·7	Æ ·6	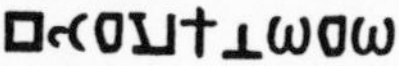	,, [Prinsep, 1847.] **Pl. XXXIX. 12.**
			Var. *b*.	
	31·5	·7	Bull to l. before  on l. 	As preceding. [Prinsep, 1847.] **Pl. XXXIX. 13.**
	22·0	·5	Traces of inscription.	,, [Cunningham, 1894.] C., *C.A.I.*, Pl. VI. 4.
	35·0	·5	,,	,, [Thomas, 1850.]

No.	Wt.	Metal. Size.	Obverse.	Reverse.
			Var. *c*.	
			Bull r. before   Uncertain inscription below.	Elephant to r.  above. Uncertain pennon-like obje behind.
25	51·0	Potin *round* ·75	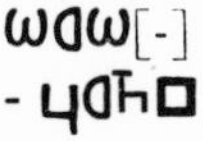	,, [Prinsep, 184
26	51·5	·7	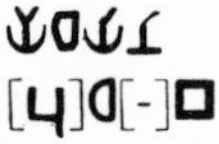	,, [Cunningham, 189 **Pl. XXXIX. 6.**
			C., *C.A.I.*, Pl. VI. 2.	
27	45·0	·7	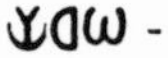	,, — **Pl. XXXIX. 15.**
28	46·5	·7		,, [Thomas, 185 **Pl. XXXIX. 14.**
29	52·5	·7		,, [Cunningham, 18
			C., *C.A.I.*, Pl. VI. 3.	
30	37·5	·7		,, [Prinsep, 18
31	*frag-ment*	·6		,, ,,
32	77·0	Æ *round* ·85		,, [Clive Bayley, 18 **Pl. XXXIX. 17.**

No.	Wt.	Metal. Size.	Obverse.	Reverse.
3	71·6	Æ *round* ·6	𑀬𑀥𑀬𑀦 [- - - - -]	As preceding. [Cunningham, 1894.]
4	72·6	·6	𑀬𑀥𑀬[-]	„ [Thomas, 1850.]
5	69·0	·75	[-]𑀥𑀬𑀦	„ [Cunningham, 1894.]
6	68·0	·8	𑀬𑀥𑀬[-] - - -	„ „
7	65·0	·7	𑀬𑀥[- -]	„ [Thomas, 1850.]
8	54·0	·6	𑀬𑀥[- -] [[illegible]𑀳 - -] - -	„ [Bush, 1862.] **Pl. XXXIX. 18.**
9	50·0	·7	𑀬𑀥𑀬𑀦 - -	„ [Bush, 1862.]
0	52·0	·7	𑀬𑀥𑀬𑀦 [illegible]𑀳𑀥[illegible] [-]	„ [Whitehead, 1922.]
1	48·0	·7	[illegible]𑀥𑀬𑀦 [illegible]𑀥[illegible]𑀫	„ [Rodgers, 1893.] **Pl. XXXIX. 19.**
2	56·5	·75	𑀬𑀥[- -] [illegible]𑀥[- -]	„ [Cunningham, 1894.]
3	44·0	·65	[- - - -] [illegible]𑀳𑀥[illegible]𑀩	„ „
4	48·5	1·0	𑀬𑀥𑀬𑀦 [illegible]𑀳𑀥 - -	„ [Thomas, 1850.]

No.	Wt.	Metal. Size.	Obverse.	Reverse.
45	69·0	Æ round ·85		As preceding. [W. S. Talbot, Esq., Pres. 1907.
46	45·5	·8	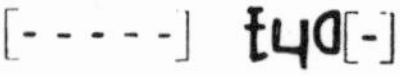	,, ,,

CLASS 3.

Silver.

No.	Wt.	Metal. Size.	Obverse.	Reverse.
47	26·0	Æ round ·7	Kārttikeya, six-headed, standing facing, holding spear in r. hand and resting l. hand on hip.  (*Bhāgavatasv*[*ā*]*min*[*o*] *Brahmaṇya-Y*[*au*]*dheya*)	Goddess standing facing on lotus.  on l.  on r.  below. [Cunningham, 1894. **Pl. XXXIX. 21.**

C., *C.A.I.*, Pl. VI. 9.

Copper.

Var. *a*.

No.	Wt.	Metal. Size.	Obverse.	Reverse.
			Kārttikeya, six-headed, standing facing, holding spear in r. hand and resting l. arm on hip. 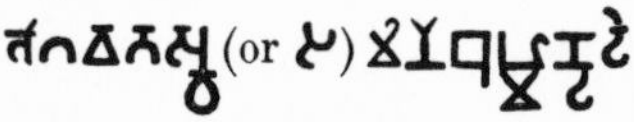 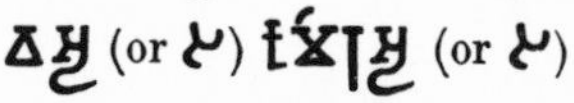 (*Bhāgavatasv*[*ā*] (or *sa*) *mino Brahmaṇyadevasya* (or *sa*) *Kumārasya* (or *sa*)) around.	Goddess with radiate head standing facing, with r. hand raised and l. hand resting on hip.  on r.  on l.  below.
48	180·0	Æ round 1·0		,, [Cunningham, 1894.

o.	Wt.	Metal. Size	Obverse.	Reverse.
		Æ round		
9	166·0	1·0	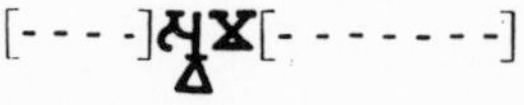	As preceding. [Cunningham, 1894.]
0	142·0	1·0		,, ,,
			C., *C.A.I.*, Pl. VI. 12.	
1	128·0	1·0	Traces of inscription.	,, [Spink, 1928.]
2	140·2	·95	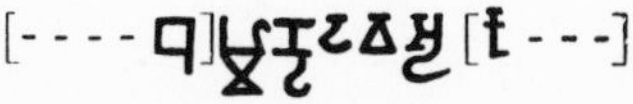	,, —
3	122·0	·95	Traces of inscription.	,, [Rodgers, 1892.]
4	30·0	·6	,,	,, [Cunningham, 1894.] **Pl. XXXIX. 20.**
			C., *C.A.I.*, Pl. VI. 10.	
5	26·0	·6		,, [J. P. Rawlins, 1922.]
6	158·5	1·0	Similar. 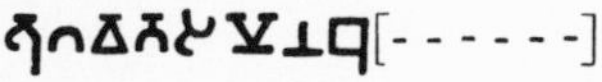	Similar. [Cunningham, 1894.] **Pl. XL. 11.**
7	175·0	1·1	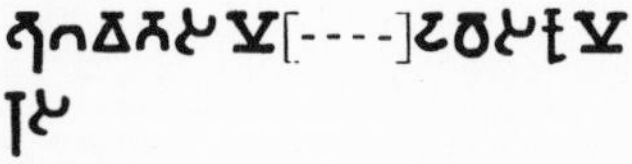	,, [Cunningham, 1894.]
a	191·0	1·1	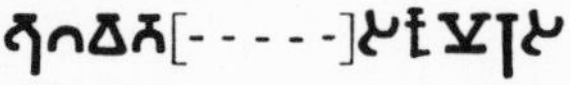	,, [Whitehead, 1922.]

No.	Wt.	Metal. Size.	Obverse.	Reverse.
			Var. *b*.	
			Kārttikeya as before, but one-headed and head radiate.	Goddess standing facing … before, but  on l. and  on r.
58	160·0	Æ *round* 1·0	Trace of inscription.	,, [Indian Museum, 1892 **Pl. XXXIX. 22.**
59	160·0	1·05	[- - - -]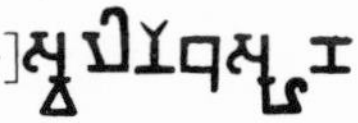 - - -  in field on r.	,, [Indian Museum, 1892
60	130·5	1·0	Trace of inscription.	,, ,,
61	141·0	1·0	,,	,, ,,
			Var. *c*.	
62	158·0	1·0	Goddess standing facing, with r. hand raised and l. resting on hip. [- - -][- - -]	Kārttikeya, six-headed, standing facing between  on … and  on r. [Cunningham, 189… **Pl. XL. 10.**
			C., *C.A.I.*, Pl. VI. 11.	

No.	Wt.	Metal. Size.	Obverse.	Reverse.
			Var. *d.*	
			Kārttikeya, six-headed, standing facing, holding spear as before. Legend as preceding, but very incomplete.	Deer r.  on r.  on l. 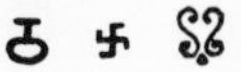 above.   below.
3	146·0	Æ *round* 1·0	  - - - - 	,, [Rodgers, 1892.]
4	144·0	1·1	 [- - -]	,, ,,
5	139·0	·95	[- -]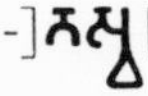[- - -]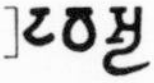	,, [Cunningham, 1894.]
			C., *C.A.I.*, Pl. VI. 13.	
6	115·0	1·0	[- -]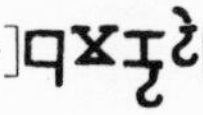[- -]	,, [Rodgers, 1892.]
7	122·0	·95	Traces of legend.	,, [J. P. Rawlins, 1922.]
			Var. *e.*	
8	126·0	1·0	Kārttikeya, six-headed, standing facing, with r. hand raised, l. on hip; spear standing on r. bound with fillet. - - -]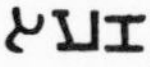[- -]	Deer l.  on r.  on l. 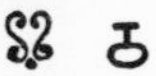   above. [Rodgers, 1892.]

No.	Wt.	Metal. Size.	Obverse.	Reverse.
			Var. *f*.	
			As preceding.	Deer to l.  below.  and  above deer.
69	121·0	Æ *round* 1·0	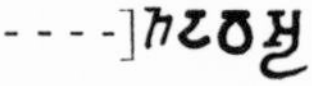	,, [Rodgers, 1892.
70	113·0	1·0		,, ,,
71	93·0	·9	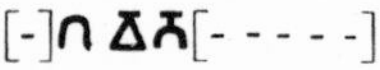	,, ,,
72	91·0	·9	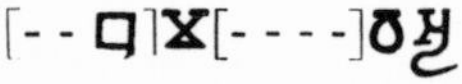	,, ,,
			Var. *g*.	
			As preceding.	Deer l.  on r.  on l.  above.
73	104·0	·95	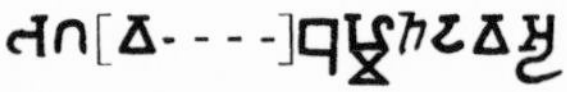	,, [Rodgers, 1892
74	80·0	·95		,, [Cunningham, 1894
75	71·0	·9	Traces of legend.	,, [Prinsep, 1847
76	75·0	·9	,,	,, [Cunningham, 1894

Var. *h*.

No.	Wt.	Metal. Size.	Obverse.	Reverse.
			Similar.	Deer r. before building.  on l.  above. 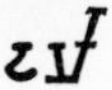 (*darma*) above deer.
77	172·4	Æ *round* 1·0	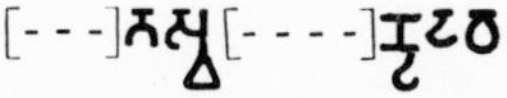	" [Cunningham, 1894.] **Pl. XL. 12.**
78	132·0	·95	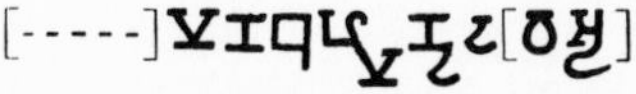	" [Cunningham, 1894.]

Var. *i*.

No.	Wt.	Metal. Size.	Obverse.	Reverse.
9	152·5	·96	Similar, but the deity is Śiva with trident. 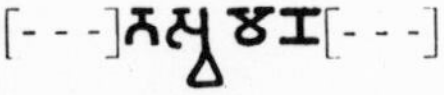	Deer r. before  Rest illegible. [Cunningham, 1894.] **Pl. XL. 13.**

CLASS 4.

No.	Wt.	Metal. Size.	Obverse.	Reverse.
0	126·0	·9	 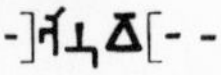 (*Bhānuva*) Snake below.	Trident and standard. [Cunningham, 1894.] **Pl. XL. 15.**

C., *C.A.I.*, Pl. VI. 14.

CLASS 5.

No.	Wt.	Metal. Size.	Obverse.	Reverse.
1	9·50	*square* ·5	Bull r. 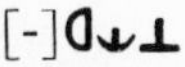 ([*Yau*]*dh*[*e*]*y*[*ā*]-*n*[*āṁ*]) above.	Illegible. [Rodgers, 1892.] **Pl. XLIV. 27.**

No.	Wt.	Metal. Size.	Obverse.	Reverse.
			CLASS 6.	
			Var. *a*.	
			Kārttikeya standing facing, holding spear in r. hand, l. hand on hip; peacock to l. at his l. foot. 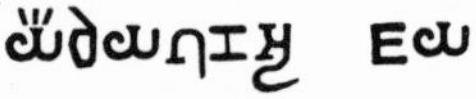 (*Yaudheyagaṇasya jaya*)	Female deity walking to l. with r. hand raised and l. hand on hip; border of dots.
82	177·0	Æ *round* 1·0		,, [Cunningham, 1894. **Pl. XL. 1.**
83	173·8	1·0	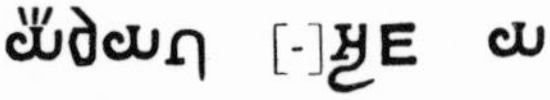	,, [Thomas, 1850.
84	167·0	·95	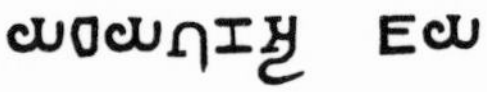	,, ,,
85	166·0	·95		,, [Spink, 1928
86	165·5	·95	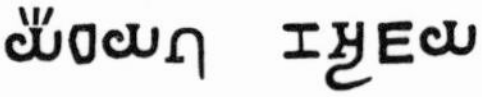	,, [Cunningham, 1894
87	163·0	·9	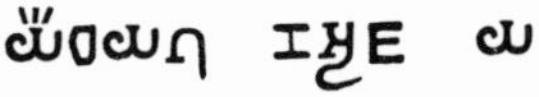	,, ,, **Pl. XL. 2.**
			C., *C.A.I.*, Pl. VI. 6.	
88	163·0	·9	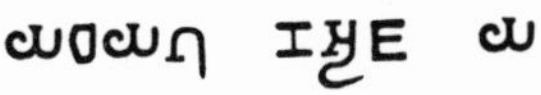	,, [Thomas, 1850
89	161·5	·9	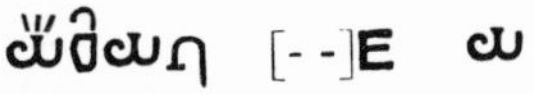	,, [Spink, 1928

o.	Wt.	Metal. Size.	Obverse.	Reverse.
		Æ *round*		
0	157·0	·9	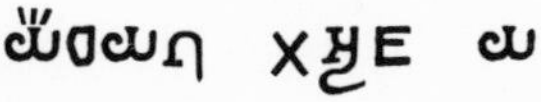	As preceding. [Thomas, 1850.]
1	159·5	1·0	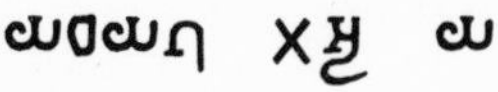	,, [Cunningham, 1894.]
			Var. *b.*	
			As preceding, with addition of  (*dve*) at end of legend.	As preceding, with addition of a flower-vase (*kalaśa*) on l. and inverted trisul on r. ()
2	177·0	1·0	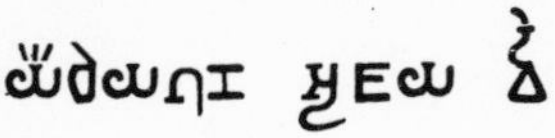	,, [Indian Museum, 1889.] **Pl. XL. 5.**
3	172·0	1·0	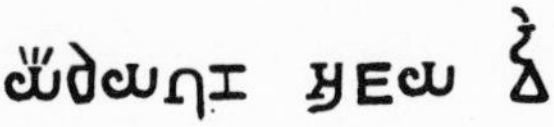	,, [Cunningham, 1894.]
4	173·0	·95	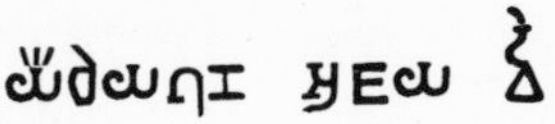	,, [Prinsep, 1847.]
5	171·6	·95	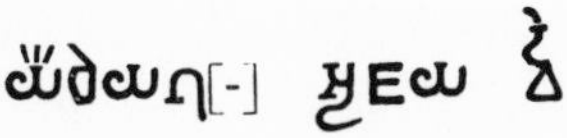	,, [Cunningham, 1894.] **Pl. XL. 6.**
6	168·2	·95	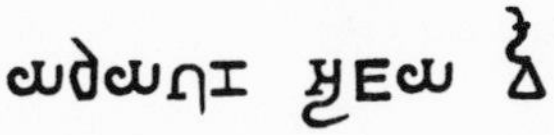	,, [Indian Museum, 1889.]
7	165·0	·9	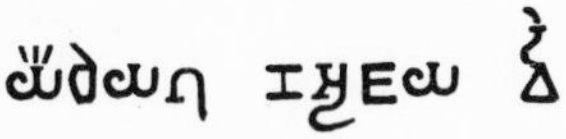	,, [Cunningham, 1894.] **Pl. XL. 4.**
			C., *C.A.I.*, Pl. VI. 7.	

No.	Wt.	Metal. Size.	Obverse.	Reverse.
98	165·0	Æ *round* ·9	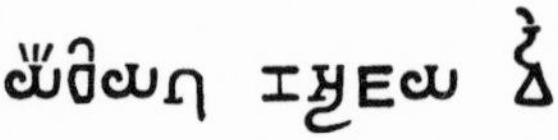	As preceding. [Prinsep, 1847
99	160·0	·95	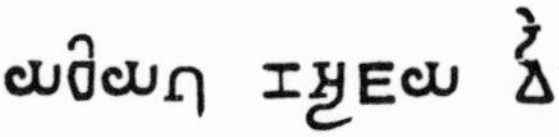	,, [J. Horne, Esq., Pres., 1916 **Pl. XL. 3.**
100	160·3	·95	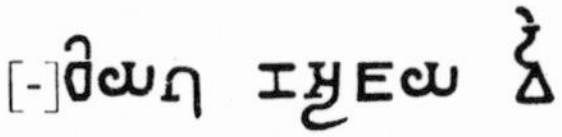	,, [Cunningham, 1894
			Var. *c.*	
			As preceding, but  (*tri*) at end of legend.	Similar, but shell (*śankhā*) o l. and *cakra* on r. 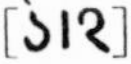
101	172·5	·95	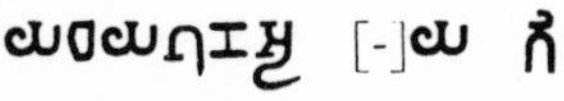	,, [Cunningham, 1894
102	163·0	1·0	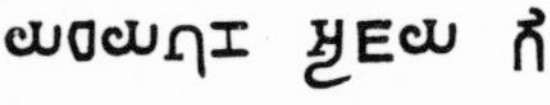	,, [Swiney, 1863
103	161·5	·9	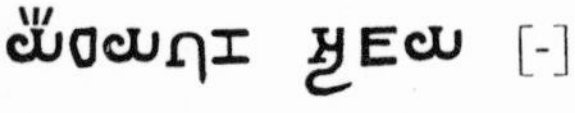	,, [Cunningham, 1894 **Pl. XL. 7** (*rev.*).
			C., *C.A.I.*, Pl. VI. 8.	
104	159·2	1·0	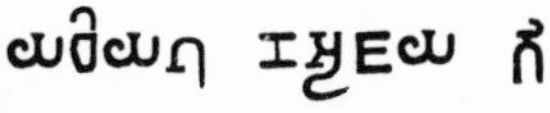	,, [Prinsep, 1847 **Pl. XL. 8** (*rev.*).
			Var. *d.*	
105	141·0	1·0	As preceding, but legend as in Var. *a.* 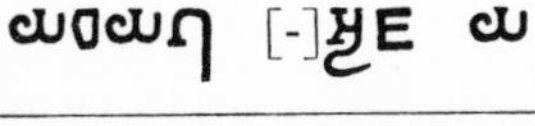	As Var. *c.* [Thomas, 1850 **Pl. XL. 9.**

UNCERTAIN COINS

No.	Wt.	Metal. Size.	Obverse.	Reverse.
			AG[- - - -]	
	50·5	Æ *square* ·6	Tree in railing. 	 **Pl. XLV. 9.**
			JYEṢṬHA[- -]	
	32·0	*round* ·55	Standing male figure on l. 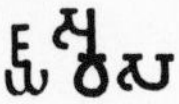 (*Jy*[-]*ṣṭhasa*) on r.	Lakṣmī standing facing. [Cunningham, 1894.] **Pl. XLV. 10.**
			MAHĀS[- -]	
	64·0	*square* ·65	Standing male figure.  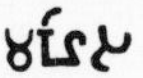 - -	Plain. **Pl. XLV. 11.**
	16·0	·4	,, Traces of legend.	,, [Cunningham, 1894.]
			PU[- -]SENA	
	20·0	·5	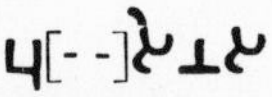  below.  above.	Tree in railing. [Cunningham, 1894.] **Pl. XLV. 12.**
	18·0	·5	,,	,, [Cunningham, 1894.]
	6·5	·4	,,	,, ,,

No.	Wt.	Metal. Size.	Obverse.	Reverse.
			ŚAŚACANDRĀTA	
8	40·0	Æ square ·55	𑀭𑀸𑀚𑀸 𑀰𑀰𑀘𑀁𑀤𑁆𑀭𑀸𑀢𑀲 (*Rājā-Śaśacandrā-tasa*)	Elephant r. [Clive Bayley, 1889 **Pl. XLV. 13.**
			VAMAK[- - -]	
9	31·5	·55	Elephant r. ☉ behind. 𑀯𑀫𑀓[- -]𑀧𑀧𑀲	Bull l. ☉ and 卐 above. [Indian Museum, 1889 **Pl. XLV. 14.**
			VASU[- -]	
10	20·5	·4	𑀯𑀲𑀼[-]𑀲 (*Vasu*[-]*sa*)	Illegible. [J. P. Rawlins, 1922 **Pl. XLV. 17.**
			VĪRASENA	
11	38·5	·5	𑀯𑀻𑀭𑀲𑁂𑀦𑀲 (*Vīrasenasa*) Tree in railing. ☉ on r. and l.	Rude standing figure of Lak-mī holding stalk of flow growing beside her in her hand. [Clive Bayley, 1889
12	23·5	·4	,,	,, ,, **Pl. XLV. 15.**
13	25·0	·4	,,	,, [C. J. Rodgers, 189

No.	Wt.	Metal. Size.	Obverse.	Reverse.
	29·5	Æ *square* ·6	As preceding.	As preceding. [Hay 1860.] **Pl. XLV. 16.**
	14·3	·45	,,	,, [Clive Bayley, 1889.]
	13·0	·45	,,	,, ,,

VRIṢṆI

No.	Wt.	Metal. Size.	Obverse.	Reverse.
	32·0	AR *round* ·6	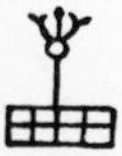 with animal half lion—half elephant in front. 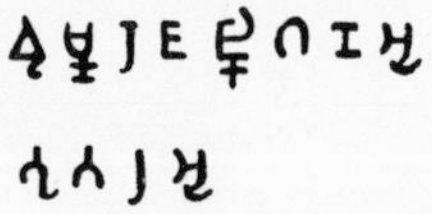 (*Vṛṣṇ[i]r[ā]jajñāgaṇasya bhūbharasya*)	Elaborate dharmacakra. 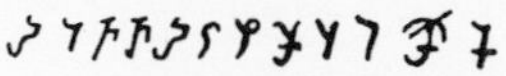 [Cunningham, 1894.] **Pl. XVI. 5.**

C., *C.A.I.*, Pl. IV. 15.

YAJÑABHU

No.	Wt.	Metal. Size.	Obverse.	Reverse.
	56·0	Æ *square* ·55	 (*Yajñabhu*)	Type uncertain. [Cunningham, 1894.] **Pl. XLV. 18.**

C., *C.M.I.*, p. 2 no. 3.

[- -]JANA

No.	Wt.	Metal. Size.	Obverse.	Reverse.
	20·0	·7 × ·4 *broken*	Type uncertain. [-]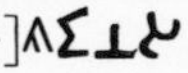 (- *śajanasa*) above.	Tree in railing.  on r. Uncertain object on l. **Pl. XLV. 19.**

J.A.S.B., 1836, Pl. LX. 9.

[-]YAŚAŚA

No.	Wt.	Metal. Size.	Obverse.	Reverse.
20	54·0	Æ *round* ·65	 on l. Bull to l.  on r. - 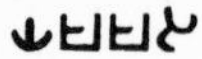 (- - *yaśaśasa*)	 [Cunningham, 189 **Pl. XLV. 20.**
21	29·0	·5	Similar, but bull to r. - - 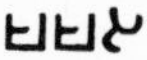	,, [Thomas, 185

NAMES UNCERTAIN

CLASS 1.

No.	Wt.	Metal. Size.	Obverse.	Reverse.
22	119·5	·95	Tree in railing. Legend around. 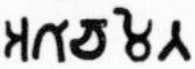 - -	Bull r. [C. J. Rodgers, 189 **Pl. XLV. 21.**
23	92·0	·7	- -][-	,, [Cunningham, 189 **Pl. XLV. 22**

C., *C.M.I.*, p. 2, no. 5.

No.	Wt.	Metal. Size.	Obverse.	Reverse.
24	52·5	·4		Lion r. [C. J. Rodgers, 189
25	73·5	·55	-  -	,, [Indian Museum, 188
26	44·5	·5	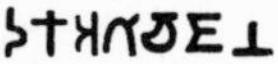 - -	,, [Thomas, 185 **Pl. XLV. 23.**

Wt.	Metal. Size.	Obverse.	Reverse.
	Æ *round*		
23·5	·4	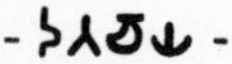	As preceding. [Clive Bayley, 1889.]
31·5	5.	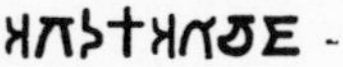	Lakṣmī standing facing, holding stalk of lotus in l. hand. [Cunningham, 1894.] **Pl. XLV. 24.**
		C., *C.A.I.*, p. 2, no. 4.	
51·0	·7	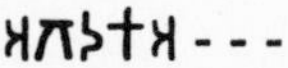	" [C. J. Rodgers, 1892.]

CLASS 2.

Wt.	Metal. Size.	Obverse.	Reverse.
49·5	·65	Lion r.  below. 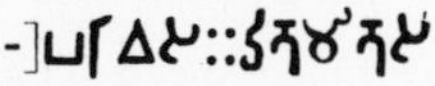	Bushy tree in railing. 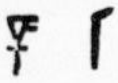 on l. 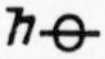 on r. [Clive Bayley, 1889.] **Pl. XLVI. 1.**
29·5	·6		" [Clive Bayley, 1889.]
34·0	·6		" " **Pl. XLVI. 2.**
36·0	·6	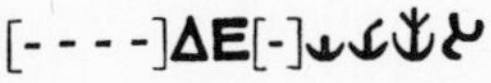	" [Clive Bayley, 1894.] **Pl. XLVI. 3.**
23·8	·6	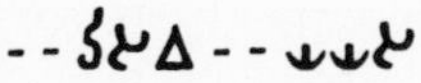	" [Clive Bayley, 1889.] **Pl. XLVI. 4.**

No.	Wt.	Metal. Size.	Obverse.	Reverse.
35	62·5	Æ *round* ·7	Similar, but different, uncertain legend.	As preceding. [C. J. Rodgers, 188 **Pl. XLVI. 6.**
36	36·0	·65	”	” [Cunningham, 189 **Pl. XLVI. 5.**
			CLASS 3. MISCELLANEOUS.	
37	85·5	·75	Tree in railing. -]⊔Xλ[-	Elephant r. [Cunningham, 189 **Pl. XLV. 25.**
38	67·8	·8	”	” [Cunningham, 189
39	47·0	·55	Sun on l. of tall tree.	Goddess standing facing. Legend ending - - ʅ𑀬 [Cunningham, 189 **Pl. XLV. 26.**
40	42·0	·45	”	Lion r. [W. S. Talbot, Esq., Pre
41	66·0	·5	Bull r. Trace of legend.	Elephant r. [Cunningham, 189 **Pl. XLVI. 13.**
42	76·5	·7	Bull l.	Three-tiered stupa. [Messrs. Spink & Son, Pre 192 **Pl. XLVI. 14.**

o.	Wt.	Metal. Size.	Obverse.	Reverse.
3	40·5	Æ *square* ·6 × ·4	Bull l. [- -] (- - *tasa*) above.	Tree in railing on l.? Stupa on r. [Thomas, 1850.] **Pl. XLVI. 8.**
4	31·0	·6	Horse to r. - - above.	 above. [Whitehead, 1922.] **Pl. XLVI. 9.**
5	84·0	·8	Bull to r. before standard surmounted by in railing. Trace of legend above.	in each angle. [Messrs. Spink & Son, Pres., 1920.] **Pl. XLVI. 7.**
6	82·5	·7	,,	,, [Prinsep, 1847.]
7	65·5	*round* ·75	Horse to r. in square.	Elaborate tree in railing. Traces of legend around. [Mrs. J. P. Rawlins, 1928.] **Pl. XLVI. 12.**
8	77·5	Pb *round* ·75	Horse r. grazing. [- -]	Female figure standing in archway with r. hand raised, wearing long robe and winged (?). [J. P. Rawlins, 1922.] **Pl. XLVI. 11.**
			(*J.A.S.B.*, 1897, Pl. XV.)	
9	27·0	Æ ·8	 Elephant to l.; traces of legend above.	[-]  [- - -] [Clive Bayley, 1889.] **Pl. XLVI. 10.**

No.	Wt.	Metal. Size.	Obverse.	Reverse.
			ADDITIONS	
			Punchmarked Silver.	
			CLASS 2. GROUP V.	
			Var. *e* (p. 42).	
20*a*	51·0	AR *round* ·65		 and traces of other punch [Director of Industries, C. Pres., 192 (from Thathari)
			GROUP VII.	
			Insert after Var. *d* (p. 46).	
15*a*	51·0	*square* ·6 × ·5		 and other stamps. [Director of Industries, C. Pres., 192 (from Thathari)
			CLASS 8 (p. 84).	
1	44·0	·4	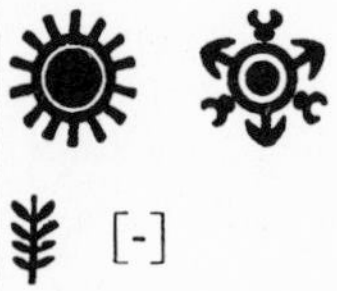 Hanuman?	Plain. [H. Nelson Wright, Esq., Pre 192 **Pl. XLVI. 17.**
			CLASS 9.	
1	2·2	*round* ·2		Plain. [H. Nelson Wright, Esq., Pre 192 **Pl. XLVI. 18.**

.	Wt.	Metal. Size.	Obverse.	Reverse.
	2·6	AR round ·2	As preceding.	As preceding. [Director of Industries, C. P., Pres., 1925.] **Pl. XLVI. 19.**
	2·7	·2	”	” [Director of Industries, C. P., Pres., 1925.] (from Thathari)
	3·0	·2	”	” ”

AUDUMBARA

ARYAMITRA

a	62·5	Æ round ·75	As no. 29. 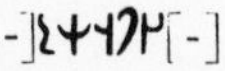	As no. 29. 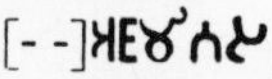 [Mrs. J. P. Rawlins, 1928.]

MAHĀBHŪTIMITRA

a	61·5	·6	As No. 26. 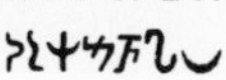	Elephant to l. with rider. Inscription illegible. [Whitehead, 1922.]

AYODHYĀ

DHANADEVA

Var. *b*.

a	93·0	*square* ·8	As no. 24. 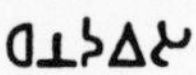	As no. 24. [Spink, 1928.]
b	96·0	·8	” but object in front with 	” ”
c	97·5	·7	”	” ”

No.	Wt.	Metal. Size.	Obverse.	Reverse.
			KUNINDA	
			AMOGHABHŪTI	
			Copper.	
		Æ	CLASS III.	
69*a*	252·0	*round* 1·1	Type as Class I, p. 162, but small; the legend above, in two lines, occupies disproportionate share of area. 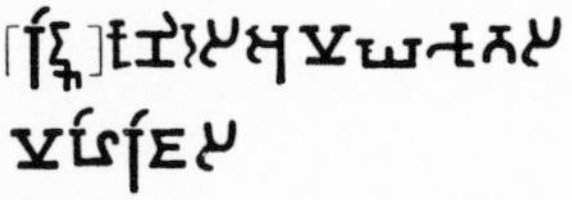	As Class I, p. 162. [C. J. Rodgers, 189 **Pl. XL. 14.**
69*b*	226·0	1·15	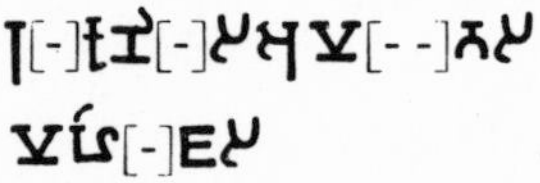	,, [Stubbs, 186
			YAUDHEYA	
			CLASS 2.	
			Var. *d*.	
			Bull r.	As in Var. *a–c*.
46*a*	51·5	·7	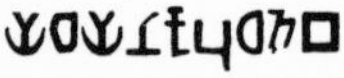	,, [Whitehead, 192
46*b*	52·5	·6	 - [-]	,, ,,
46*c*	47·5	·6	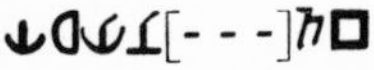	,, [Clive Bayley, 188
			? YAUDHEYA or KANAUJ	
			[- - -]MITRA	
1	46·0	·6	 [-] 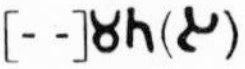 (- -)*mitasa*	Type illegible. [Thomas, 185 **Pl. XXXIX. 9.**

INDEXES

INDEX I

ATTRIBUTIONS

INDEX II

RULERS

A

Acyuta, lxxix–lxxx, 117–19.
Agnimitra (Kauśāmbī), xcvi, 153.
— (Pañcāla), cxvii, 199–201.
Ajavarman, lxxxix–xc.
Amoghabhūti, ci–ciii, 159–67, 288.
Aparānta, lxxxi, cx.
Ārjunāyana, lxxxii–lxxxiii, 121.
Āryamitra (Audumbara), lxxxvi, 125–6.
— (Ayodhyā), xc, 137–8.
Aśvaghoṣa, xcvi, 150.

B

Balabhūti, cx, 178.
Bhadrāghoṣa, cxvii, 197.
Bhānumitra (Audumbara), lxxxvi, 127–8.
— (Pañcāla), cxvii, 195–7.
Bhāvadatta, cx–cxi.
Bhūmimitra, cxvii, 198.
Brahmamitra (Kanauj), xciii, 147.
— (Mathurā), cx, 173.
Bṛhaspatimitra I, xcvi–xcviii, 150.
— II, xcvi–xcviii, 151–3.

D

Devamitra, xc.
Dhanadeva (Ayodhyā), lxxxix, 132–3, 287.
— (Kauśāmbī), xcvii, 153.
Dharaghoṣa, lxxxiii, 124–5.
Dharmapala, xci, 140.
Dhruvamitra, cxvii, 199.
Dṛḍhamitra, cx, 174.

G

Gomitra I, cviii, 169.
— II, cix, 170–2.
Goṣadatta, 174; correct to Śesadatta (q.v.).

H

Hagāmaṣa, cxi–cxii, 183–4.
Hagāna, cxi–cxii, 184.
Haridatta, lxxxi, 120.

I

Indramitra, cxvii, 203–4.

J

Jayagupta, cxvii, 202.
Jayamitra, cxvii, 203.
Jyeṣṭhadatta, cliii, 279.
Jyeṣṭhamitra, xcvi, 154.

K

Kāḍa, xcii–xciii, 145–6.
Kāmadatta, cx, 182.
Kumudasena, lxxxix–xc, 137.

M

Mahābbhūtimitra, lxxxvi, 287.
Mahādeva, lxxxiii, 123–4.
Mahāsena, cliv, 279.
Mahīmitra, lxxxvi, 126–7.
Mūladeva, lxxxviii, 130.

N

Naradatta, lxxxix, 134.

P

Parvata, xcvi, 150.
Phalgunīmitra, cxvii, 194–5.
Puṅgasena, cliv, 279.
Puruṣadatta, cx, 176–7.

R

Rājuvula, cxi–cxiv, 185–9.
Rāmadatta, cx, 178–81.

INDEX III

INSCRIPTIONS

(*a*) Greek

(*b*) Brāhmī

[illegible] xcvi, 153.
[illegible] cxvii, 199, 201.
[illegible] lxxix–lxxx, 117–19.
[illegible] lxxxvi, 125–6.
[illegible] lxxxii, 121.
[illegible], cxxv, 215.
[illegible] xc, 137.
[illegible] xcvi, 150.
[illegible] 203–4.
[illegible] cxlv, 262.
[illegible] cx, 177.
[illegible] cxli, 240.
[illegible] lxxxiii–lxxxvi, 122–5.
[illegible] cxlv, 263.
[illegible] cxlvi, 264.
[illegible] xcii, 145–6.
[illegible] xcviii.
[illegible] cxlviii, 267–70, correct to [illegible] (q.v.).
[illegible] cxii, 184.
[illegible] cxii, 183.
[illegible] cxii, 183–1.
[illegible] cxii.
[illegible] cviii–cix, 169–72.
[illegible] cxvii, 202.
[illegible] cxvii, 203.
[illegible] xcvi, 154.
[illegible] cxxvi, 214.
[illegible], cxl, 212.
[illegible] cxxvi, 214.
[illegible] lxxxix, 132–3.
[illegible] xci, 140.
[illegible] cxvii, 193.
[illegible] cx, 174.
[illegible] lxxxix, 134.
[illegible] cxxvi–cxxviii, 214–17.
[illegible] xcvi, 150.

𑀮𑀶𑀦𑀲𑀶 cxvii, 192.	𑀥𑀶𑀤𑀤𑀶 cxi, cliv, 280.
𑀤𑀘𑀲𑀢 cxlvi, 264.	𑀥𑀚𑀫𑀤𑀲𑀚𑀟𑀢𑀲𑀫𑀤𑀳 c,158.
𑀥𑀶𑀲𑀤𑀶 lxxxix, 130-1.	𑀤𑀳𑀚𑀏𑀤𑀟𑀶𑀦𑀘𑀳𑀩𑀩𑀚 clvi, 281.
𑀤𑀦 [- -] cliv, 280.	𑀶𑀥𑀏𑀢𑀩𑀳𑀶 cxxiv, 213.
𑀤𑀏𑀶𑀢𑀭𑀶 xc, 138-9.	𑀭 𑀤 𑀩 𑀩 [𑀩] [⁻] lxxx–lxxxi, 120.
𑀥𑀏𑀶𑀢(𑁇𑀤𑀢𑀢𑀶𑀚𑀟𑀤𑀶 lxxxv, 125.	𑀢𑀸𑀶𑀭𑀶 xc, 138.
𑀥𑀶𑀲𑀲𑀤𑀶 lxxxix, 127.	𑀫𑀝𑀶𑀶𑀫 xc, 135-6.
𑀥𑀪𑀲𑀤𑀶 xciv, 147.	𑀳𑀤𑀲𑀳𑀶 lxxx, lxxxix, 120, 133.
𑀥𑀪𑀶𑀭𑀶 cx, 175-6.	𑀶𑀤𑀲𑀢𑀢 lxxxiii, 122-3.
𑀥𑀪𑀢𑀡𑀶 cxvii, 202.	𑀶𑀢𑀤𑀢 xcvi, 150.
𑀥𑀝𑀩𑀡𑀶 cxvii, 192.	𑀳𑀶𑀶𑀭𑀶 xciii, cx, 147, 174-5.
	𑀩 𑀢[𑀲] 𑀳 𑀶 lxxxi, 120.

(c) KHAROṢṬHĪ

cxiv, 185-6. 𐨤𐨟𐨢𐨩𐨫𐨤𐨬𐨪𐨢𐨟𐨩𐨡𐨮𐨏	lxxxiii, 123 𐨤𐨟𐨪𐨕𐨫𐨪𐨟𐨩𐨢
cxxvi, 215 𐨢𐨩𐨤	lxxxiv, 124-5 𐨤𐨟𐨲𐨪𐨫𐨪𐨤𐨟𐨮𐨕
lxxxiii–lxxxv, 122-5 𐨤𐨢𐨩𐨮𐨤	lxxxiv, 124 𐨢𐨲𐨢𐨲
cxxviii, 216-17 𐨆𐨥𐨍𐨢𐨩	cxiv, 187 𐨤𐨟𐨢𐨟𐨡𐨳𐨟𐨩𐨮𐨏𐨪𐨟𐨕
lxxxvi, 287 𐨤𐨫𐨲𐨳𐨥𐨪𐨕	lxxxiii, 122-3 𐨤𐨤𐨫𐨳
ci–ciii, 159, 161. 𐨤𐨳𐨪𐨲𐨩𐨤𐨟𐨐𐨩𐨢𐨥𐨪𐨤𐨪𐨟𐨩𐨕	lxxxvi, 127-8 𐨤𐨫𐨲𐨍𐨥𐨤𐨪
cxxiii, 211-12 𐨤𐨪𐨢𐨫𐨬𐨤𐨪	lxxxv, 123 𐨢𐨳𐨬𐨪
lxxxvi, 125-6 𐨤𐨫𐨲𐨢𐨤𐨪	lxxxiii, 122 𐨤𐨤𐨢𐨤
xxxv, 125 𐨀𐨀𐨬𐨪𐨲𐨐𐨲𐨤𐨳𐨮𐨮𐨤𐨪	clvi, 281 𐨢 𐨢 𐨮𐨮𐨟𐨲 𐨬 𐨤 𐨳 𐨬 𐨡 𐨏 𐨢
lxxxvi, 126-7 𐨤𐨫𐨲𐨟𐨫𐨪	cxxix, cxxxi–cxxxii, 218 𐨲𐨤[-]𐨲
	cxxvi, 215 𐨲𐨥 [-] 𐨲𐨢 [-]

INDEX IV

SYMBOLS ON PUNCH-MARKED SILVER COINS

 xvi, 1.

 xvi, 1.

 xvi, 1.

 xvi, 2.

 xvi, 3.

 xvi, 3.

 xvi, 2.

 xvii, 4.

 xvii, 5.

 xvii, 8.

 xviii, 9.

 xix, 10.

10.

10.

xvii, 6–7.

xvii, 6–7.

xxii, lix–lxiii, 1–51, 64–5, 79–82, 84.

xxii, xxxvii, lxiv–lxvii, 52–63, 68–76, 83.

xxii, 58–9.

xxii, xxxvii, 44.

xvii, 7.

xxiii, lix–lxi, lxix, 11–20, 25–34, 38, 40–1, 43–50, 55, 56, 82.

or xxiii, lxvii, 59, 72, 79–81, 82.

xxiii, xxviii, lxii, 35, 36.

xxiii, 37, 38.

 xxvii, lx, 23–4.

 xxvii, lxi, 31.

 xxviii, lxi, lxii, 32–6.

 lxi, 36.

 xxviii, 26, 37, 38.

 xxviii, lxv, 60–3.

 xxviii, 44.

 xxviii, lxiv, 57.

 xxviii, 76–8.

 xxviii, lxv, 62, 77, 78.

 xxviii, lxvi, 74, 75.

 xxviii, 41.

 xxxix, 58.

 xxix, 78, 82.

 xxix, lxv, 64, 71, 72.

 xxix, 51.

 xxix, 84.

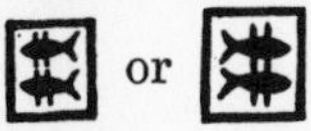

xxix, 44, 56[?], 83.

 xxix, lxii, lxvi, 41, 42, 71, 74.

 xxix, lxiv, 60–2.

 xxx, 55.

 xxx, 83.

 xxx, 55, 67.

 xxx, 55.

 xxx, lxi, 31.

 xxx, lxi, 28, 29.

 xxx, lxviii, 82.

 xxx, lxvii, 68–9, 78, 80, 83.

 xxx, 59, 62.

 xxx, 32.

 xxx, 43, 54.

 xxx, lxiv, 62.

 xxx, lxvi, 74, 78.

 xxx, lxvi, 74.

 xxx, 27, 29.

 xxxi, xxxviii, xxxix, xl, 38, 42–4, 52, 55, 68, 72.

 xxxi, 43, 55.

 xxxi, xl, 20, 32–5, 38–9.

 xxxi, lxii, 38, 39.

 xxxi, 56.

xxxiii, 56.

xxxiii, 58.

xxxiii, 58, 59.

xxxiii, lxiv, 59, 72.

xxxiii, 59.

xxxiii, lxvi, 71, 72.

xxxiii, 80.

xxxiii, 83.

xxxiii, lxi, 29.

xxxiii, 29.

xxxiii, lxviii, 82.

xxxiii, xxxviii, lxiv, lxv, lxvi, 39, 43, 47, 49, 52, 57, 61, 62, 63, 70, 78, 79, 81, 82.

27, 56.

xxxiv.

xxxiv, xxxviii, xl.

xxxiii, lxv, 63–5.

xxxiii, 63.

xxxiii, lxiv, 59, 72.

xxxiii, 52, 53.

xxxv, 78.

xxxiv, xxxviii, xxxix, xl, xliii, lxi, 26–39, 49, 54.

xxxiv, lxvi, 73–4.

xxxiv, lxiv, 54.

xviii, 9.

xxxiv, lxviii, 55, 68, 80.

58.

xviii, 6, 9.

xix, 10.

xxxiv, lxviii, 80.

59, 61, 73, 79.

xxxiv, lxix, 59.

lxix, 48, 59, 61, 62, 73, 78, 79.

59, 76.

68, 73.

68.

xxxv, lxiv, 55.

xxxv, 55.

xxxv, xlv, lxiii, lxiv, 23–4, 44–9, 55.

xxxv, lxiii, 46–52.

xxxv, xxxviii, lx, 20, 23, 24.

xxxv, lxviii, 82.

INDEX V

SYMBOLS ON PUNCH-MARKED COPPER COINS

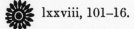

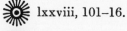

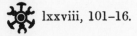

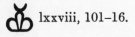

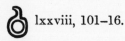

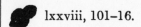

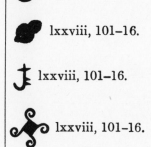

INDEX VI

SYMBOLS AND TYPES ON UNINSCRIBED CAST COINS

INDEX VII

SYMBOLS ON TRIBAL COINS

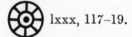

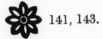

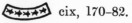

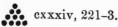

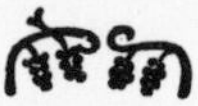 cxxxiv, 222.

 lxxxii, 121, 213.

 cxxv–cxxxvi, 226–7, 229–30.

 cxxxvi, 229.

 cxxxv, 227.

 123.

 lxxxviii, 130–5.

 xcvii, xcviii, 151–3, 181–2.

 ci, cxxiv, cxlix, 152, 153, 159–67, 270–5.

 xcvii, xcviii, cxii, 152–5, 182–3, 190–2.

 xcvii, 150, 157, 158.

 cviii, 169.

 xciii, xcix, 147.

 lxxxi, clvii, 120, 282.

 xcviii, 150.

 xciii, 147.

 clv, 282.

 xci, 140–3.

 cxxxvi, cxxxviii, 229.

 cxlvi, 267–8.

 cxlviii, 267.

 133.

 lxxxii, 121.

 lxxxi, lxxxix, 120, 282.

 lxxxviii, 130–2, 134–5.

 cxxxiv, 220.

 cxxxiv, 220.

 cxxxiv, 219–20.

 xc, xciii, xcviii–xcix, cxlii–cxlv, 134, 140, 144, 147, 148–9, 150, 154, 213, 240, 241–4, 247, 249, 257–60.

 lxxxviii, xcv, cix, cxlii–cxliii, 130–4, 152, 173, 174, 241, 243, 244, 247–9, 252, 258, 260, 262.

INDEX VIII

TYPES ON TRIBAL COINS

INDEX IX

GENERAL

A

Acyuta coins, provenance of, lxxix.
Afghanistan, alleged find of punch-marked coins from, xlv.
Agathocles, finds of coins of, xiv, cxxxv.
— suggested translation of name, cxxx–cxxxi.
— coins of Taxila of, cxxxv.
Agodaka, unidentified *janapada*, cliii, clvii.
Ahicchatra, coins from, lxxix, cxix, cxx.
Alexander the Great and Omphis, xiv.
— finds of coins of, xiv, xvii, xli, xlii.
Almorā, coins from, lxxx–lxxxi.
Amoghabhūti, king of the Kuṇindas, cii.
Amohinī, inscription of, cxiv.
Āndhra coins, symbols on, xxxiv.
Antialkidas, find of coins of, xlv.
Antimachus, finds of coins of, lvii.
Antiochus II, find of coins of, xlv.
Aonla, Pañcāla coins from, cxix.
Aparānta, no coins of, lxxxii.
Apollodotos I Sotēr, coins of, copied by Audumbaras, xv, lxxxv.
— finds of coins of, lxxxvi, ciii.
Ārjunāyana coins, lxxxii.
Atakatakā, legend on coins from Taxila, cxxvi.
Audumbara coins, lxxiii–lxxxiv.
Augustus, denarius of, from Coimbatore, liv.
Bairaṅt, punch-marked coins from, l, lxxvii.
Ballia, punch-marked coins from, xlix.
Bārānāye, alleged inscription on Mathurā coins, cviii–cix.
Behat, Kuṇinda coins from, cli.
— Yaudheya coins from, cxlvii, cli.
Belwa, punch-marked coins from, xlviii, lvii.
Besnagar, punch-marked coins from, li, lxxvii.
— coins of Eran from, cxlii.
Bhagalpur, coins from, xlvi, xlvii, lxxix.
Bhanjakia, Purī coins from, cxxi.
Bharhut stupa, xv.
Bhāvadatta of Mathurā, coins of, cxi.
Bhir mound (Taxila), coins found in, xvi, xlii, xliv, xlvii, lvi.
Bhitari, copper coins from, lxxvii.
Bhuila, punch-marked coins from, xlix.
— Pañcāla coins from, cxix.
Bimlipatan, punch-marked coins from, liv.
Bṛhaspatimitra, several rulers of this name, xcvii–xcviii.
Bodh Gayā, punch-marked coins from, xlviii.
— inscription from, cxiii.
Bua-dih, punch-marked coins from, xlix.
Bulandshahr, Mathurā coins from, cviii.

B

Badaon, Pañcāla coins from, cxix.
Bahudhañake, legend on Yaudheya coins, cxlviii.

C

Campā = Bhagalpur, lxxix.
Caitya symbol really a mountain, xxiv.

TABLE

FOR

CONVERTING ENGLISH INCHES INTO MILLIMETRES

AND THE

MEASURES OF MIONNET'S SCALE

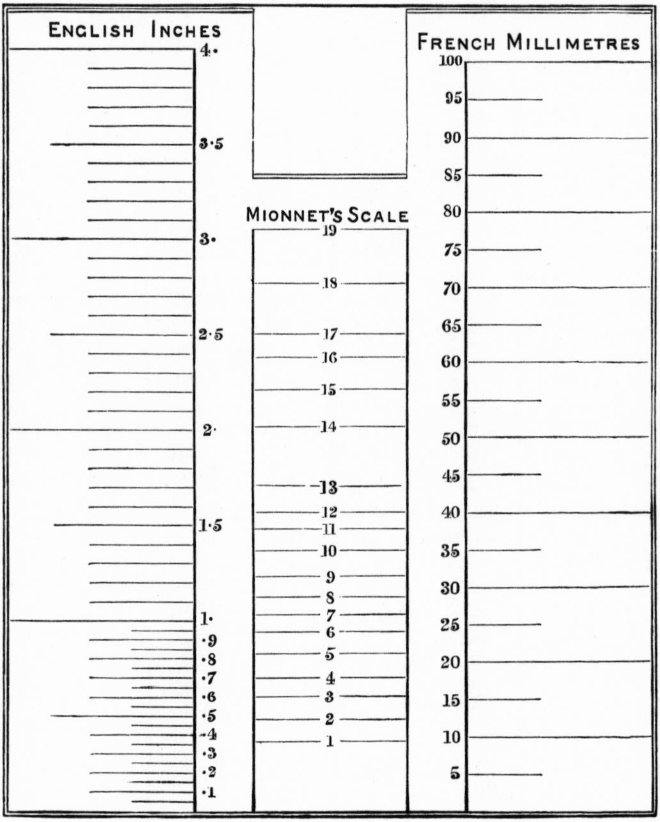

TABLE

OF

THE RELATIVE WEIGHTS OF ENGLISH GRAINS AND METRIC GRAMMES

Grains.	Grammes.	Grains.	Grammes.	Grains.	Grammes.	Grains.	Grammes.
1	·064	41	2·656	81	5·248	121	7·840
2	·129	42	2·720	82	5·312	122	7·905
3	·194	43	2·785	83	5·378	123	7·970
4	·259	44	2·850	84	5·442	124	8·035
5	·324	45	2·915	85	5·508	125	8·100
6	·388	46	2·980	86	5·572	126	8·164
7	·453	47	3·045	87	5·637	127	8·229
8	·518	48	3·110	88	5·702	128	8·294
9	·583	49	3·175	89	5·767	129	8·359
10	·648	50	3·240	90	5·832	130	8·424
11	·712	51	3·304	91	5·896	131	8·488
12	·777	52	3·368	92	5·961	132	8·553
13	·842	53	3·434	93	6·026	133	8·618
14	·907	54	3·498	94	6·091	134	8·682
15	·972	55	3·564	95	6·156	135	8·747
16	1·036	56	3·628	96	6·220	136	8·812
17	1·101	57	3·693	97	6·285	137	8·877
18	1·166	58	3·758	98	6·350	138	8·942
19	1·231	59	3·823	99	6·415	139	9·007
20	1·296	60	3·888	100	6·480	140	9·072
21	1·360	61	3·952	101	6·544	141	9·136
22	1·425	62	4·017	102	6·609	142	9·200
23	1·490	63	4·082	103	6·674	143	9·265
24	1·555	64	4·146	104	6·739	144	9·330
25	1·620	65	4·211	105	6·804	145	9·395
26	1·684	66	4·276	106	6·868	146	9·460
27	1·749	67	4·341	107	6·933	147	9·525
28	1·814	68	4·406	108	6·998	148	9·590
29	1·879	69	4·471	109	7·063	149	9·655
30	1·944	70	4·536	110	7·128	150	9·720
31	2·008	71	4·600	111	7·192	151	9·784
32	2·073	72	4·665	112	7·257	152	9·848
33	2·138	73	4·729	113	7·322	153	9·914
34	2·202	74	4·794	114	7·387	154	9·978
35	2·267	75	4·859	115	7·452	155	10·044
36	2·332	76	4·924	116	7·516	156	10·108
37	2·397	77	4·989	117	7·581	157	10·173
38	2·462	78	5·054	118	7·646	158	10·238
39	2·527	79	5·119	119	7·711	159	10·303
40	2·592	80	5·184	120	7·776	160	10·368

TABLE

OF

THE RELATIVE WEIGHTS OF ENGLISH GRAINS AND METRIC GRAMMES

Grains.	Grammes.	Grains.	Grammes.	Grains.	Grammes.	Grains.	Grammes.
161	10·432	201	13·024	241	15·616	290	18·79
162	10·497	202	13·089	242	15·680	300	19·44
163	10·562	203	13·154	243	15·745	310	20·08
164	10·626	204	13·219	244	15·810	320	20·73
165	10·691	205	13·284	245	15·875	330	21·38
166	10·756	206	13·348	246	15·940	340	22·02
167	10·821	207	13·413	247	16·005	350	22·67
168	10·886	208	13.478	248	16·070	360	23·32
169	10·951	209	13·543	249	16·135	370	23·97
170	11·016	210	13·608	250	16·200	380	24·62
171	11·080	211	13·672	251	16·264	390	25·27
172	11·145	212	13·737	252	16·328	400	25·92
173	11·209	213	13·802	253	16·394	410	26·56
174	11·274	214	13·867	254	16·458	420	27·20
175	11·339	215	13·932	255	16·524	430	27·85
176	11·404	216	13·996	256	16·588	440	28·50
177	11·469	217	14.061	257	16·653	450	29·15
178	11·534	218	14·126	258	16.718	460	29·80
179	11·599	219	14·191	259	16·783	470	30·45
180	11·664	220	14·256	260	16·848	480	31·10
181	11·728	221	14·320	261	16·912	490	31·75
182	11·792	222	14·385	262	16·977	500	32·40
183	11·858	223	14·450	263	17·042	510	33·04
184	11·922	224	14·515	264	17·106	520	33·68
185	11·988	225	14·580	265	17·171	530	34·34
186	12·052	226	14·644	266	17·236	540	34·98
187	12·117	227	14·709	267	17·301	550	35·64
188	12·182	228	14·774	268	17·366	560	36·28
189	12·247	229	14·839	269	17·431	570	36·93
190	12·312	230	14·904	270	17·496	580	37·58
191	12·376	231	14·968	271	17·560	590	38·23
192	12·441	232	15·033	272	17·625	600	38·88
193	12·506	233	15·098	273	17·689	700	45·36
194	12·571	234	15·162	274	17·754	800	51·84
195	12·636	235	15·227	275	17·819	900	58·32
196	12·700	236	15·292	276	17·884	1000	64·80
197	12·765	237	15·357	277	17·949	2000	129·60
198	12·830	238	15·422	278	18·014	3000	194·40
199	12·895	239	15·487	279	18·079	4000	259·20
200	12·960	240	15·552	280	18·144	5000	324·00

PLATES

PLATE I

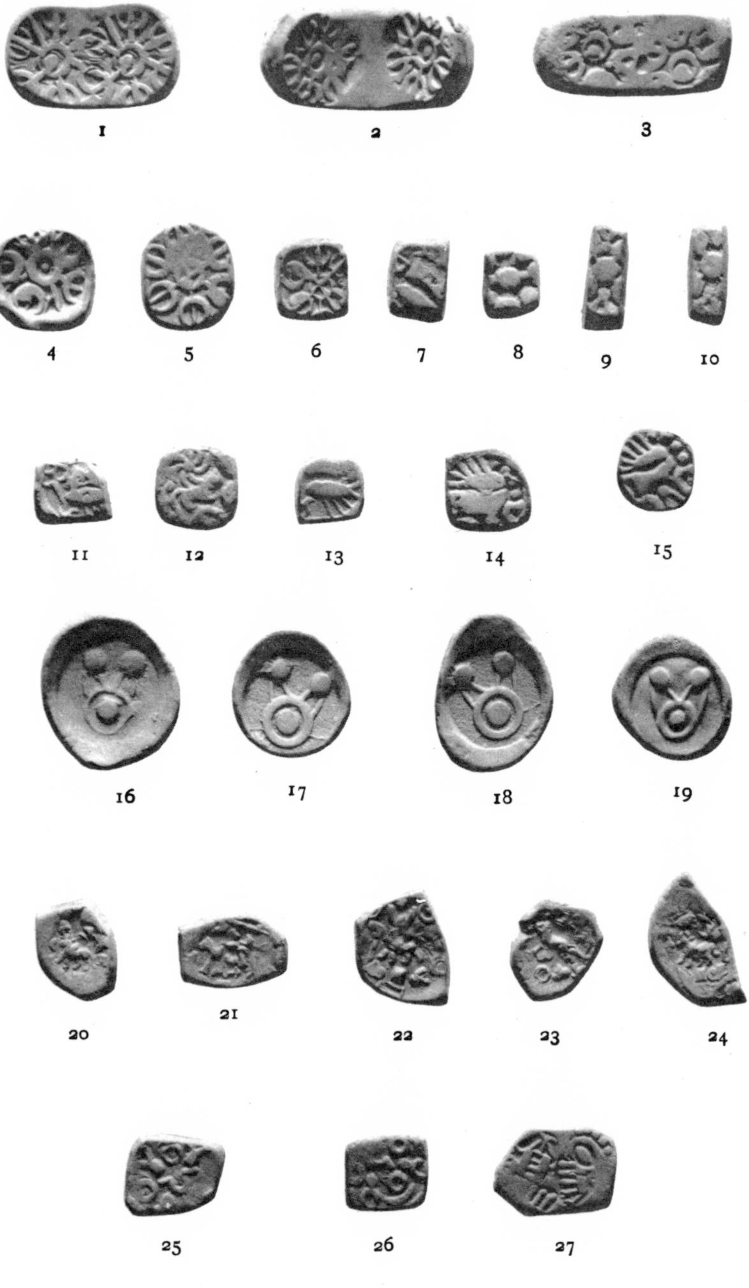

VARIOUS EARLY SILVER

PUNCH-MARKED SILVER

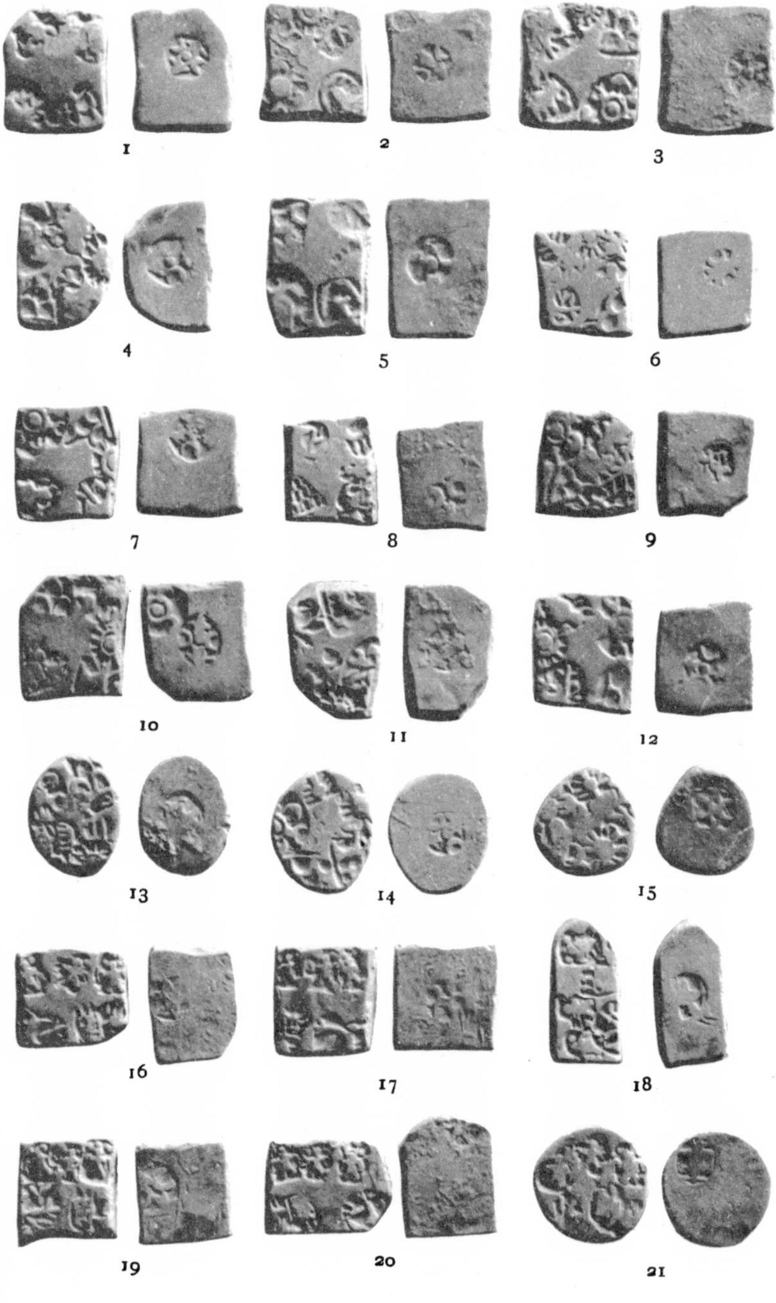

PUNCH-MARKED SILVER

PUNCH-MARKED SILVER

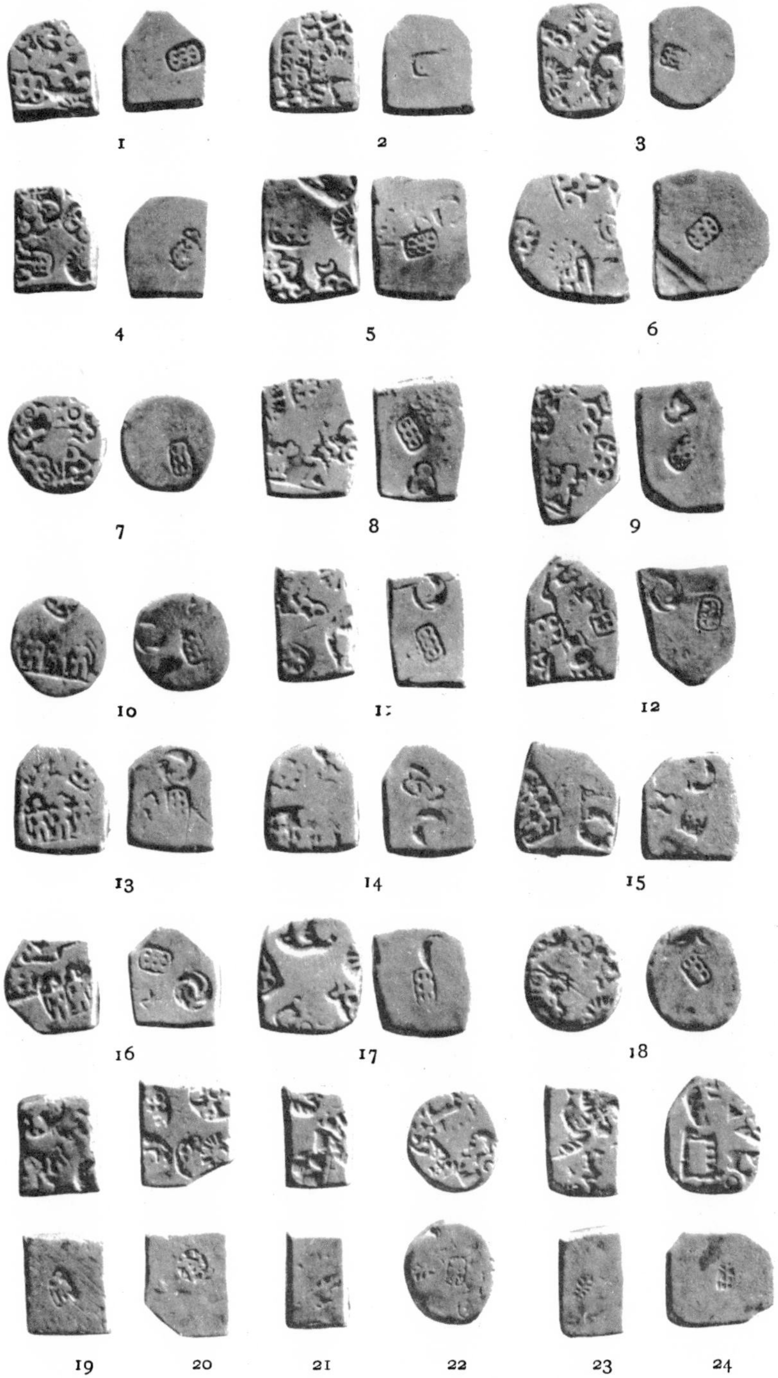

PUNCH-MARKED SILVER

PLATE VI

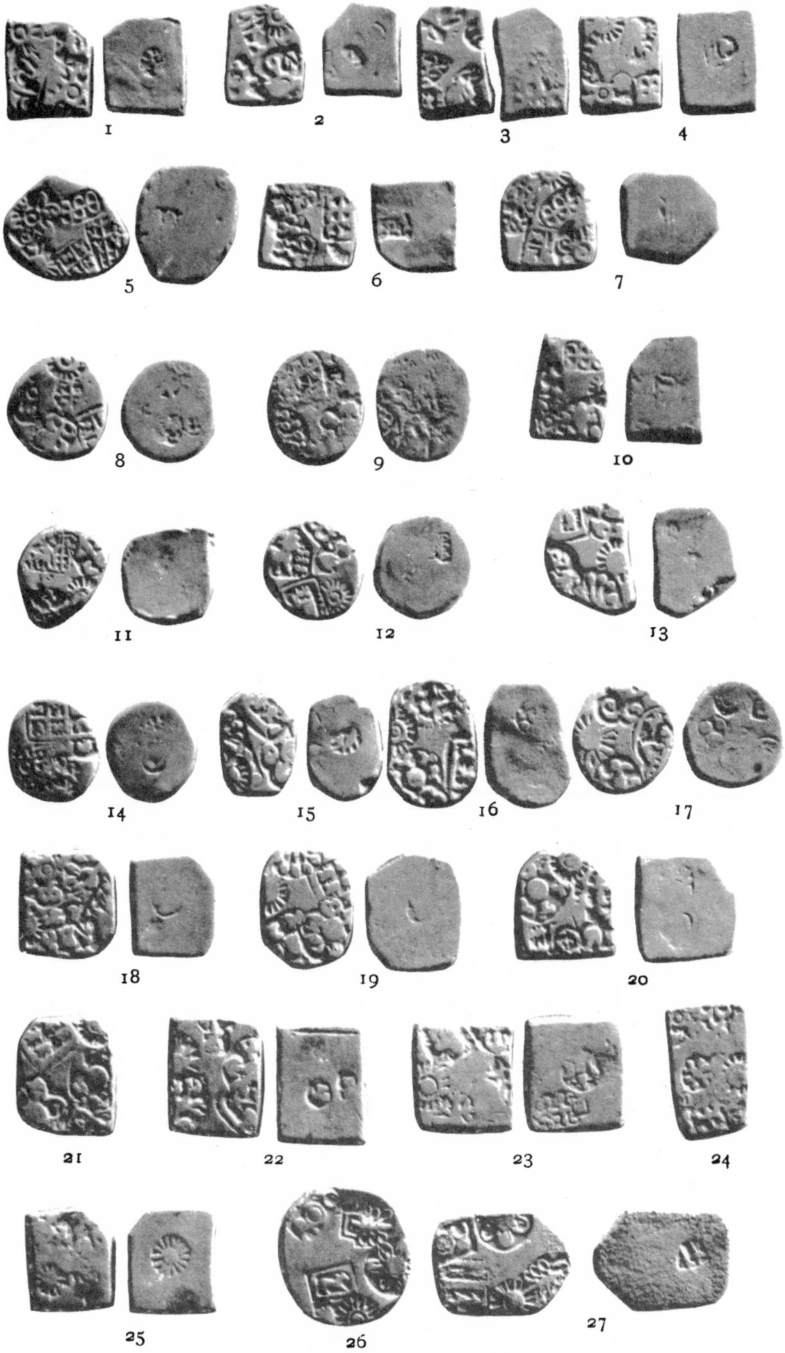

PUNCH-MARKED SILVER

PLATE VII

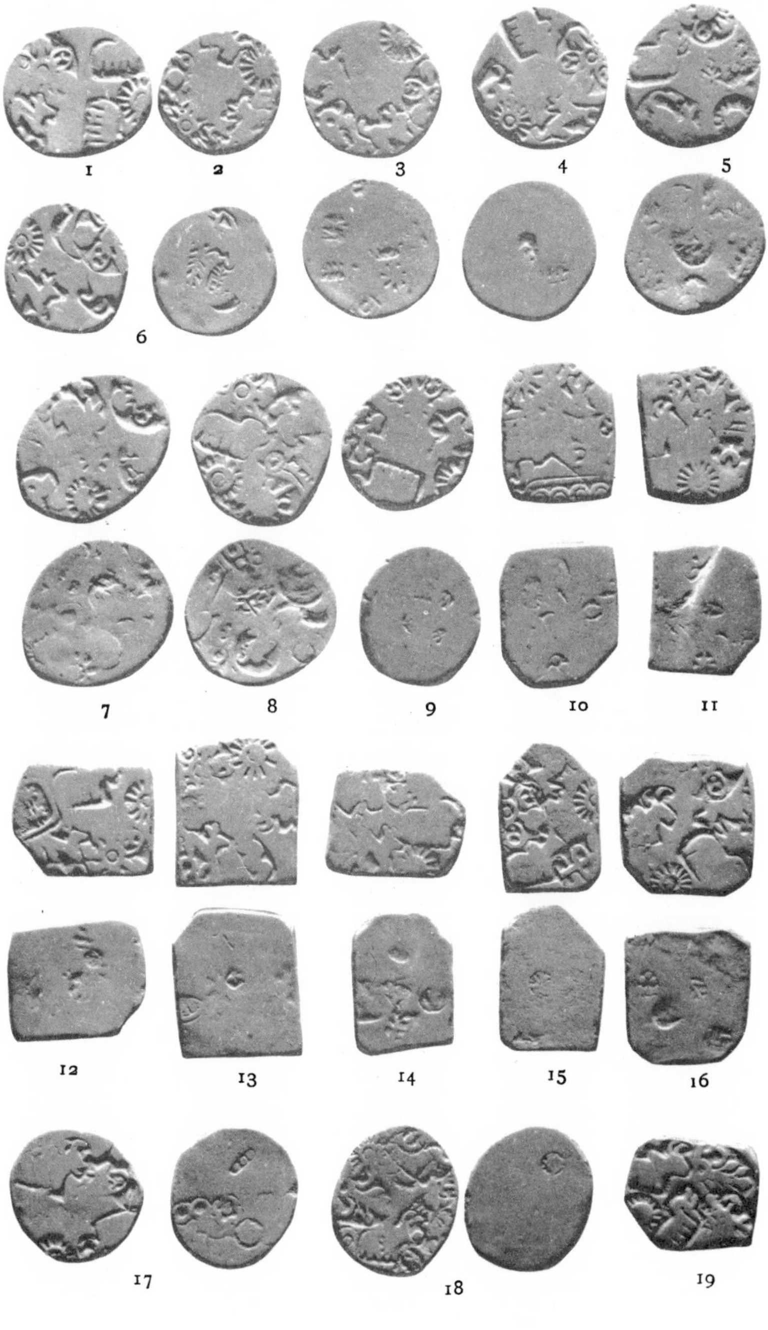

PUNCH-MARKED SILVER

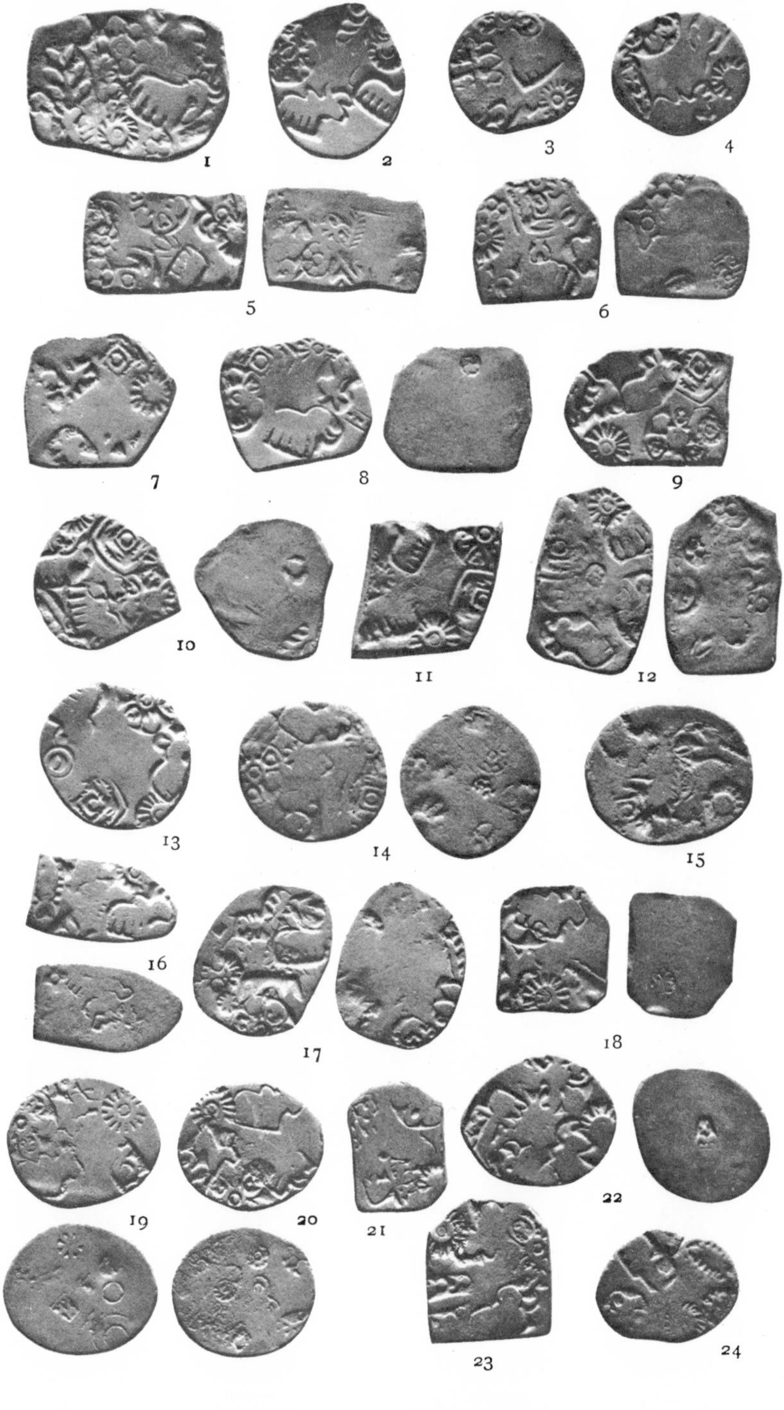

PUNCH-MARKED SILVER

PLATE IX

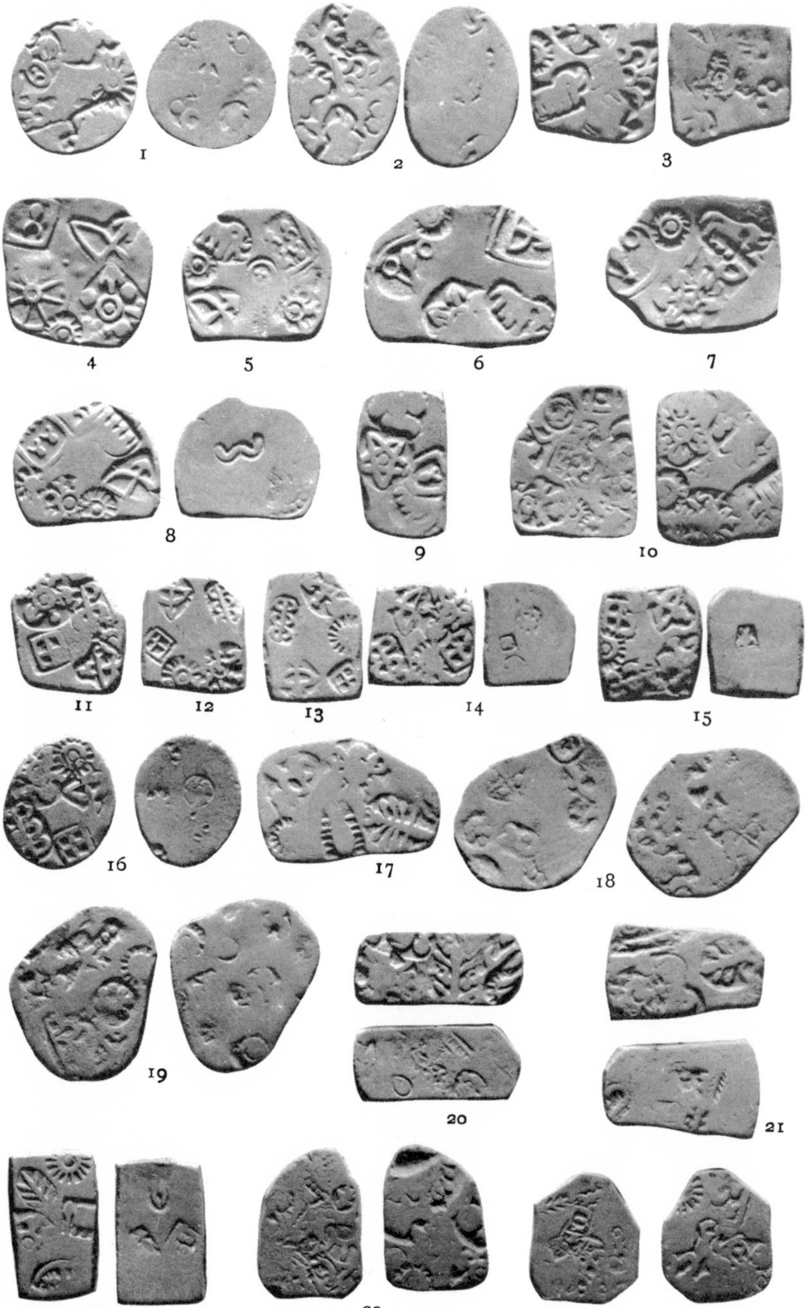

PUNCH-MARKED SILVER

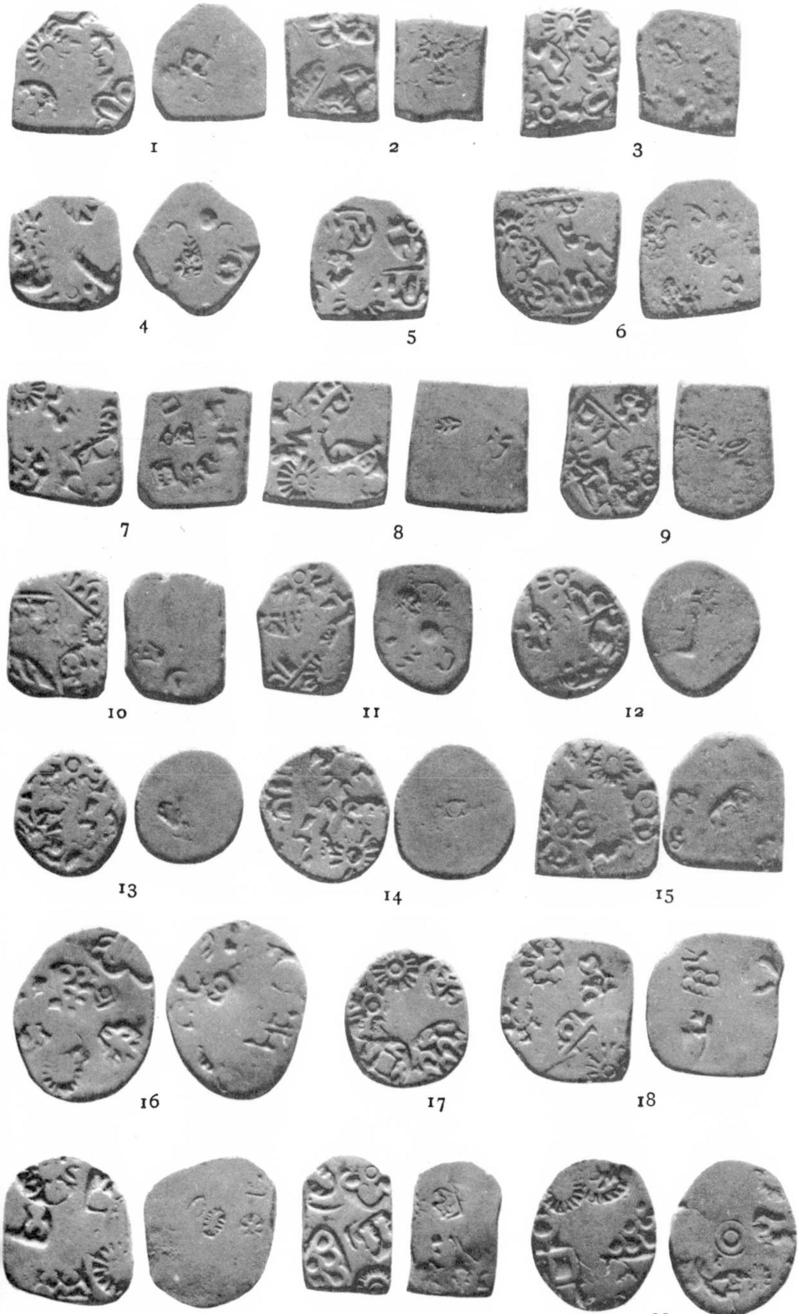

PUNCH-MARKED SILVER

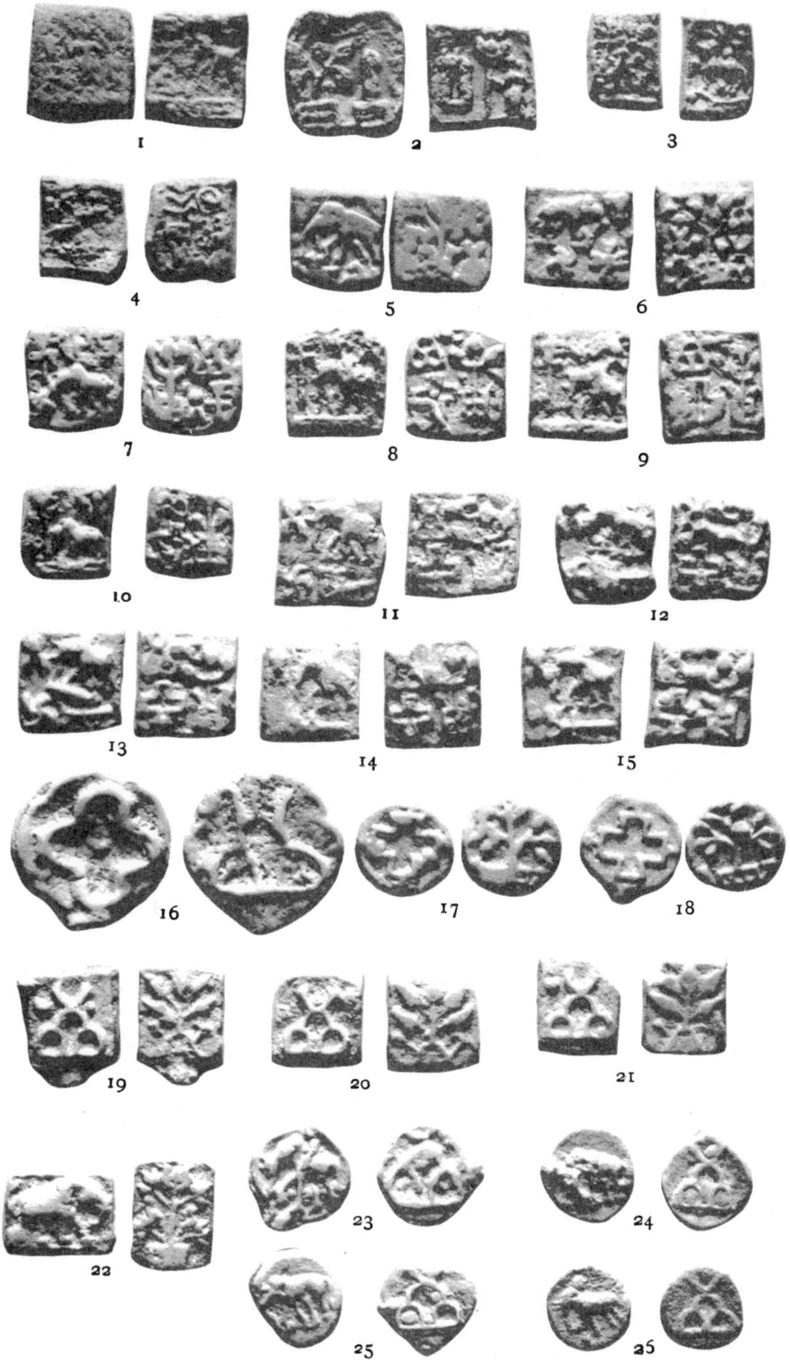

CAST COPPER

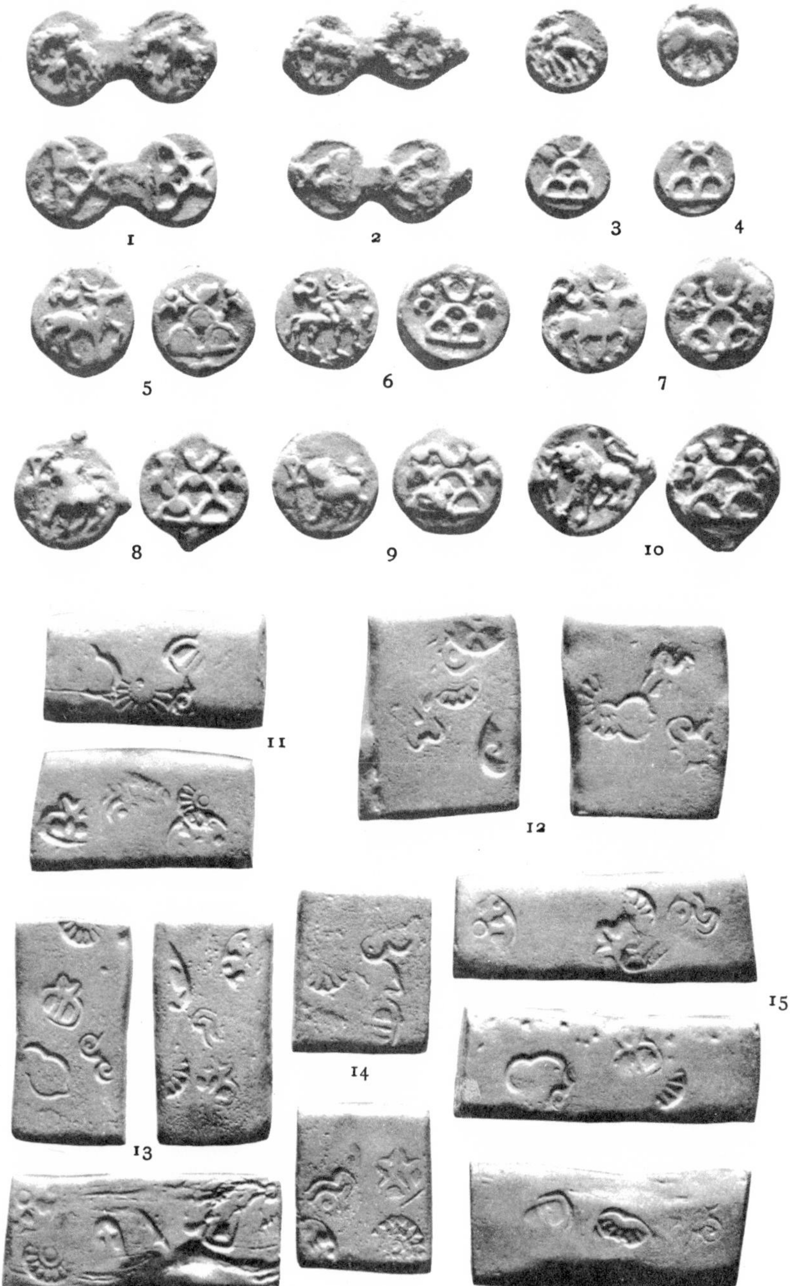

CAST AND PUNCH-MARKED COPPER

1

2

3

4

5

6

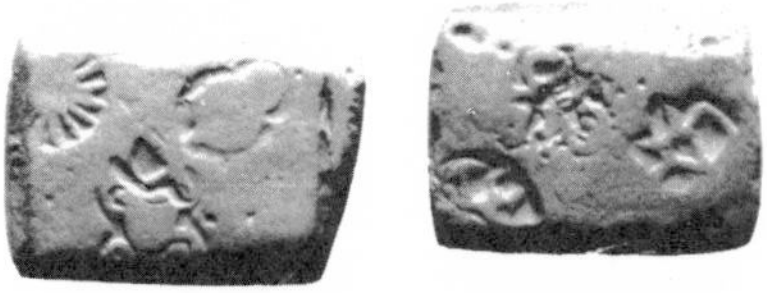

7

8

9

10

11

12

13

14

PUNCH-MARKED COPPER

PLATE XIV

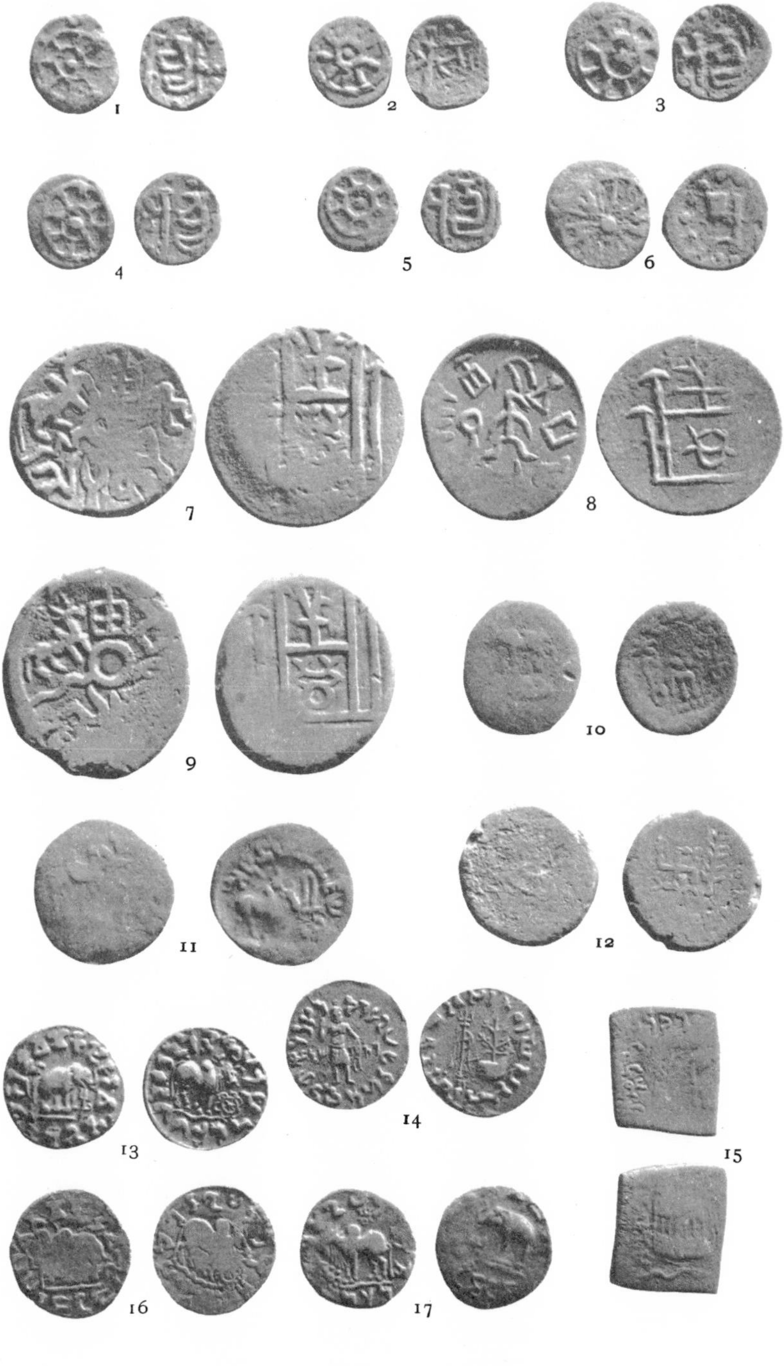

AHICCHATRA—AUDUMBARA

AUDUMBARA

AUDUMBARA—AYODHYĀ

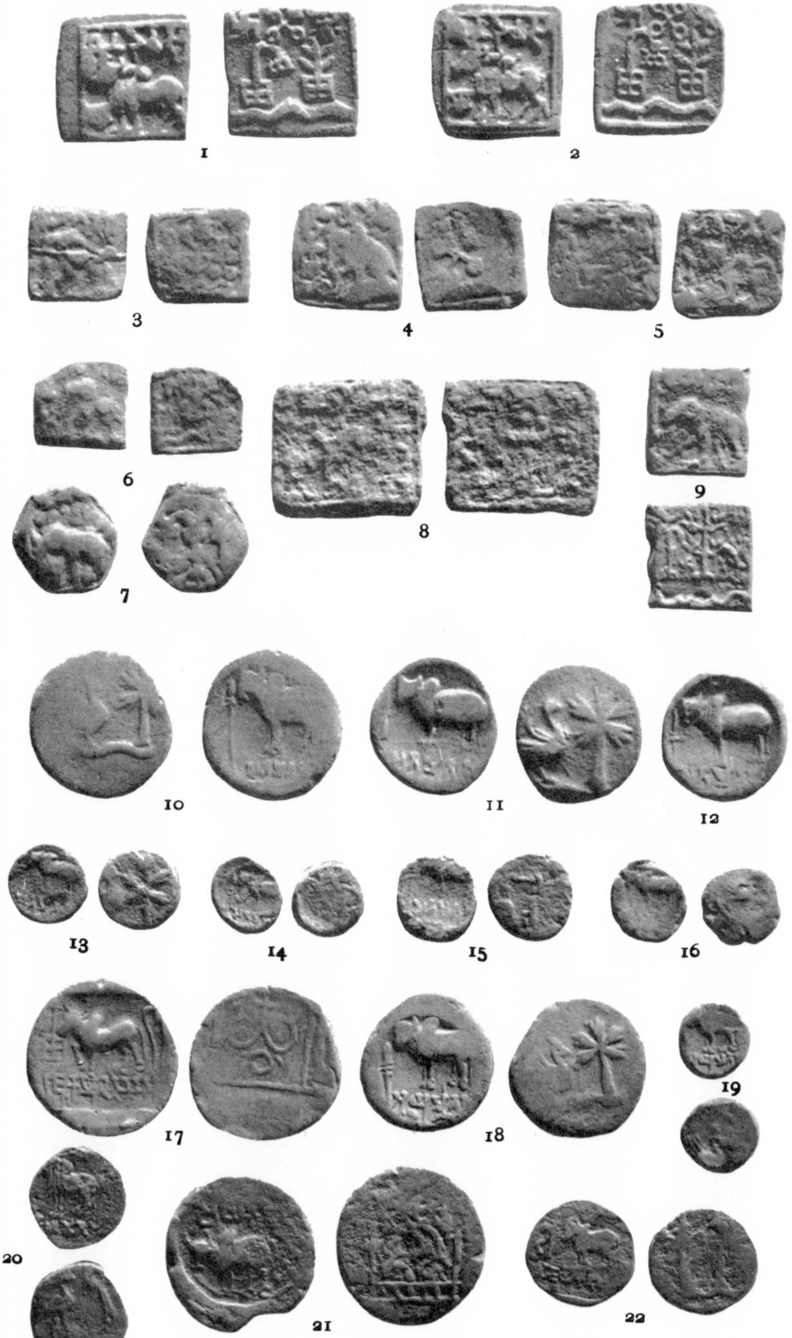

AYODHYĀ

PLATE XVIII

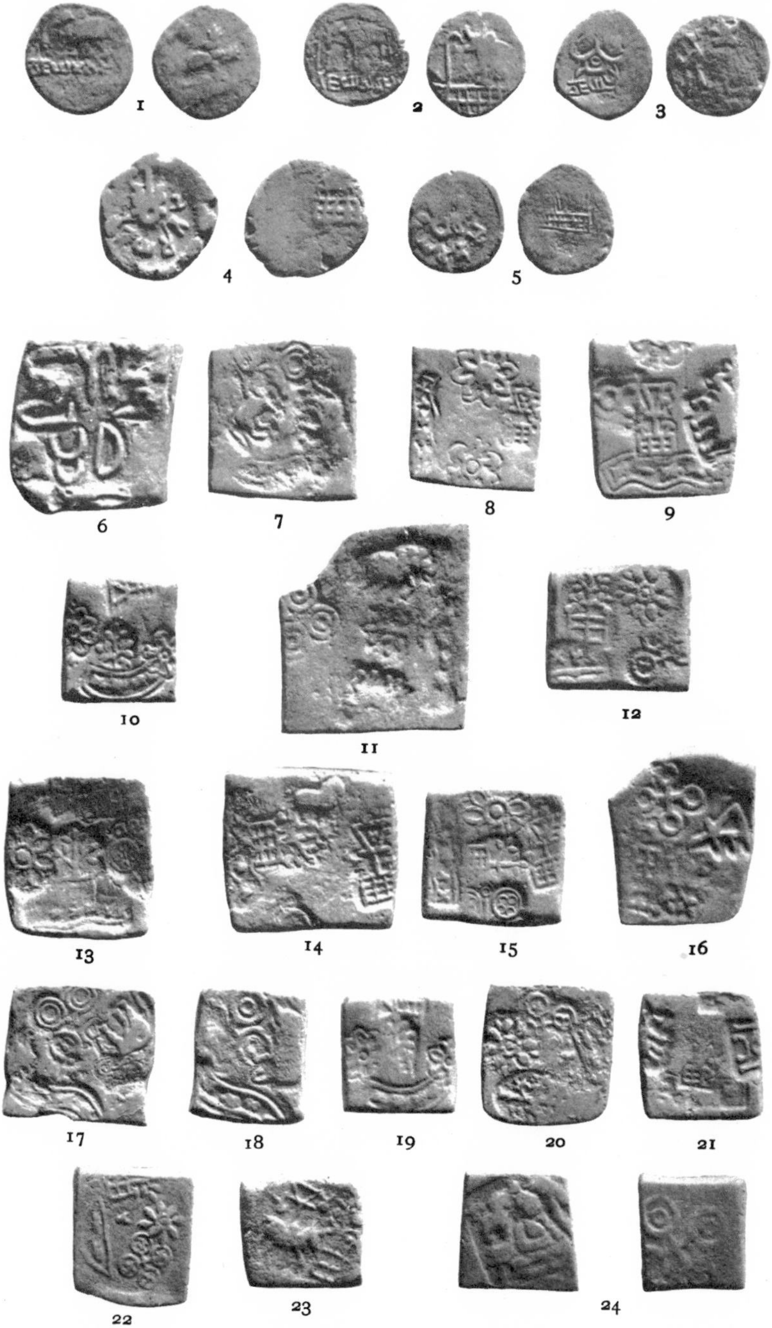

AYODHYĀ—ERAN

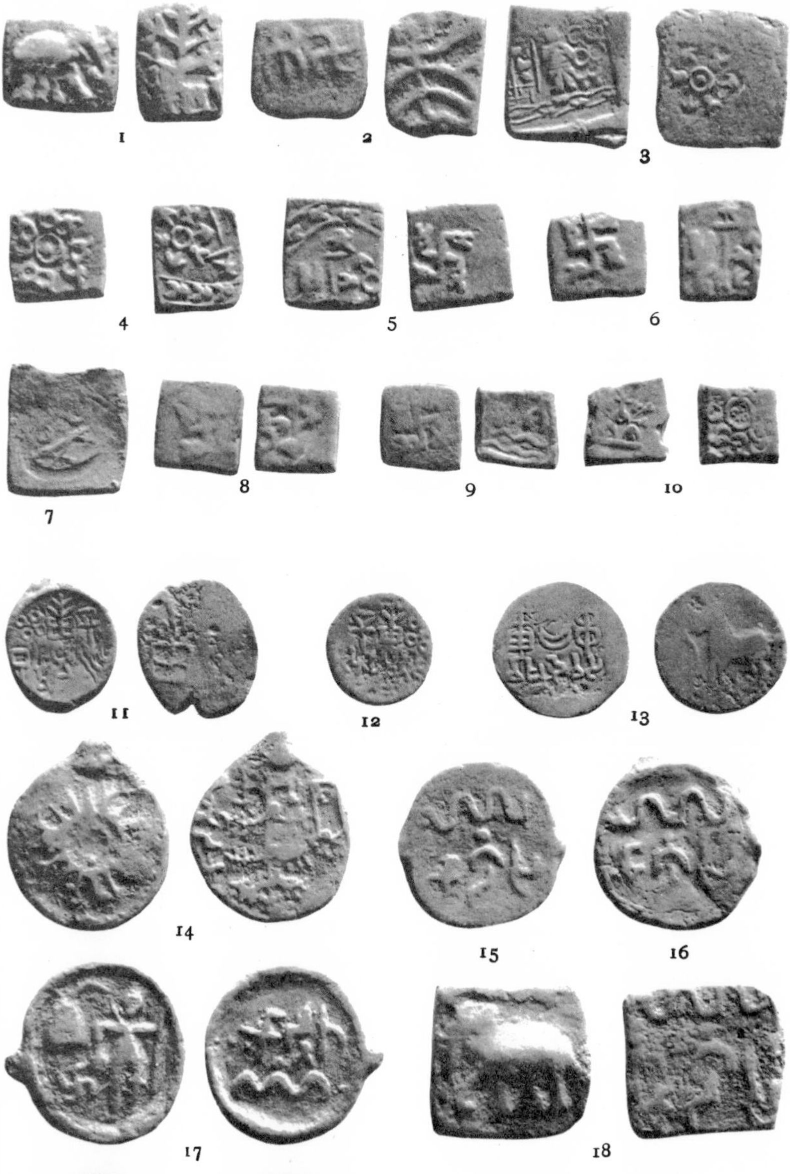

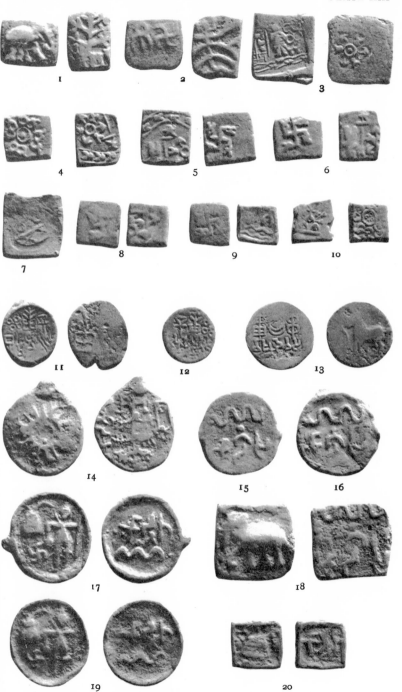

ERAṆ—KANAUJ-KĀḌA

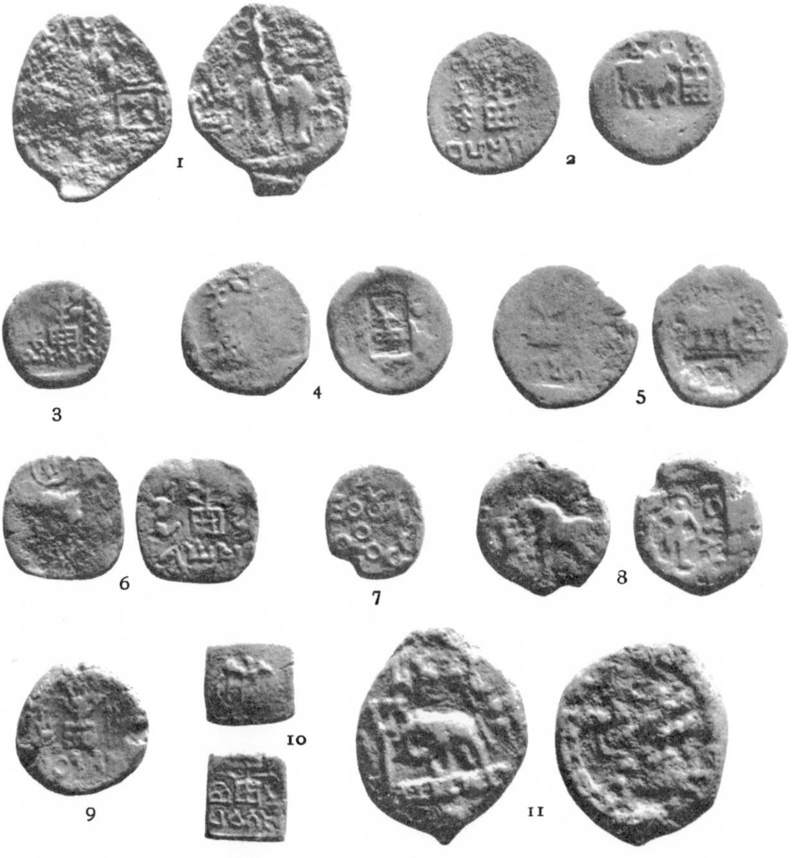
1
2
3
4
5
6
7
8
9
10
11
12
13
14
15

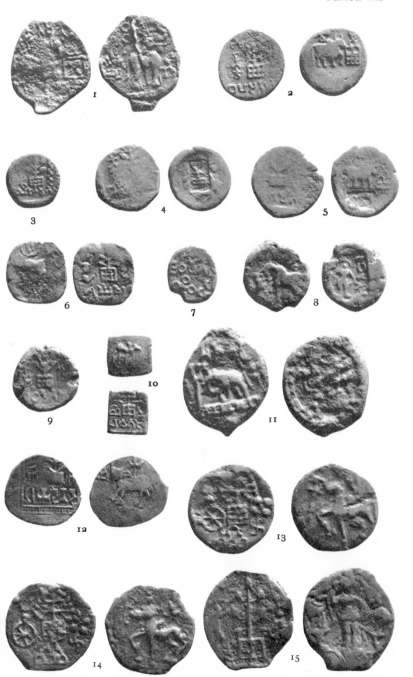

KAUŚĀMBĪ

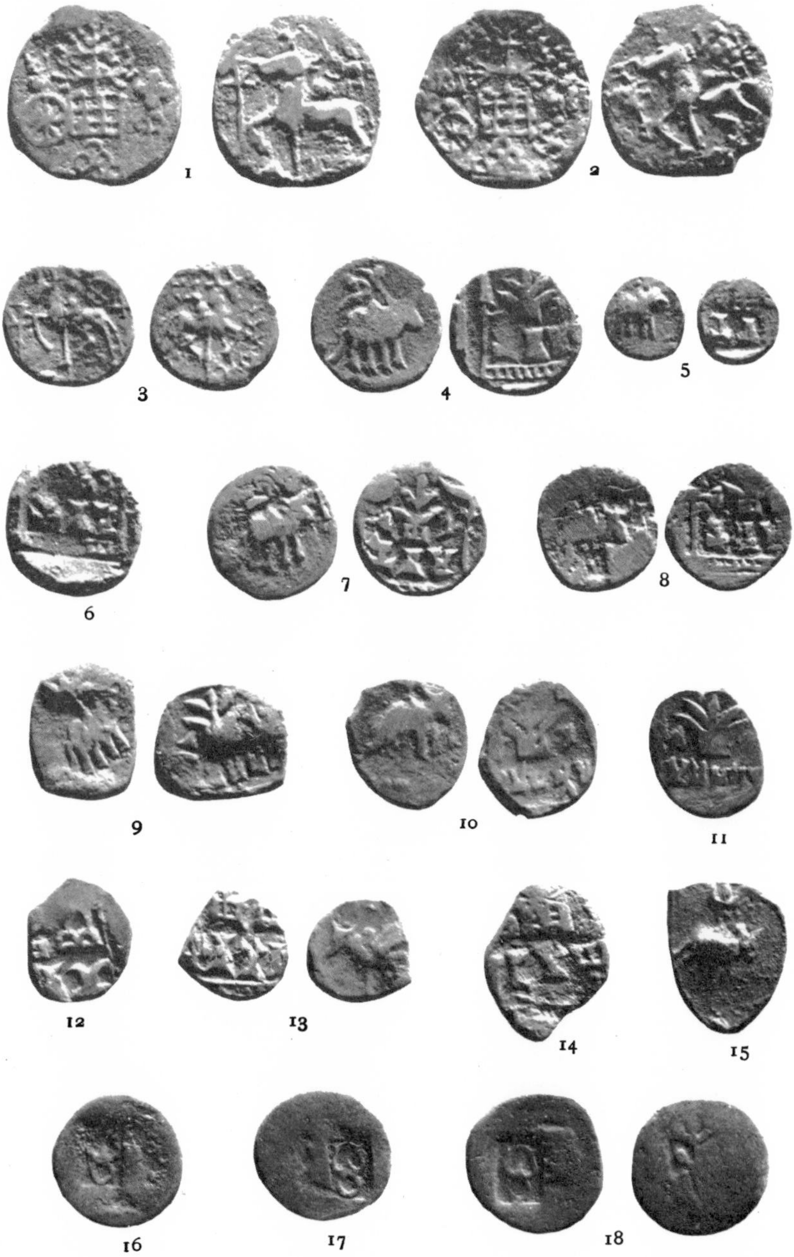

KAUŚĀMBĪ

1

2

3

4

5

6

7

8

9

10

11

12

13

14

15

16

KUṆINDA

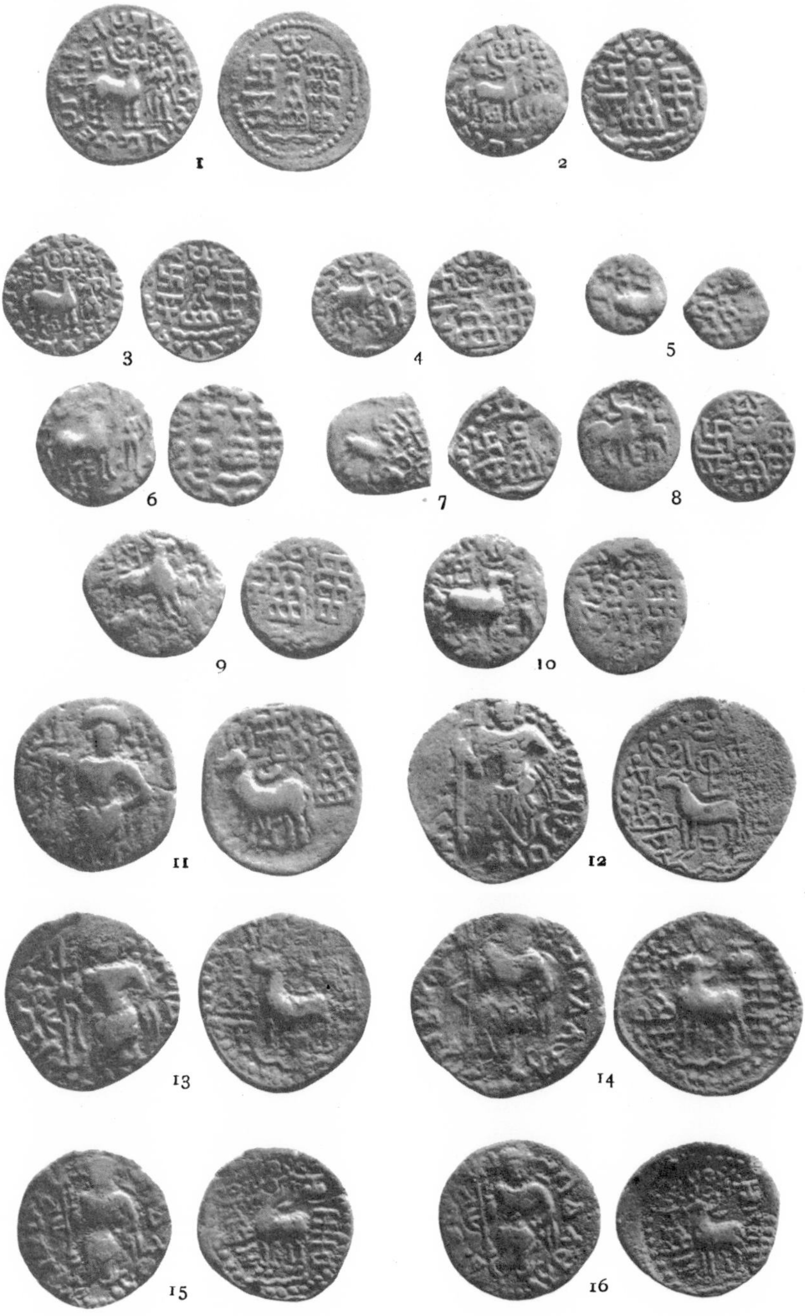

KUṆINDA

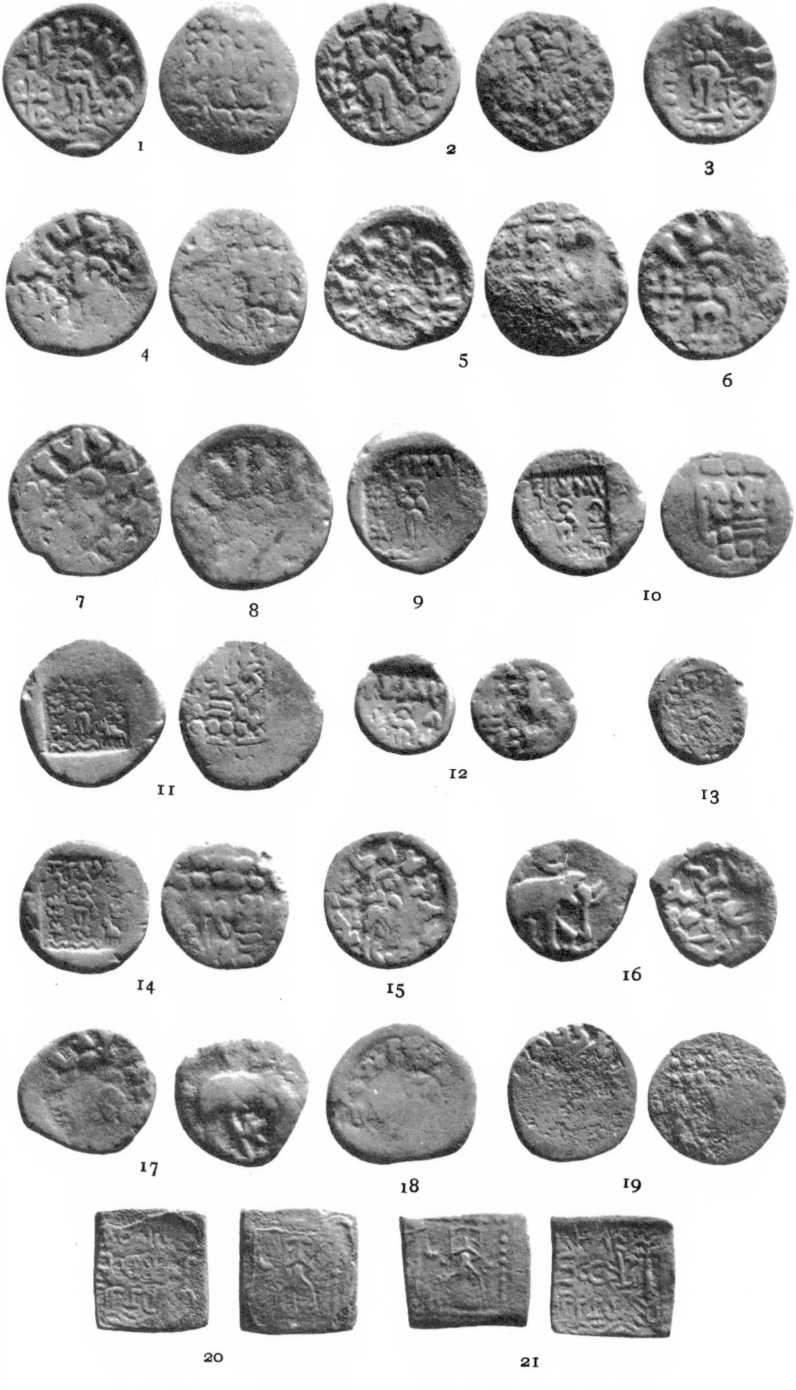

1 2 3 4 5 6 7 8 9 10 11 12 13 14 15 16 17 18 19 20 21

MATHURA

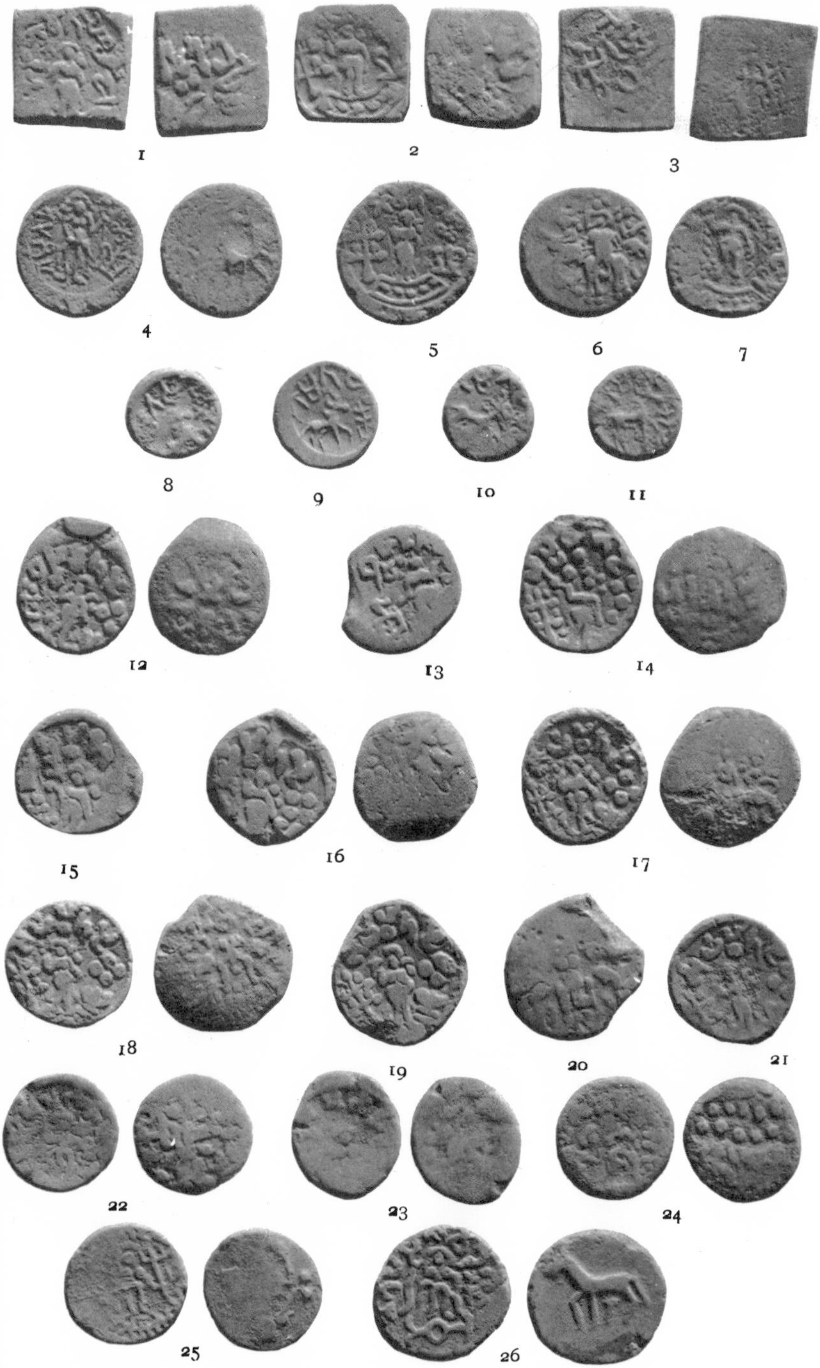
1
2
3
4
5
6
7
8
9
10
11
12
13
14
15
16
17
18
19
20
21
22
23
24
25
26

MATHURA

PLATE XXVI

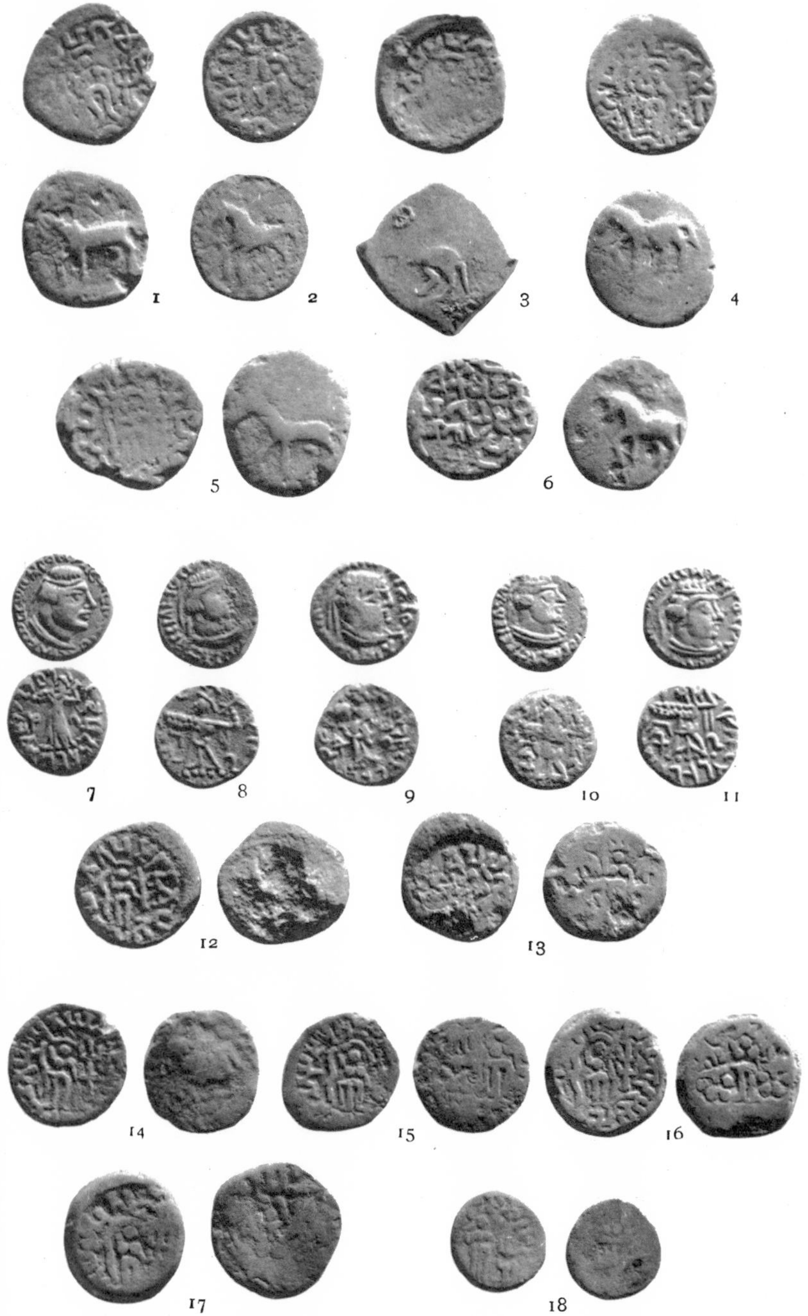

MATHURA

PAÑCĀLA

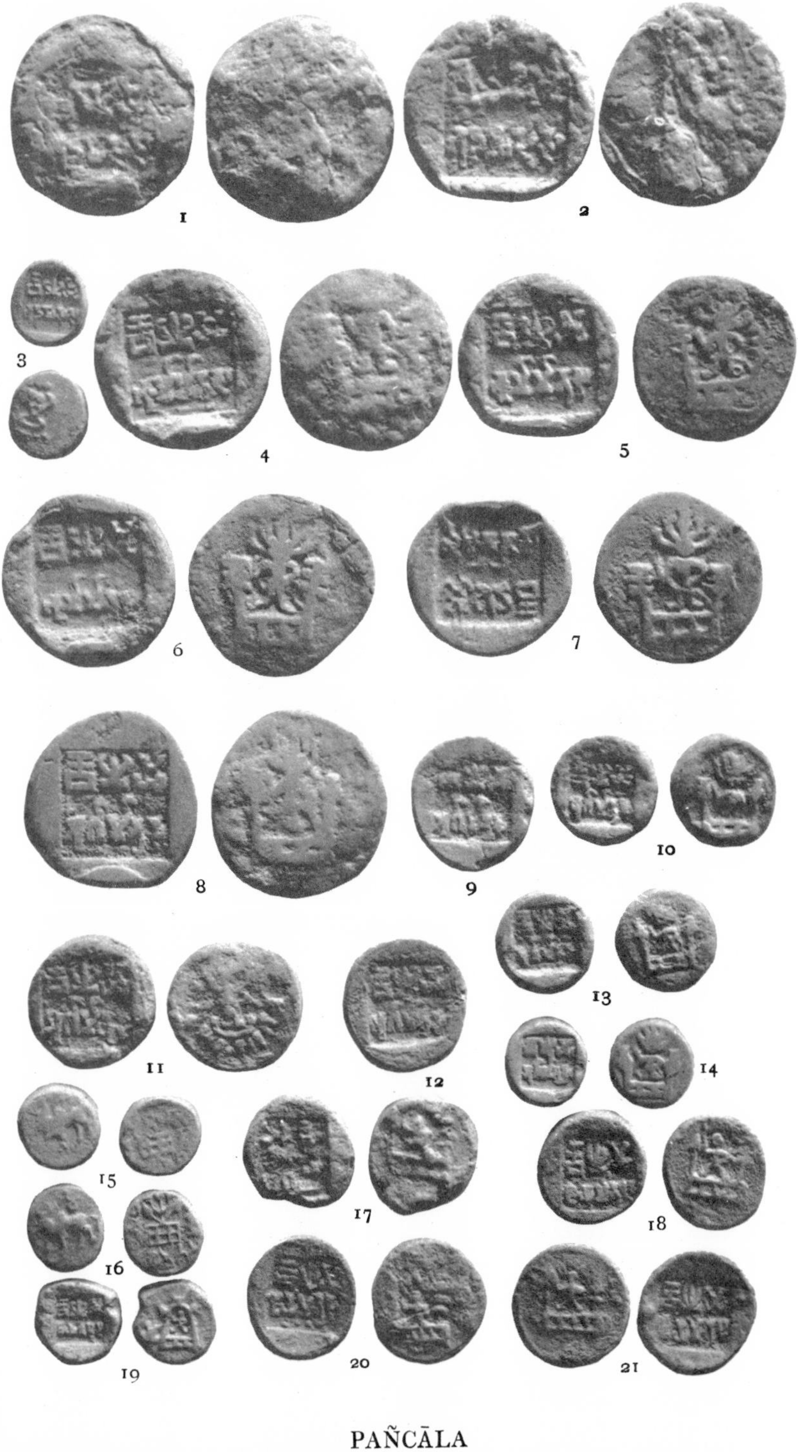

PAÑCĀLA

PAÑCĀLA—RĀJANYA

1 2 3 4 5 6 7 8 9 10 11 12

PURĪ

TAXILA

TAXILA

TAXILA

TAXILA

TAXILA-TRIPURĪ-UDDEHIKA-UPAGODA-UPĀTIKYA

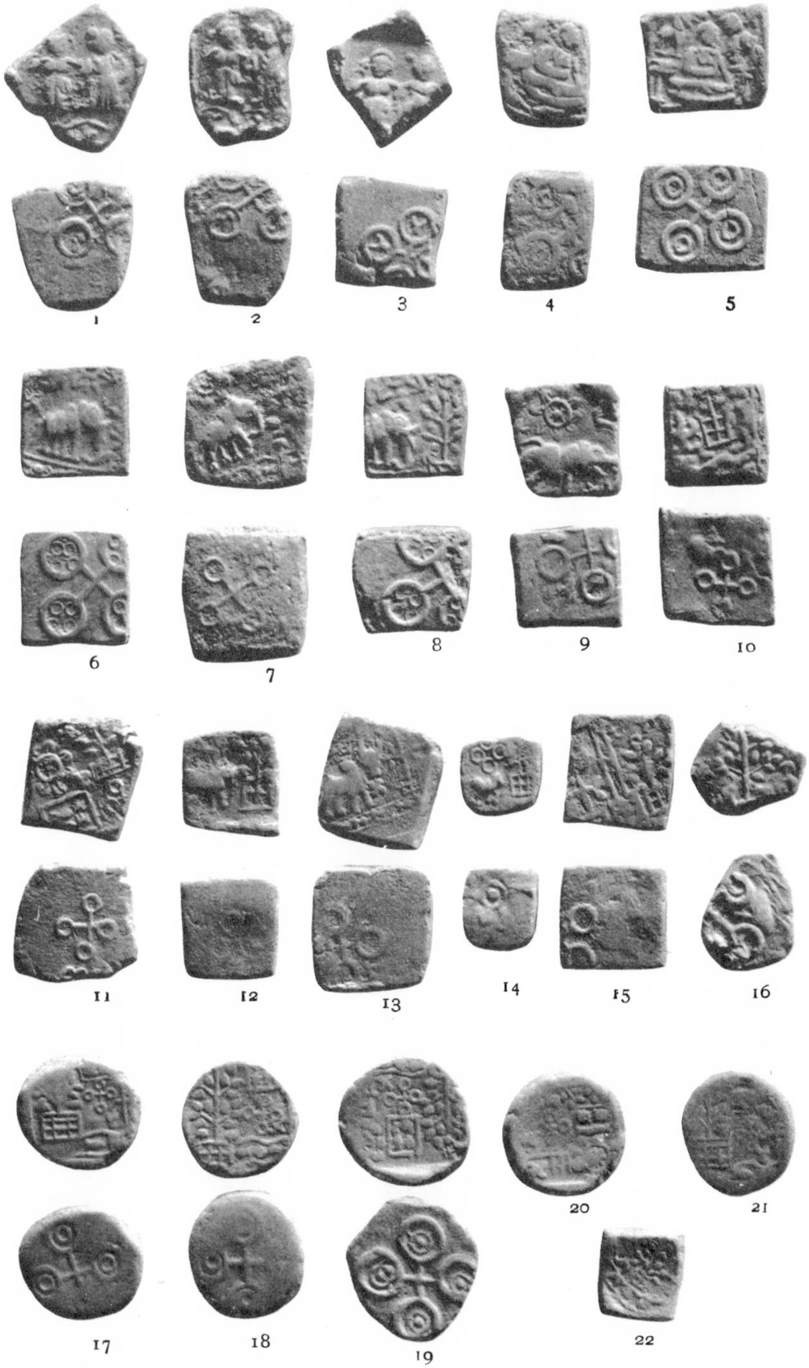

UJJAYINĪ

UJJAYINĪ

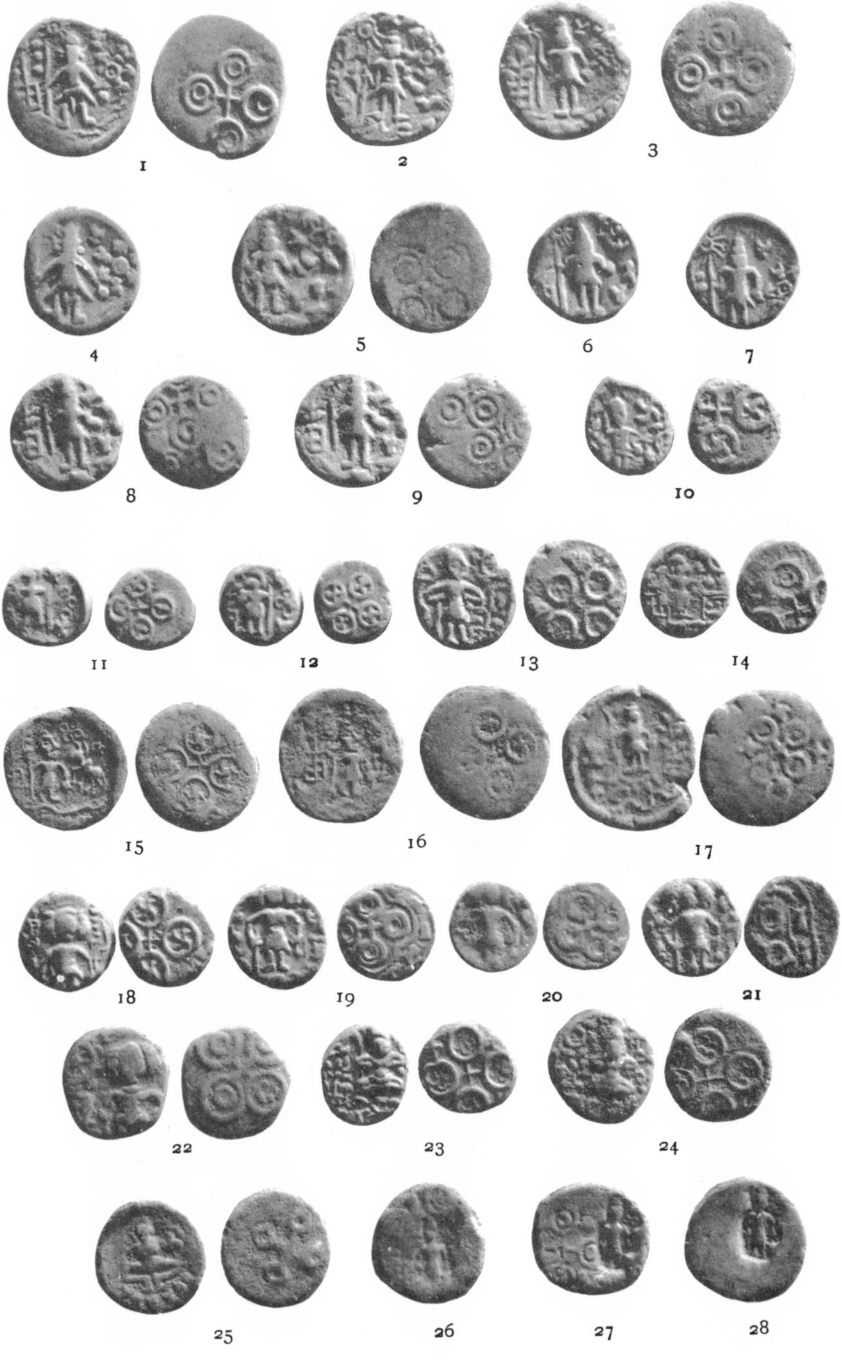

UJJAYINĪ

PLATE XXXIX

YAUDHEYA

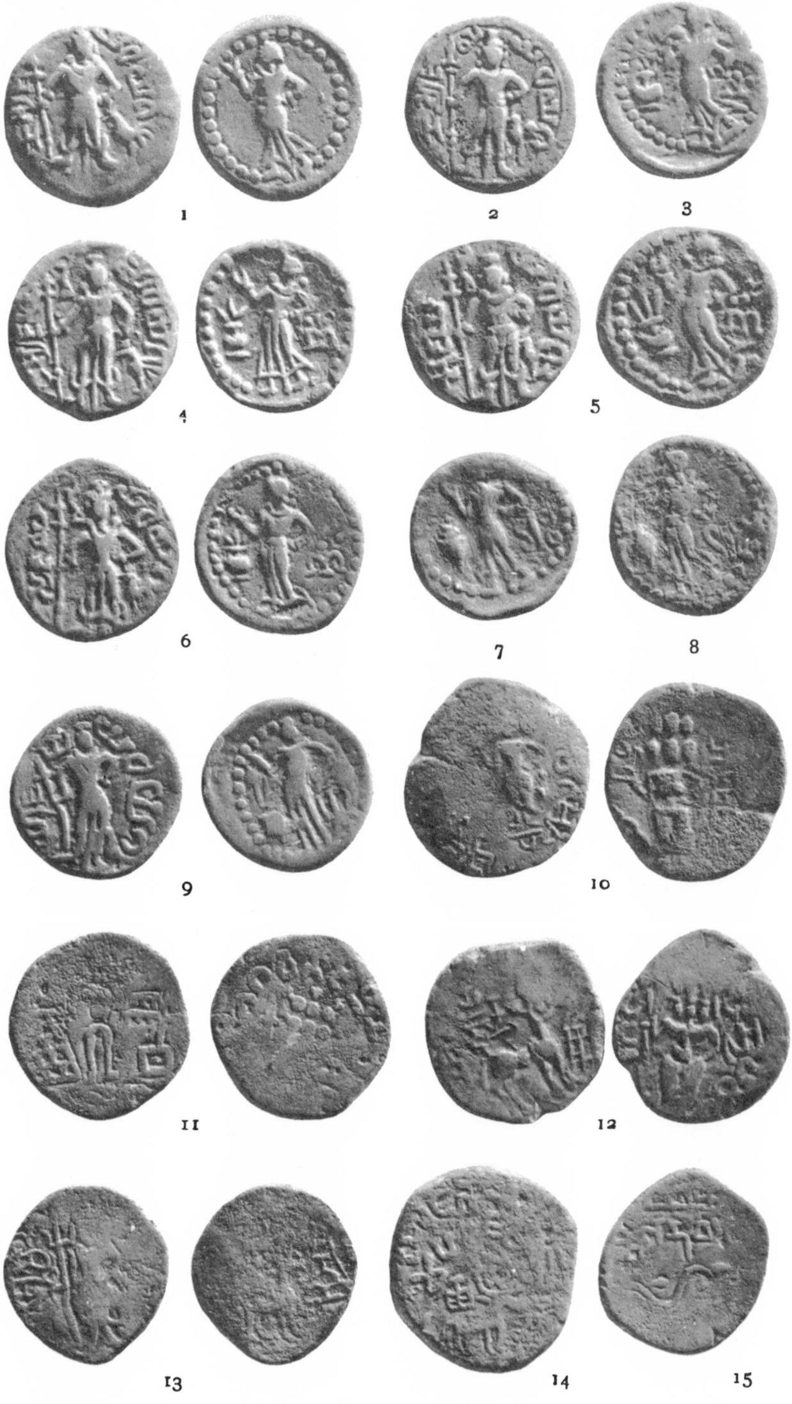

YAUDHEYA

PUNCH-MARKED SILVER (ADDITIONAL)

PUNCH-MARKED SILVER (ADDITIONAL)

ADDITIONAL: AUDUMBARA—MATHURĀ

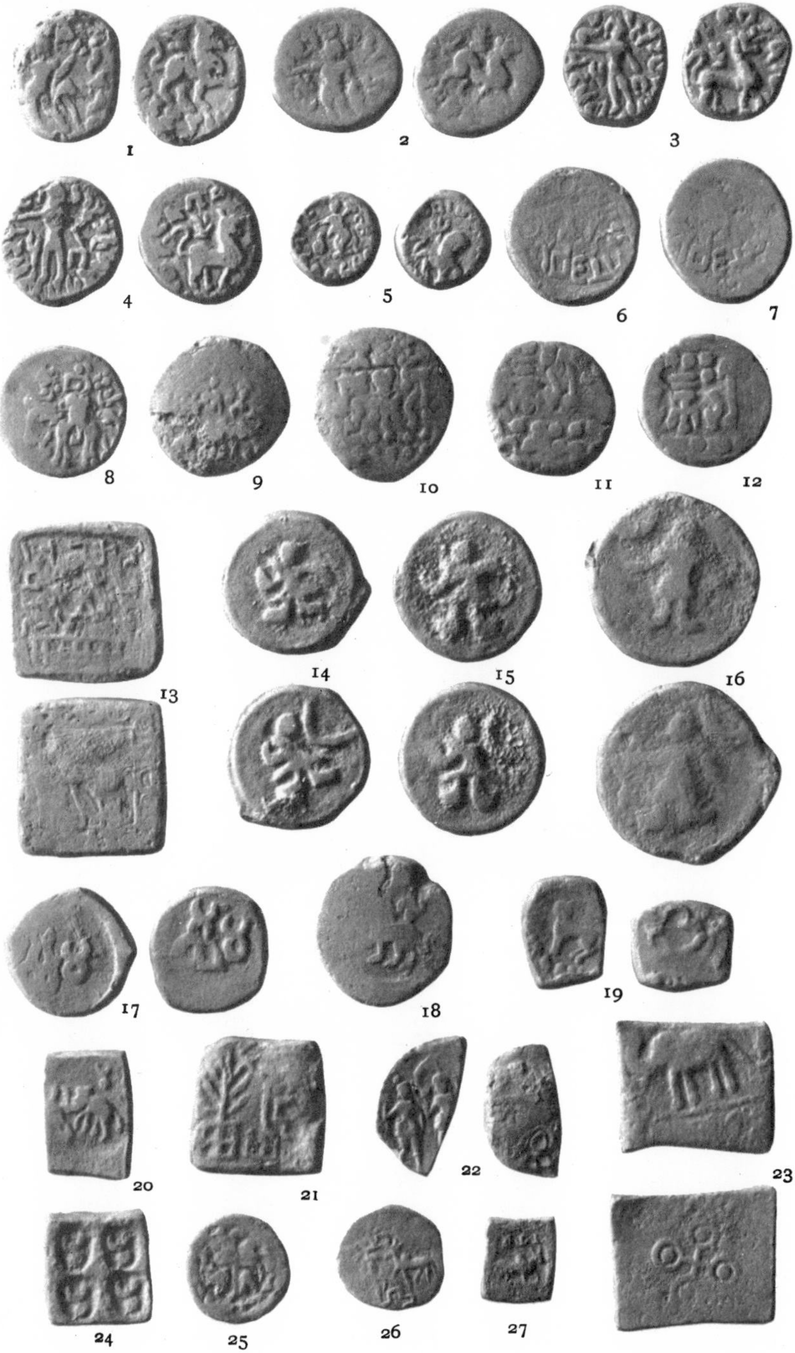

ADDITIONAL: MATHURĀ—YAUDHEYA

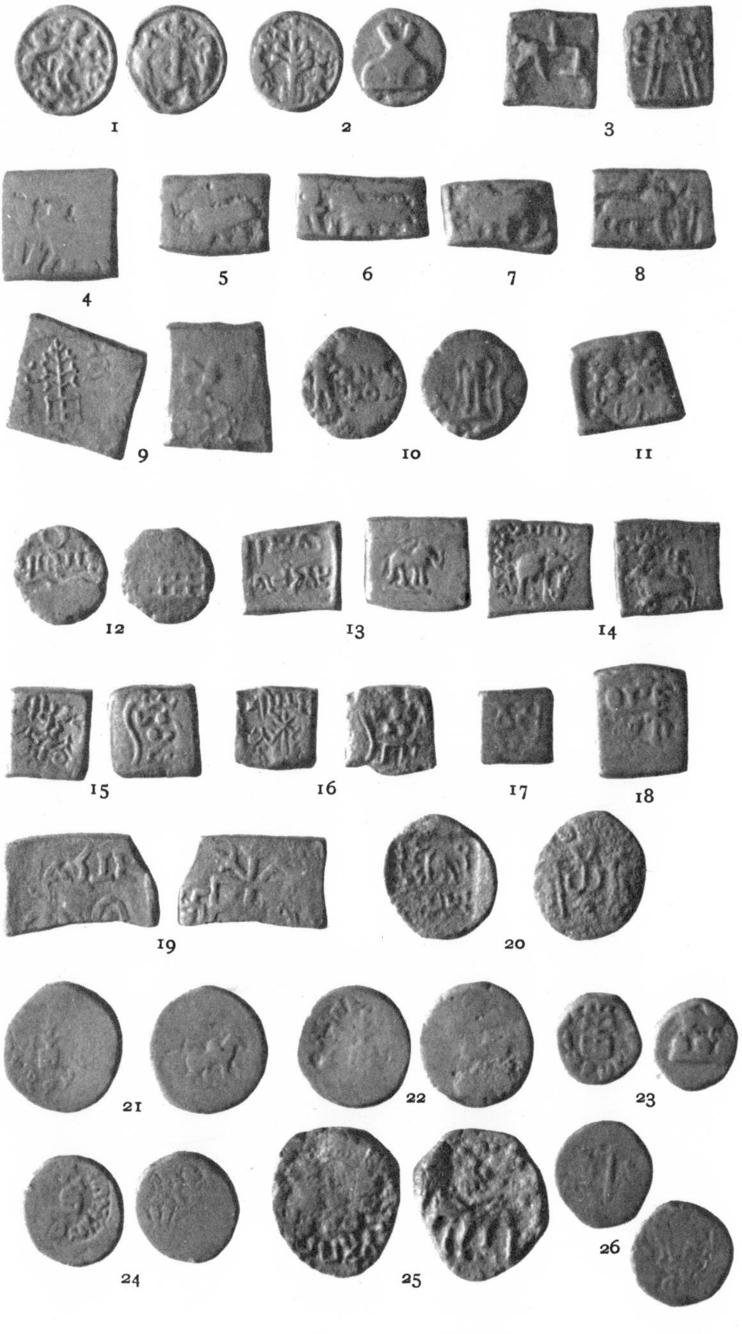

TAXILA—UNCERTAIN

UNCERTAIN—ADDITIONAL